THE WHICH? GUIDE TO
Co
Sho

G000139141

THE WHICH? GUIDE TO
Country
Shopping

Compiled by CHRISTOPHER ROUNDELL

CONSUMERS' ASSOCIATION

Which? Books are commissioned and researched by
Consumers' Association and published by
Which? Ltd, 2 Marylebone Road, London NW1 4DF

Distributed by The Penguin Group:
Penguin Books Ltd, 27 Wrights Lane, London W8 5TZ

First edition 1995

British Library Cataloguing-in-Publication Data
Consumers' Association
Which? Guide to Country Shopping
I. Title
381.10941

ISBN 0 85202 552 1

Cover photograph by Johanna Fernihough
Items lent by: Ruth Pringle Textiles, Pamela Woods Accessories, Compton
Marbling, From the Wood, MacGregor and Michael, Melanie Sproat, The
Glanarrow Box Co, Dunford Wood, Patricia Hamilton, Paul Barcroft, Jim
Edmiston, Architectural Fine Art, Peter Snagge, Sarah Thyssen, Wendy
Brandon, Rosebud Preserves
Designed by Paul Saunders
Maps by European Map Graphics Ltd
Index by Marie Lorimer
Typeset by Saxon Graphics Ltd, Derby
Printed and bound in England by Clays Ltd, St Ives plc

CONTENTS

Introduction

This guide is for anyone who travels about Britain and likes seeking out the unusual. High-street shopping holds few surprises, now that so many small shops have given way to the might of the nationwide chains, so for goods that are less homogenised, possibly unique – things which cannot be bought throughout the length and breadth of Britain – it is to the small country retail outlets that we must turn.

The outlets in this book sell regional and local food specialities, handmade products of every description, items to wear, articles for the home and garden and much more besides. There are potters, silversmiths, cheese-makers, weavers, wood-carvers, cider-makers, jewellers, confectioners, milliners, clock-makers, bakers, brewers and leather-workers. Some are keeping disappearing rural skills alive; others are bringing back the fresh, country flavours of real food that may be sadly missing from those well-stocked supermarket shelves. In this guide you'll find small studio workshops, smoke-houses and smithies, nurseries, herb farms, saddleries and dairies, selling goods as humble as a bread roll and as grand as a dining-room suite, as fragrant as pot-pourri and as fragile as glass. You'll find dolls, dolls' houses and rocking-horses that make you wish you were a child again, garden furniture quite unlike your local superstore's, artefacts in wood, tapestries and paper products that bid fair to be called works of art, items in silver and gold which are the heirlooms of tomorrow, silk ties and scarves and hand-knitted garments that are one of a kind . . .

When you arrive, you may find, for example, a solitary potter selling what he makes, or a group of people making and decorating their stock in trade; you may discover that refreshments are available, too. A cheese-maker's output may consist of one distinctive cheese; on the other hand, you may find a large dairy with cream, yoghurt, several different cheeses and a nearby farm walk to detain you a little longer. Some outlets have repair facilities or run training courses in the skills and crafts they market. Some places will appeal to just a few enthusiasts. Some will strike a chord that launches their visitors on a new hobby.

Some businesses are seasonal. Some require you to make an appointment in advance. Some of the featured outlets are *very* small, family-run businesses – maybe even one-man bands – and you may arrive at a moment when the proprietor has left the premises for a moment to post a letter or collect the children from school. Should this happen, don't blame us! Someone will no doubt be back shortly.

We hope that wherever you're headed, or wherever you're staying on holiday, you'll remember to glance at the maps for the areas accessible to you and find out what's on your route or in your region. We know you'll enjoy exploring.

Note This guide differs from most Consumers' Association guides in that we make no claims to have assessed the goods on sale; availability of specific items would in any case be impossible to guarantee. We simply tell you what sorts of wares are being sold and at what address, and we provide you with the directions, and the maps, that will help you find these places.

To find what's on your route, or in a particular area, look at the map pages in colour at the back of the book. Each outlet has its own number, such as 1/34: the first part (1) is the map number, the second (34) the number of the outlet as it appears both on the map and in the entries. To find the corresponding entry, turn to the listings for map page 1 and find the 34th entry. Each entry gives a brief description of the products on offer, opening times (note that some require you to telephone), and directions.

We have divided the entries into three: those selling food products are marked with ■; those selling non-food or craft products are marked with ●; and multiples are marked with ✻.

A multiple is an outlet where several businesses are operating under one roof. For example, 1/1 Greeb Cottage Craft Workshop is a multiple. Here, several craftspeople produce ceramics, glass, silverware, leather goods and items in wood.

Another way to use the guide is to look at the Category index at the back, find 'Cheese', 'Dried flowers', 'Toys' or whatever type of goods interests you, and see what outlets are listed; then turn to the entry for fuller information and the map for the exact location.

In due course, we hope to publish further editions of this guide, so if you want to recommend for inclusion next time a place you have discovered, please let us have details of it: write to Dept VF, The Which? Guide to Country Shopping, Freepost, 2 Marylebone Road, London NW1 1YN (no stamp required).

MAP 1

1/1
✱ MULTIPLE
Greeb Cottage Craft Workshop
Greeb Cottage, Land's End,
Cornwall TR19 7AA
Tel: (01736) 871501
Fax: (01736) 871812

Pottery, glass, woodwork, silver and
leather.
Open: Daily 10am-5.30pm, often to
7pm in Jul-Aug
Cards: No

DIRECTIONS: Follow A30 to Land's
End. Craft centre is left of main
complex.

1/2
● CERAMICS
Delan Cookson
Lissadell, St Buryan, Penzance,
Cornwall TR19 6HP
Tel: (01736) 810347

Hand-thrown porcelain bowls, bottles
and vases.
Open: By appointment only
Cards: No

DIRECTIONS: 500 yards along road
to St Just from village of St Buryan.

1/3
● TEXTILES
Noah's Ark Studio
Anne Sicher, c/o Wolf at the Door Gallery,
Bread Street, Penzance,
Cornwall TR18 6EQ
Tel: (01736) 60573/731686

Hand-painted silk, scarves,
bedspreads, wall hangings, banners.
Open: Mon, Tue, Thur, Fri 10am-
5pm, Sat 10am-4pm. Closed Jan-
Easter
Cards: Access, Visa

DIRECTIONS: From Market Jew
Street take the steps up the arcade. At
the top of the arcade turn left.

1/4
● ENGRAVING
Jack Trowbridge
Gorselands, Newmill, Penzance,
Cornwall TR20 8UX
Tel: (01736) 62105

Hand letter-cutting in stone, slate,
wood and metal.
Open: By appointment only
Cards: Access, Visa

DIRECTIONS: Between Penzance
and Gurnards Head.

1/5
● KNITWEAR
Corinne Carr Designs
Bolenna, Towednack, St Ives,
Cornwall TR26 3AP
Tel/Fax: (01736) 796176

Fair Isle knitwear, necklaces,
handmade beads with wood and bone.
Open: By appointment only
Cards: No

DIRECTIONS: At the roundabout in
Lelant take back road to St Ives in
direction of Nancledra. Turn left at
T-Junction towards Towednack. 500
yards on take the left-hand fork.
Third house on the right (a
cottage/barn).

1/6
● CERAMICS
Bob Berry Raku Ceramics
Coldharbour Studios, Towednack, St Ives,
Cornwall TR26 3AU
Tel: (01736) 798316

Japanese-style decorative pieces.
Open: Mon, Tue, Thur-Sat 10am-
4pm, Sun by appointment. Closed 24
Dec-4 Jan
Cards: No

DIRECTIONS: From B3311 St Ives to
Penzance road, signposted
Towednack approx 1 mile south-west
of Halse Town. Converted barn
opposite converted Methodist Chapel.

1/7
● CERAMICS
Leach Pottery Ltd
Upper Stennack, St Ives,
Cornwall TR26 2HE
Tel: (01736) 796398

Pottery.
Open: Mon-Fri 10am-5pm, summer
also Sat and holidays. Closed 25 Dec
Cards: Access, Diners, Visa

DIRECTIONS: Edge of town on
Nancledra and St Just road.

1/8
✳ MULTIPLE
Sloop Craft Market
Capel Court, St Ives, Cornwall TR26 1LS
Tel: (01736) 796051

Jewellery, leather, wood carvings,
painting, pottery, walking sticks,
stained glass and teddy bears.
Open: Mon-Sat 10am-5.30pm, but
telephone first during winter months
Cards: Visa

DIRECTIONS: Behind Sloop pub on
the wharf.

1/9
● CERAMICS
Jon Middlemiss Ceramics
Wheal Vor, Tyringham Road, Lelant,
St Ives, Cornwall TR26 3LF
Tel/Fax: (01736) 754832

Handmade ceramics, pieces are
thrown, carved and lustred. Mainly
non-functional.
Open: By appointment only
Cards: No

DIRECTIONS: From A30 to Lelant
roundabout, past Garden Centre to
centre of village. Past Post Office on
the left. 100 yards further, second
cottage on the left.

1/10
● GLASS
Norman Stuart Clarke Glass
The Glass Gallery, St Erth,
Cornwall TR27 6HT
Tel: (01736) 756577

Glass bottles, vases and paperweights.

Open: Mon-Fri 10am-1pm, 2.30pm-
5pm, Sat 10am-1pm. Closed 25-26
Dec
Cards: Access, Switch, Visa

DIRECTIONS: On A30 to Hayle turn
left at St Erth station. Proceed to
village, the Glass Gallery is opposite
the Star Inn car park.

1/11
● WOOD
Roy Hewson Woodcarver
Steppy Downs Studio, 13 St Erth Hill, St
Erth, Hayle, Cornwall TR27 6EX
Tel: (01736) 753342

Woodcarvings of wildlife subjects,
walking sticks, staffs and bird mobiles.
Open: Mon-Sat 9am-6pm. Easter-Oct
Sun 9am-6pm. Nov-Easter by
appointment only. Closed 24 Dec-
1 Jan
Cards: Access, Switch, Visa

DIRECTIONS: Turn off A30 at St
Erth station. Continue through
village. Climb St Erth Hill. Studio is
on left at top of hill.

1/12
■ FISH/SHELLFISH
Quayside Fish
Porthleven, Nr Helston, Cornwall TR13 9JU
Tel: (01326) 562008
Fax: (01326) 574386

Fresh fish, shellfish and smoked fish.
Open: Mon-Sun 9am-5pm, closed
bank hols except Good Fri. Closed 25
Dec-1 Jan
Cards: No

DIRECTIONS: Harbourside at
Porthleven, which is 2½ miles south
of Helston, off the A394.

1/13
■ PRESERVES
Phillimore Fine Foods
The Lugger Restaurant, Harbour Head,
Porthleven, Cornwall TR13 9JA
Tel: (01326) 562761

Chutneys and mustards.
Open: Easter-Oct, Mon-Sun 10am-
late
Cards: Access, Visa.

DIRECTIONS: On the A393 Helston to Breage road, take turning marked for Porthleven. Follow this into Porthleven and to the harbour.

1/14
■ BEER

Blue Anchor Inn
50 Coinagehall Street, Helston,
Cornwall TR13 8EX
Tel: (01326) 562821

Brewers.
Open: Mon-Sat 11am-11pm. Sun 12-3pm, 7pm-10.30pm
Cards: No

DIRECTIONS: At bottom of Coinagehall Street, opposite Woolworths.

1/15
● CERAMICS

Norman Underhill
Trecarne, Meaver Road, Mullion,
Cornwall TR12 7DN
Tel: (01326) 240667

Handmade figurines.
Open: Daily 10am to dusk
Cards: Access, Switch, Visa

DIRECTIONS: Take A3083 Helston to Lizard road. After about 6 miles turn right on B3296, signposted Mullion Cove. First building on right.

1/16
■ WINE

Pemboa Vineyards
Mellangoose Mill, Pemboa, Helston,
Cornwall TR13 0QF
Tel: (01326) 563116

White wines, tours.
Open: May-Oct. Thur-Sat 2pm-5pm
Cards: No

DIRECTIONS: 1 mile beyond the entrance to Flambards Theme Park on the road to Gweek.

1/17
● CERAMICS

Golden Goose Pottery & Gallery
c/o Cornish Goldsmiths, New Portreath Road, Portreath, Nr Redruth,
Cornwall TR16 4HN
Tel: (01209) 314027

Decorated pottery, paintings, prints, glass.
Open: Mon-Sat 10am-5.30pm, Sun 10am-4pm. Closed Christmas
Cards: Access, Visa

DIRECTIONS: On B3300, off A30, halfway between Portreath and Redruth. Next door to Cornish Goldsmiths.

1/18
● CERAMICS

Kennack Pottery
Kennack Sands, Ruan Minor, Nr Helston,
Cornwall TR12 7LX
Tel: (01326) 290592

Detailed porcelain models of old laced working boots from 2-35cms, 4 wellington sizes in various colours, mice, elephants, seals and dolphins, etc.
Open: 9am-9pm peak holiday season, 9am-5pm rest of year. Available by phone out of season
Cards: No

DIRECTIONS: From Helston take the A3083 Lizard Road, left on to B3293. After Goonhilly satellite station turn right for Kennack Sands. In Kuggar turn left and it is beside Treasure Island Gifts and Beach Goods shop.

1/19
● CERAMICS

Trelowarren Pottery
Trelowarren, Mawgan, Cornwall TR12 6AF
Tel: (01326) 221583

Hand-thrown pottery in locally-produced stoneware clay
Open: July-Aug Mon-Sun 10am-10pm, mid-Jan-March Mon-Fri 11am-4pm. Closed Christmas and New Year
Cards: Access, Visa

DIRECTIONS: From Helston take the A3083 Lizard Road, at the roundabout past RNAS Culdrose, turn left on the B3293 towards St Keverne. At Garras turn left at the Trelowarren sign and follow the mile-long drive.

1/20
■ FARM PRODUCE

Cheese Farm Shop
Menallack Farm, Treverva, Penryn,
Cornwall TR10 9BP
Tel: (01326) 40333

Farmhouse cheeses, bread rolls, local ham, cream, sausages, lamb.
Open: Any reasonable hour
Cards: No

DIRECTIONS: On Falmouth to Gweek road, unclassified, ½ mile west of Treverva.

1/21
● PASTILLE-BURNERS

The Dragons Lair
The Cottage Piece; Carnkie, Nr Redruth,
Cornwall TR16 6SF
Tel: (01209) 216902

Handmade synthetic-stone pastille-burners, in the shape of dragons and fantasy characters.
Open: Mon-Sat 9am-5pm
Cards: No

DIRECTIONS: Leave A30 at Pool, turn off towards Four Lanes, opposite Countryman pub.

1/22
● PLANTS

Burncoose Nurseries
Gwennap, Redruth, Cornwall TR16 6BJ
Tel: (01209) 861112
Fax: (01209) 860011

Nursery specialising in rhododendrons and conservatory plants.
Open: Mon-Sat 9am-5pm, Sun 11am-5pm. Closed 25 Dec
Cards: Access, Amex, Switch, Visa

DIRECTIONS: Situated directly on A393 Redruth to Falmouth road between Lanner and Ponsanooth.

1/23
■ CIDER

Callestock Cider Farm
Penhallow, Truro, Cornwall TR4 9LW
Tel: (01872) 573356
Fax: (01872) 573056

Scrumpy ciders, country wines, jams and preserves.
Open: Mid-Jan-mid-Dec Mon-Fri 9am-5pm, also Easter-Oct Sat 9am-5pm, July-Aug Sun 12-3pm
Cards: No

DIRECTIONS: Signposted off the A3075, Newquay to Redruth Road at Penhallow.

1/24
■ ICE-CREAM

Callestick Farm Dairy Ice Cream
Callestick Farm, Callestick, Truro,
Cornwall TR4 9LL
Tel: (01872) 573126

Ice-cream.
Open: Mid-Feb-mid-Oct, 1 Dec-24 Dec, daily 10am-5pm
Cards: No

DIRECTIONS: Callestick lies between A30 and A3075, 5 miles north of Truro.

1/25
■ ICE-CREAM

Roskilly Cream and Ice Cream
Tregellast Barton, St Keverne, Helston,
Cornwall TR12 6NX
Tel/Fax: (01326) 280479

Cream, ice-cream, fudge, chutney, mustard, jams, honey.
Open: All year round
Cards: No

DIRECTIONS: Take Lizard road from Helston then follow signposts to St Keverne. At St Keverne square leave war memorial to your left and take road ahead. Immediately out of square turn right and follow road for ½ mile. Turn right at first junction. Farm on your left.

1/26
● CERAMICS
Jenny Beavan
White Lady's Cottage, Pickett's Yard, St
Thomas Street, Penryn, Cornwall TR10 8JR
Tel/Fax: (01326) 373524

Handmade ceramic vessel forms.
Open: By appointment
Cards: No

DIRECTIONS: St Thomas Street is in
the heart of Penryn town. Head for
the town car park. Pickett's Yard is
through wrought iron gates 25 yards
from the fish and chip shop.

1/27
● CERAMICS
Carnon Downs Pottery
Carnon Downs Garden Centre,
Quenchwell Road, Carnon Downs, Truro,
Cornwall TR3 6LN
Tel: (01872) 863374

Hand-thrown raku-fired individual
pieces, terracotta pots for garden and
home, gallery.
Open: Mon-Sat 9am-5pm, Sun, bank
hols 10am-5pm. Closed 25-26 Dec,
1 Jan
Cards: Access, Visa

DIRECTIONS: Take A39 out of
Truro to Carnon Downs roundabout,
turn right into village, first right into
Quenchwell Road. Garden centre on
left.

1/28
● TOYS
It's Childsplay
Treworthal Barn, Treworthal, Crantock,
Nr Newquay, Cornwall TR8 5PJ
Tel/Fax: (01637) 830896

Wooden toys and children's furniture,
including rocking and armchairs.
Open: Mon-Fri 8.30am-5.30pm, Sat
10.30am-4.30pm. Closed 25 Dec-1
Jan
Cards: Access, Visa

DIRECTIONS: Signposted off A3075
Newquay to Redruth Road. Approx 3
miles from Newquay.

1/29
■ MEAT PRODUCTS
Merrivale Charcuterie
1 Coombes Lane, Truro, Cornwall TR1 2BJ
Tel: (01872) 222227
Fax: (01326) 377717

Charcuterie and pork products.
Open: Mon-Sat 9am-5pm
Cards: No

DIRECTIONS: From Pydar Street,
lane between Body Shop and W H
Smith. 15 yards down lane on left.

1/30
● METALWORK/WOOD
Truro Agencies
14a Kenwyn Street, Truro, Cornwall TR1 3DJ
Tel: (01872) 73381
Fax: (01872) 225738

Wrought iron and wooden house
accessories and local crafts.
Open: Mon-Sat 9.30am-5pm
Cards: Access, Amex, Diners, Visa

DIRECTIONS: Kenwyn Street is 100
yards off Victoria Square.

1/31
● CANDLES
St Eval Candle Company
Great Engollan Farm, Engollan, St Eval,
Wadebridge, Cornwall PL27 7UL
Tel: (01841) 540850
Fax: (01841) 541114

Hand-finished church, dinner, garden
and fraganced candles.
Open: Mon-Fri 9am-5pm
Cards: No

DIRECTIONS: On B3276 Trenance
to Porthcothan road. Pass Bedruthan
Steps. Turn right through Treburrick
towards St Eval. At telephone kiosk
turn right to Engollan to find factory.

1/32
● CERAMICS
John Davidson
The Pottery, New Mills, Ladock, Truro,
Cornwall TR2 4NN
Tel: (01726) 882209

Handmade porcelain and stoneware
pottery.

Open: Mon-Fri 10am-6pm, summer
Sat 10am-1pm. Closed 24 Dec-1 Jan
Cards: No

DIRECTIONS: On A39, 8 miles east
of Truro, 4 miles west of Indian
Queens.

1/33
■ FARM PRODUCE
Trudgian Farm Shop
Probus, Truro, Cornwall TR2 4JN
Tel: (01726) 883946

Home-produced beef, lamb and pork.
Sausages, pies, cakes, cream and ice-
cream.
Open: Mon-Sat 8.45am-6pm
Cards: No

DIRECTIONS: On A390 between
Truro and St Austell, in Probus beside
church.

1/34
■ FISH/SHELLFISH
**Mellingey Smoked Fish & Trout
Farm**
St Issey, Wadebridge, Cornwall PL27 7QU
Tel: (01841) 540551
Fax: (01841) 540476

Trout, smoked trout, haddock,
kippers and fish pâtés.
Open: Daily 8am-9pm
Cards: No

DIRECTIONS: From A39 Wadebridge
to Padstow road, take A389 to St Issey.

1/35
■ DELICATESSEN FOODS
Stein's Delicatessen
8 Middle Street, Padstow,
Cornwall PL28 8AR
Tel: (01841) 532221
Fax: (01841) 533344

Pasties, pies, bread, jams, preserves.
Open: Mon-Sat 9am-5pm. Closed
Sun
Cards: Access, Visa

DIRECTIONS: In Middle Street in
centre of Padstow, a few minutes'
walk from harbour.

1/36
● KNITWEAR
The Wool Workshop
Padstow, Cornwall PL28 8LE
Tel/Fax: (01841) 533046

Wool fibres for spinning, knitwear.
Open: Mon-Sat 10am-6pm. Closed
Jan-Easter, telephone first
Cards: No

DIRECTIONS: Follow A389 to
Padstow. Workshop on left ¼ mile
before Padstow.

1/37
■ WINE
Veryan Vineyard
Tregenna, Portloe, Nr Truro,
Cornwall TR2 5PS
Tel: (01872) 501404

Wines, Cornish ciders and apple
juice.
Open: Mon-Sun 2pm-6pm. Closed
harvest-Easter
Cards: No

DIRECTIONS: South-east of Truro, 2
miles east of Veryan, on road between
Portloe and Portholland.

1/38
■ SMOKED PRODUCE
Atlantis Smoked Fish
Fore Street, Grampound, Truro,
Cornwall TR2 5SB
Tel: (01726) 883201

Smoked fish, shellfish, meat and
cheese.
Open: Mon-Sun 8.30am-6.30pm,
closed Jan-March Tue-Sat 10am-5pm
Cards: No

DIRECTIONS: On A390 at
Grampound mid-way between Truro
and St Austell. In main street at
bottom of hill.

1/39
■ BAKED GOODS
Di's Dairy & Pantry
Rock Road, Rock, Wadebridge,
Cornwall PL27 6NW
Tel/Fax: (01208) 863531

Steak and kidney pies, quiches, cakes,
treacle tarts, pasta sauces and cheese.
Open: Easter-Oct Mon-Sat 8am-7pm
Sun 8am-1pm. Oct-Easter Mon-Fri
8am-5.30pm, Sun 8.30am-12. Closed
25, 26 Dec
Cards: Access, Switch, Visa

DIRECTIONS: Take B3314 from
Wadebridge to Port Isaac. After 3
miles turn left to Rock. Second shop
on right as enter main part of village.

1/40
■ WINE
Polmassick Vineyard
Polmassick, Nr St Ewe, Cornwall PL26 6HA
Tel: (01726) 842239

Wines and vineyard tours.
Open: June-Sept Tue-Sat and bank
hols 11am-5pm
Cards: No

DIRECTIONS: From Truro, follow
signs on B3287 after Tregony. It is
signposted at Polmassick crossroads.

1/41
● CERAMICS
Rashleigh Pottery
Wheal Martyn China Clay Heritage Centre,
Carthew, St Austell, Cornwall PL26 8XG
Tel: (01726) 850362

Pottery made from white stoneware
clay.
Open: April-Oct Mon-Fri 10am-6pm
Cards: No

DIRECTIONS: 3 miles north of St
Austell on the A391 Bodmin road,
follow brown holiday route road
signs.

1/42
■ SMOKED PRODUCE
The Cornish Smoked Fish Co. Ltd
Charlestown, St Austell, Cornwall PL25 3NY
Tel: (01726) 72356

Smoked foods, mostly fish. Smoked
and sliced mackerel, hot smoked
salmon, gravad mackerel.
Open: Mon-Fri 8am-5pm, in summer
also Sat 10am-12pm
Cards: No

DIRECTIONS: At head of dock in
small port of Charlestown; ½ mile
south of St Austell.

1/43
● PLANTS
Wall Cottage Nursery
Lockengate, Bugle, St Austell,
Cornwall PL26 8RU
Tel: (01208) 831259

Rhododendron and azalea nursery.
Open: Mon-Sat 8.30am-5pm. Out of
season telephone in advance.
Cards: No

DIRECTIONS: On the A391 ½ mile
from the A30 roundabout, and 6 miles
north of St Austell.

1/44
● CERAMICS
Heather Swain Pottery
Prywyth Cottage, Newhall Green, Delabole,
Cornwall PL33 9ES
Tel: (01840) 212885

Countryside breakfast tableware,
animal toast racks and handmade
earthenware pottery in animal themes.
Open: By appointment only
Cards: No

DIRECTIONS: On A39, 3 miles after
Camelford, turn right to St Teath,
through village. After 1 mile turn
right to Trewalder, the 3rd house after
the bridge.

1/45
■ PRESERVES

Trevervan Jams
Trevervan House, Trewarmett, Tintagel,
Cornwall PL34 0ES
Tel: (01840) 770486

Preserves, chutneys and pickles.
Open: 11am-5pm. Closed Christmas
Cards: Access, Amex, Diners, Visa

DIRECTIONS: 4 miles from
Camelford on B3263 about 1½ miles
from Tintagel. Near end of village,
overlooking Port Isaac Bay.

1/46
■ WINE

Camel Valley Wine
Little Denby Vineyard, Nanstallon, Bodmin,
Cornwall PL30 5LG
Tel: (01208) 77959

Red and white wines, vineyard tours.
Open: June-Sept Mon-Fri 2pm-4pm,
other times telephone first
Cards: No

DIRECTIONS: From Bodmin take
A389 Wadebridge road, after 2 miles
turn left to Nanstallon. After 1 mile
turn right at Vineyard sign.

1/47
■ BAKED GOODS

Proper Cornish
19 Paardeberg Road, Bodmin,
Cornwall PL31 1EY
Tel: (01208) 78712
Fax: (01208) 78713

Cornish pasties, pies, sausage rolls.
Open: Mon-Sat 6am-6pm. Closed 25,
26 Dec
Cards: No

DIRECTIONS: Off A30 to Bodmin.
Signs to industrial estates avoiding
town centre. Look for Walker Lines
Industrial Estate, near large factories.

1/48
● CERAMICS

Helland Bridge Pottery
Helland Bridge, Bodmin,
Cornwall PL30 4QR
Tel: (01208) 75240

Hand-thrown and decorated pottery.
Open: Mon-Sun 10am-5pm. Closed
15 July-31 Aug 3pm-6pm
Cards: No

DIRECTIONS: 2 miles north of
Bodmin, off A30. Follow signs to
Helland, situated beside bridge over
river Camel.

1/49
■ SAUSAGES

Tywardreath Butchers
41 Church Street, Tywardreath, Par,
Cornwall PL24 2QQ
Tel: (01726) 812051

28 varieties of sausage.
Open: Mon-Fri 7.30am-5pm Sat
7.30am-1pm
Cards: No

DIRECTIONS: Opposite New Inn
pub in middle of Tywardreath, just
off A390.

1/50
● LEATHER

The Leather Shop
The Old Mill, Boscastle, Cornwall PL35 0AA
Tel: (01840) 250515
Fax: (01840) 250539

Leather shoes, sandals, coats, jackets,
bags, purses, tankards, silver and
ethnic jewellery.
Open: Winter-daily 10am-6pm,
summer 9am-10pm
Cards: Access, Visa

DIRECTIONS: In main street next to
Wellington Hotel.

1/51
■ SAUSAGES
Richard Kittow and Son
1-3 South Street, Fowey,
Cornwall PL23 2AH
Tel: (01208) 873762

Sausages from pork, beef, lamb, wild
boar and venison.
Open: Mon-Sat 8am-5pm. Closed 25,
26 Dec, 1 Jan
Cards: No

DIRECTIONS: Liskeard to Bodmin
main road, signposted Trago Mills,
shop is right of main doors.

1/52
● PLANTS
Duchy of Cornwall Nursery
Cott Road, Lostwithiel, Cornwall PL22 0BW
Tel: (01208) 872668
Fax: (01208) 872835

Trees and shrubs.
Open: Mon-Sat 9am-5pm, Sun 10am-
5pm. Closed bank hols
Cards: Access, Amex, Switch, Visa

DIRECTIONS: From Lostwithiel,
head east on A390. Turn left as you
leave town, signposted to Golf Club.
One mile after Golf Club.

1/53
● CERAMICS
Wenford Bridge Pottery
St Breward, Bodmin, Cornwall PL30 3PN
Tel: (01208) 850471

Wood-fired functional stoneware.
Open: Mon-Sun 8.30am-5.30pm.
Closed 25 Dec
Cards: Access, Visa

DIRECTIONS: Signposted midway
along the Bodmin to Camelford
B3266 road.

1/54
● SADDLERY GOODS
Blisland Harness Makers
Higher Harrowbridge, Bolventor, Liskeard,
Cornwall PL14 6SD
Tel: (01579) 320593

Saddlery, dog equipment, cases, boxes,
bellows, cartridge bags and belts.

Open: Mon-Sun 9am-5pm, by
appointment only
Cards: No

DIRECTIONS: A30 Launceston to
Bodmin road, 2½ miles south of
Bolventur on the St Cleer road, which
follows the river Fowey.

1/55
● CERAMICS
Marylyn Hyde Pottery
Lower Stursdon, Morwenstow, Bude,
Cornwall EX23 9HU
Tel: (0288 331) 412

Hand-built pots with stoneware clay
used for containers, but mainly for
decorative purposes.
Open: Summer daily 10am-5pm, in
winter by appointment
Cards: No

DIRECTIONS: Off the A39, turn
towards the coast at Stursdon Cross,
cottage on right 1½ miles.

1/56
● WOOD
Lynn Muir
Aboukir House, Marhamchurch, Bude,
Cornwall EX23 0HB
Tel: (01288) 361561

Collectors' toys made from painted
reclaimed wood.
Open: By appointment only
Cards: Access, Switch, Visa

DIRECTIONS: 1 mile off A39 near
Bude. In middle of Marhamchurch,
opposite the Bullers Arms pub.

1/57
● CERAMICS
Springfield Pottery
Hartland, Bideford, Devon EX39 6BG
Tel: (01237) 441506

Earthenware pottery from local clays,
oven to tableware, tiles, garden and
individual pots.
Open: Mon-Sat 9am-6pm. Closed 25-
26 Dec, 1 Jan.
Cards: Access, Visa

DIRECTIONS: A39 Bideford to Bude
road, 12 miles west turn right for

Hartland. In village watch out for signs on left-hand side after the war memorial.

1/58
● FURNITURE
Millthorne Chairs
10 Fore Street, Hartland, Nr Bideford, Devon EX39 6BD
Tel: (01237) 441590

Adults' and children's Windsor chairs and stools in beech, ash and elm.
Open: Mon-Fri 8.30am-6pm
Cards: No

DIRECTIONS: From Bideford head towards Clovelly Cross, 200 yards on right of A39 to Hartland, 3 miles into village on left, first house before Anchor Inn.

1/59
● PLANTS
Bregover Plants
Middlewood, Nr Launceston, Cornwall PL15 7NN
Tel: (01566) 782661

Garden nursery, hardy perennials, asters, geraniums, primula, unusual annuals/biennials in season.
Open: Wed-Fri 11am-5pm. Mid Oct-mid-Mar, weekends and by appointment only
Cards: No

DIRECTIONS: Halfway between Liskeard and Launceston on the B3254.

1/60
● DOLLS' HOUSES
Treasure Houses
Lane End Cottage, Widegates, Looe, Cornwall PL13 1QB
Tel: (01503) 240665

Twelfth-scale dolls' houses. Thatched cottages, Regency townhouses and associated miniatures. Ranges for adults and children.
Open: Telephone first, but usually Mon-Sat 10am-5pm. Closed end Sept for 2 weeks
Cards: No

DIRECTIONS: On A387 westbound Looe Road. 4 miles north-east of Looe. 100 yards past Splinters Antiques on left.

1/61
■ CHEESE
Lynher Valley Dairy
D H Horrell Ltd
Netherton Farm, Upton Cross, Liskeard, Cornwall PL14 5BD
Tel: (01579) 62244
Fax: (01579) 62666

Makers of nettlecoated Cornish Yarg cheese and soft cheeses.
Open: Mon-Sat 10am-4pm. Closed Nov-1 April
Cards: No

DIRECTIONS: From A30 take B3257 towards Callington. 1 mile after Coads Green turn right to Rilla Mill/Upton Cross. Sign at lane end.

1/62
■ CHEESE
North Beer Farm
Boyton, Launceston, Cornwall PL15 8NR
Tel: (01566) 785607

Ewes' milk, cheese.
Open: Telephone first
Cards: No

DIRECTIONS: 6 miles north of Launceston, off B3254 to Bude. First right (tiny lane, no signpost) after Bennacott Kennels.

1/63
■ ICE-CREAM
Thorne Farm Natural Dairy Ice Cream Ltd
Thorne Manor, Holsworthy, Devon EX22 7JD
Tel: (01409) 253342
Fax: (01409) 253751

Natural dairy ice-cream.
Open: Daily 9am-5pm
Cards: No

DIRECTIONS: From Holsworthy take Bude road. After 2 miles turn right, signposted to Chilsworthy, Bradworthy. First farm lane ½ mile.

1/64
● TEXTILES

South Worden Farm Enterprises
South Worden Farm, Bradworthy,
Holsworthy, Devon EX22 7TW
Tel: (01409) 241827

Pure wool yarn and garments from
crossbred sheep.
Open: Telephone for appointment
Cards: No

DIRECTIONS: South of Clovelly and
east of Morwenstow. From
Bradworthy village square follow
signs to Kilkhampton/Bude. Turn 1st
left down lane after crossing stream.
3rd property on right.

1/65
■ WINE

Clawford Vineyard
Clawton, Holsworthy, Devon EX22 6PN
Tel: (01409) 254177

English wines, country wines, meads,
apple juices, ciders.
Open: Mon-Fri 9am-6.30pm, Sat
10am-6pm, June-Oct Sun 10am-6pm.
Closed 25-26 Dec
Cards: No

DIRECTIONS: On A388 Holsworthy
to Launceston road turn left at
Clawton crossroads. 2½ miles to T-
junction, turn left. After ½ mile turn
left into Clawford driveway, up to old
white Devon farmhouse.

1/66
■ CONFECTIONERY

Duchy Confectionery Company
Stoke Climsland, Callington,
Cornwall PL17 8NZ
Tel: (01579) 370331
Fax: (01579) 370191

Cornish cream fudge.
Open: Daily 9am-5pm
Cards: No

DIRECTIONS: In village by church.

1/67
● CERAMICS

Haytown Pottery
Haytown, Holsworthy, Devon EX22 7UW
Tel/Fax: (01409) 261476

Decorative, coloured domestic ware
and individual pieces, modelled
animals.
Open: Mon-Sun 10am-5pm
Cards: Visa

DIRECTIONS: 3 miles north-west of
the A388 Holsworthy to Torrington
road. Turn at Venn Green and follow
sign to Haytown at next crossroads.

1/68
● FURNITURE

David Savage Furniture Makers
21 Westcombe Lane, Bideford,
Devon EX39 3JQ
Tel: (01237) 479202
Fax: (01237) 479306

Furniture.
Open: Mon-Fri 9.30am-1pm, 2pm to
4.30pm, weekends by appointment
only. Closed Christmas to New Year
Cards: Access, Visa

DIRECTIONS: From Bideford quay,
pass statue of Charles Kingsley, turn
left at garage on right. Turn right at
junction of Chingswell Street and
North Road. At end of North Road
turn right then first left.

1/69
● PLANTS

The Fortescue Garden Trust, Garden House Enterprises Ltd
The Garden House, Buckland
Monachorum, Yelverton, Devon PL20 7LQ
Tel: (01822) 854769

Plant centre specialising in unusual
plants. Refreshments.
Open: Mar-Oct daily 10.30am-5pm
Cards: No

DIRECTIONS: 2 miles west of
Yelverton, clearly signposted off A386
Plymouth to Tavistock road. Once
through the village of Crapstone, 200
yards on the right.

1/70
■ HONEY

Vivian's Honey Farm
Hatherleigh, Devon EX20 3LJ
Tel/Fax: (01837) 810437

Honey from own 400 hives.
Open: Usually 9.30am-5.30pm, but
telephone in advance
Cards: No

DIRECTIONS: ½ mile from
Hatherleigh on Winterleigh road,
unmade lane on left.

1/71
■ CIDER

Inch's Cider Ltd
Hatherleigh Road, Winkleigh,
Devon EX19 8AP
Tel: (01837) 83560
Fax: (01837) 83552

Range of ciders (manufacturers since
1916).
Open: Summer Mon-Sat 9am-
5.30pm, winter Mon-Fri 9am-
4.30pm, Sat 9am-1pm
Cards: No

DIRECTIONS: A30 to Okehampton/
Bodmin, at first roundabout (10
miles) left to Winkleigh, left at
crossroads in village.

1/72
■ MEAT/POULTRY/GAME

**Higher Hacknell Farm
Partnership**
Higher Hacknell Farm, Burrington,
Umberleigh, Devon EX37 9LX
Tel: (01769) 560292

Lamb and beef.
Open: By appointment
Cards: No

DIRECTIONS: 1 mile outside
Burrington village, just off A377
Barnstaple to Exeter road.

1/73
■ CIDER

Saul's Farm
Wembworthy, nr Chulmleigh,
Devon EX18 7RW
Tel: (01769) 580750

Cider, apple juice and wine.
Open: Mon-Sat 9am-5pm, Sun
12noon-3pm
Cards: No

DIRECTIONS: 2 miles from
Wembworthy on back road to Bridge
Reeve.

1/74
■ FISH/SHELLFISH

Avon Oysters
Bigbury Cottage, Bigbury, Kingsbridge,
Devon TQ7 4AP
Tel: (01548) 810876
Fax: (01548) 830274

Oyster and mussel farm; in summer
crabs and lobsters.
Open: 8am-1pm. Telephone first for
afternoon times
Cards: No

DIRECTIONS: Follow A379 out of
Kingsbridge. 1 mile out of Modbury
turn right. Follow road to Bigbury. At
Pickwick Inn turn left. After 1 mile
Avon Oysters on left.

1/75
● CERAMICS

Rose Cottage Pottery
Harbourneford, South Brent,
Devon TQ10 9DT
Tel: (01364) 72550

Hand-thrown domestic and
ornamental earthenware.
Open: Mon-Sun 10am-5.30pm,
advisable to telephone first
Cards: No

DIRECTIONS: Harbourneford is on a
lane leading from South Brent
towards Dean Prior, approx 1½ miles.
Third house on the left as you enter
the hamlet.

MAP 2

2/76
■ BEER
The Royal Inn
Horsebridge, Tavistock, Devon PL19 8PJ
Tel: (01822) 870214

Four varieties of home-brewed beer.
Open: Mon-Sun 12-2.30pm, 7-11pm.
Closed 25 Dec 7-11pm
Cards: No

DIRECTIONS: From Tavistock take
A384. ½ mile past Lamerton take first
left (signpost to Gullworthy) keep
straight for 3 miles, follow signs to
Horsebridge. Or from the A390 to
Gunnislake to B3257, second right to
Luckett, keep straight for 3 miles.

2/77
■ CIDER
Countryman Cider
Felldownhead, Milton Abbot, Tavistock,
Devon PL19 0QR
Tel: (01822) 870226

Farm ciders using English cider
apples.
Open: Mon-Fri 9am-6.30pm, also
May-Sept Sat 9am-6.30pm
Cards: No

DIRECTIONS: Off B3362 Launceston
to Tavistock road at either junction
leading to Kell and Bradstone,
between Greystone Bridge and
Milton Abbot.

2/78
● PLANTS
Rowden Gardens
Brentor, nr Tavistock, Devon PL19 0NG
Tel: (01822) 810275

Aquatic and rare plants. Gardens open.
Open: Mar-Sept Sat-Sun and bank
hols 10am-5pm. Other times by
appointment
Cards: No

DIRECTIONS: On Lydford/Tavistock
road take turn off signposted
Lidditon, ¼ mile on.

2/79
● TOYS
Hilary Bix Puzzles
36 Lower Gunstone, Bideford,
Devon EX39 2DE
Tel: (01237) 470792

Children's wooden jigsaw puzzles,
clocks and door plaques.
Open: Mon-Fri 9am-12.30pm, 2.30-
5pm. Closed 27 June-9 Aug, 19 Dec-
10 Jan
Cards: Access, Visa

DIRECTIONS: Up Cooper Street,
cross over Mill Street and into Lower
Gunstone (the Heavitree pub is on
the corner). 150 yards up the hill on
the right.

2/80
● CERAMICS
Wren Pottery
The Village Craft Arcade, 10 Brook Street,
Tavistock, Devon PL19 0HD
Tel: (01822) 616896

Stoneware pottery, coffee sets, dinner
services, casseroles.
Open: Mon-Sat 9am-5pm
Cards: Access, Visa

DIRECTIONS: In the village arcade.

2/81
■ CHEESE
Country Cheeses
Market Road, Tavistock, Devon PL19 0BW
Tel: (01822) 615035

Cheeses, including Trehill, St Rumon
and St Petroc.
Open: Mon-Sat 9.30am-5pm. Closed
25-27 Dec
Cards: Access, Diners, Visa

DIRECTIONS: From Bedford Square
in Tavistock through the main gates
to Pannier Market. On right. Well
signposted.

2/82
● FORGEWORK

Redferns Smithy
Redferns, Brentor, Tavistock,
Devon PL19 0LR
Tel: (01822) 810496

Ironwork, windvanes, fireside
furniture, grilles.
Open: Mon-Sat 9am-12noon. Closed
25 Dec and Easter
Cards: No

DIRECTIONS: Leave the A386 at
Tavistock main square, head north for
5 miles to North Brentor.

2/83
● CERAMICS

**The Pottery at Duckpool
Cottage**
Duckpool Cottage, Sheepwash, Beaworthy,
Devon EX21 5PW
Tel: (01409) 231282

Wood-fired stoneware, garden and
domestic pots.
Open: By appointment only
Cards: No

DIRECTIONS: 1¼ miles north of
Sheepwash.

2/84
■ MEAT/POULTRY/GAME

Mid Devon Fallow
Keyethern Farm, Hatherleigh, Okehampton,
Devon EX20 3LG
Tel/Fax: (01837) 810028

Fresh and smoked venison. Also
deerskin rugs and antlers.
Open: Daily 11am-3pm
Cards: No

DIRECTIONS: North out of
Hatherleigh, take first left on
Sheepwash road for about 1½ miles.
Signposted.

2/85
● PLANTS

The High Garden
Newton Ferrers, Devon PL8 1BW
Tel: (01752) 872528

Pieris, rhododendron and azaleas.
Open: By appointment
Cards: No

DIRECTIONS: At Beacon Hill off
Court Road, 3 miles south of
Yealmpton on the Plymouth to
Kingsbridge road.

2/86
● CERAMICS

Hatherleigh Pottery
20 Market Street, Hatherleigh,
Devon EX20 3JP
Tel: (01837) 810624

Stoneware, domestic and garden pots.
Open: Mon-Sat 10am-6pm
Cards: Access, Visa

DIRECTIONS: On the A386 between
Okehampton and Torrington, the
pottery is on the main street just
above the town square.

2/87
● CERAMICS

Newport Pottery
72 Newport Road, Barnstaple,
Devon EX32 9BG
Tel: (01271) 72103

Pottery: house names, number plates,
decorative and functional bowls,
dishes, flower containers.
Open: Mon-Fri 10am-6pm, Sat 10am-
1pm and by appointment. Closed
some public holidays.
Cards: No

DIRECTIONS: From Tiverton A361
to Barnstaple, left after Tesco's, right
at traffic lights, 250 yards on left.

2/88
● SADDLERY GOODS

Ermington Mill Saddlery
National Shire Horse Centre, Yealmpton,
Plymouth, Devon PL8 2EL
Tel: (01752) 881133
Fax: (01752) 881014

Heavy horse harnesses, leather belts
and handbags.
Open: Oct-Mar Mon-Fri 8.30am-
5.30pm, Apr-Sept Mon-Sun 8.30am-
5.30pm. Closed Christmas.
Cards: Access, Visa

DIRECTIONS: Just off A379, 1½ miles
east of Yealmpton, follow all brown
horse signs on A38 east and west.

2/89
● PLANTS

Hostas Ann and Roger Bowden
Sticklepath, Okehampton,
Devon EX20 2NN
Tel: (01837) 840481
Fax: (01837) 840482

Over 400 varieties of hostas.
Open: By appointment
Cards: Access, Visa

DIRECTIONS: Off A30 Exeter to
Cornwall. Leave dual carriageway 15
miles west of Exeter at Merrymeet
roundabout. 3 miles to Sticklepath. In
middle of village.

2/90
● CERAMICS

Chittlehampton Pottery
Chittlehampton, Umberleigh,
Devon EX37 9PX
Tel: (01769) 540420

Handmade pottery and other
ceramics, functional domestic pottery,
candlesticks.
Open: Tue-Fri 10am-5pm, weekends
by appointment
Cards: Access, Visa

DIRECTIONS: Between the A377 and
A361 roads to North Devon. Just off
B3227, 4 miles west of South
Moulton.

2/91
● PLANTS

Glebe Cottage Plants
Pixie Lane, Warkleigh, Umberleigh,
Devon EX37 9DH
Tel/Fax: (01769) 540554

Herbaceous plants. Garden open.
Open: Tue-Fri 10am-5pm
Cards: No

DIRECTIONS: 4 miles south-west of
South Molton on B3226. Right
towards Warkleigh, right towards
Umberleigh, left towards
Chittlehamholt and Chulmleigh.

2/92
● WOOD

Woodturners Craft Centre
New Road, Modbury, Devon PL21 0QH
Tel: (01548) 830405

Woodturning, furniture, carving.
Open: Mon-Sat 10.30am-5.30pm. 25
Dec-31 Jan by appointment only.
Cards: No

DIRECTIONS: Craft Centre is the last
building on the right leaving
Modbury for Kingsbridge. Look for
the red cartwheels.

2/93
● LEATHER GOODS

A & J Piper
7 Exeter Street, North Tawton,
Devon EX20 1HB
Tel/Fax: (01837) 82548

Leather bags, briefcases and travelling
bags.
Open: By appointment
Cards: Access, Visa

DIRECTIONS: Travelling west from
Exeter take North Tawton exit at first
roundabout (15 miles). After 500
yards take turning at the Post Inn
through Widdon Down, then
immediate right to North Tawton.

2/94
■ FISH/SHELLFISH

Head Mill Trout Farm
Umberleigh, Devon EX37 9HA
Tel: (01769) 580862
Fax: (01769) 580950

Fresh and smoked trout products.
Open: Daily 9.30-5.30pm. Closed
Christmas
Cards: Access, Visa

DIRECTIONS: On B3226 South
Molton to Exeter road shortly before
junction of B3226 and A377
Barnstaple/Exeter road at King's
Nympton station.

2/95
■ MEAT/POULTRY/GAME
Heal Farm Meats Ltd
Heal Farm, King's Nympton, Umberleigh,
Devon EX37 9TB
Tel: (01769) 574341
Fax: (01769) 572839

Fresh meat, sausages, bacon, ham,
pâté, potted beef and brawn from rare
breeds.
Open: Mon-Fri 9am-5pm, Sat 10am-
4pm. Closed bank hols and Christmas
to New Year
Cards: Access, Diners

DIRECTIONS: From South Molton
go to George Nympton. After village
take first right turn, follow through
Sampson Cross. Take first right then
next left at Heal Farm sign.

2/96
■ MEAT/POULTRY/GAME
Wild Beef
Hillhead Farm, Chagford, Devon TQ13 8DY
Tel/Fax: (01647) 433433

Organic beef.
Open: By appointment only
Cards: No

DIRECTIONS: At square in Chagford
take road at top and follow signs to
Fernworthy Reservoir for about 2½
miles. Hillhead Farm is on right.

2/97
■ ICE-CREAM
Devonshire Farmhouse Ice Cream
Higher Murchington Farm, Chagford,
Newton Abbot, Devon TQ13 8HJ
Tel: (01647) 433648

Clotted cream, dairy ice-cream,
sorbets and yoghurt.
Open: Daily
Cards: Access, Switch, Visa

DIRECTIONS: South of Whiddon
Down on A30, 16 miles west of
Exeter. Take Moretonhampstead
road, 2 miles west on Murchington
road.

2/98
● WOOD
Wood & Rush
1A The Square, Chagford, Devon TQ13 8AA
Tel: (01647) 231330

Willow basket-maker and woodturner.
Open: Thur-Sat 10.30am-5pm
Cards: No

DIRECTIONS: Chagford is 2 miles
off A382 between Moretonhampstead
and Whiddon Down. The shop is
opposite Old Forge Tea Rooms in the
centre of the village.

2/99
● CLOTHES
Sleepy Hollow
South Hams Business Park, Churchstow,
Devon TQ7 3QR
Tel: (01548) 857060
Fax: (01548) 857061

Hats and country wear, equestrian
comfort products.
Open: Mon-Fri 9am-5pm
Cards: Access, Visa

DIRECTIONS: Follow A379
(Kingsbridge-Plymouth) road. On the
left about 600 yards after first
roundabout.

2/100
■ HONEY
Quince Honey Farm
North Road, South Molton, Devon
EX36 3AZ
Tel: (01769) 572401
Fax: (01769) 574704

Devon and Exmoor honey in jars,
combs. Beeswax candles, polish.
Open: 9am-5pm. Closed Christmas
and New Year
Cards: Access, Switch, Visa

DIRECTIONS: Signposted from A361
(North Devon Link Road).

2/101
■ BAKED GOODS

Moorland Larder
113 East Street, South Molton,
Devon EX36 3DB
Tel: (01769) 573554

Farmed venison, country foods and
homemade products.
Open: Mon-Sat 9.30am-5pm. Winter
Wed 9.30am-2pm. Closed Sun, 25, 26
Dec, 1 Jan
Cards: No

DIRECTIONS: Signposted South
Molton on A361.

2/102
■ CHEESE

Loddiswell Cheese
Blackdown Farm, Rings Lane, Loddiswell,
Kingsbridge, Devon TQ7 4EA
Tel: (01548) 821387

Goats'- and cows'-milk cheeses.
Open: Mon-Sun 11am-6pm
Cards: No

DIRECTIONS: From A38 road follow
signs to Blackdown Rings.

2/103
■ MEAT/POULTRY/GAME

Tordean Farm
Dean Prior, Buckfastleigh, Devon TQ11 0LY
Tel: (01364) 643305
Fax: (01364) 643011

Meat and meat products.
Open: Mon-Thur 7am-5pm, Fri 7am-
6.30pm. Sat by appointment. Closed
24 Dec to 2 Jan
Cards: No

DIRECTIONS: On Exeter-bound
A38, halfway between Plymouth and
Exeter. Also halfway between South
Brent and Buckfastleigh. Near the
Rattery flyover.

2/104
■ MEAT/POULTRY/GAME

Deer Force 10
Village Farm, Holne, Newton Abbot,
Devon TQ13 7SL
Tel: (01364) 631532

Venison, including sausages, pâté,
terrines and smoked meat.
Open: Daily 8am-7pm, but advisable
to telephone first
Cards: Access, Visa

DIRECTIONS: On A38 Exeter to
Plymouth road, take Ashburton exit
marked Peartree. Follow signs for
Princetown and Holne. After crossing
River Dart, turn left for Holne. 30
yards above the Church House Inn.

2/105
● PLANTS

Stone Lane Gardens
Stone Farm, Chagford, Devon TQ13 8JU
Tel: (01647) 231311

Birch and alder arboretum.
Open: By appointment
Cards: No

DIRECTIONS: Just south of lane
connecting Whiddon Down with
Drewsteignton, on a branch lane at
midway point, running a short
distance south to the A382.

2/106
■ ICE-CREAM

Salcombe Dairy
Shadycombe Road, Salcombe,
Devon TQ8 8DX
Tel: (01548) 843228
Fax: (01548) 843096

Ice-cream. Shop and café.
Open: Summer daily 9am-5pm, spring
and autumn Mon-Sat 9am-5pm,
winter Mon-Sat 9.30am-2pm
Cards: No

DIRECTIONS: Turn off A38 to
Kingsbridge. Follow signs to
Salcombe. Situated in the main short
stay car park.

2/107
■ FISH/SHELLFISH

Salcombe Smokers
54 Fore Street, Kingsbridge,
Devon TQ7 1NY
Tel/Fax: (01548) 852006

Smoked salmon, mackerel, cods' roe,
prawns, cod, haddock.
Open: Mon and Thur 8am-4pm. Tue,
Wed, Fri 8am-5pm. Sat 8am-1pm
Cards: No

DIRECTIONS: At top of Fore Street,
on left just below town clock.

2/108
■ WINE

Loddiswell Vineyard and Winery
Lilwell, Loddiswell, Kingsbridge,
Devon TQ7 4EF
Tel: (01548) 550221

Grapes and wines.
Open: Easter-Oct Mon-Fri 1pm-6pm,
at other times by appointment
Cards: No

DIRECTIONS: 5 miles north of
Kingsbridge, 7 miles south of
Wrangaton Cross on A38 Exeter to
Plymouth.

2/109
● BASKETS

Honeyford Baskets
Honeyford Cottage, Drewsteignton, Exeter,
Devon EX6 6NQ
Tel: (01647) 281603

English willow and hedgerow baskets.
Open: By appointment only
Cards: No

DIRECTIONS: From Exeter take the
A30. Follow signs for Crockernwell,
at Crockernwell take left turn
signposted Drewsteignton and Castle
Drogo. Honeyford is ¼ mile on the
right.

2/110
■ WINE

The Down-St-Mary Vineyard
Down-St-Mary, Nr Crediton,
Devon EX17 6EE
Tel/Fax: (01363) 82300 (ask for fax)

Vineyard and winery operation
making white wine. Also bottle other
products.
Open: Tue-Sat 11.30am-5.30pm, Sun
12-3pm
Cards: No

DIRECTIONS: Through the village of
Down-St-Mary ¾ mile down the
lane, leading to Zeal Monachorum.
Down-St-Mary is off the A377,
Crediton–Barnstaple Road.

2/111
■ WINE

Cuprea Vineyard
Diptford Downs, Diptford, Nr Totnes,
Devon TQ9 7PB
Tel: (01364) 73205

English wines.
Open: May-Oct Mon-Fri 2pm-5pm,
also July-Aug Sat-Sun 2pm-5pm
Cards: No

DIRECTIONS: On B3210 Totnes to
Avonwick road, 4 miles west of
Totnes. Follow signs for village and
vineyard.

2/112
● NEEDLECRAFTS

Presence
21-23 East Street, Ashburton,
Devon TQ13 7AQ
Tel: (01364) 653369

Patchwork, quilts, appliqué cushions,
papier mâché.
Open: Mon-Sat 9.30am-5.30pm.
Closed bank hols
Cards: Access, Visa

DIRECTIONS: On the A38 between
Exeter and Plymouth next to NatWest
bank.

2/113
● CERAMICS

Simonsbath Pottery
Pound Cottage, Simonsbath, Exmoor,
Somerset TA24 7SH
Tel/Fax: (0164383) 443

High-fired stoneware, casseroles,
mugs, jugs, lampbases and vases.
Open: Mon-Fri 9.30am-5.30pm, Sat-
Sun 10am-5pm. Closed winter Mon-
Tue
Cards: Access, Visa

DIRECTIONS: On main road
through Simonsbath between Exmoor
Forest and Simonsbath House Hotel.

2/114
● CERAMICS

Fuchsia Ceramics
Cutlands Pottery, Chillington, Nr
Kingsbridge, Devon TQ7 2HS
Tel: (01548) 580390

Hand-thrown domestic stoneware
decorated with fuchsia design.
Open: Mon-Fri 9am-1pm, 2pm-
5.45pm. Telephone first at weekends
Cards: No

DIRECTIONS: 4 miles from
Kingsbridge on A379 coastal road to
Dartmouth, on right in village of
Chillington.

2/115
■ CIDER

**Stancombe Traditional
Farmhouse Cyder**
Stancombe, Sherford, Kingsbridge,
Devon TQ7 2BE
Tel: (01548) 531634
Fax: (01548) 531012

Cider fermented in oak barrels.
Open: Mon-Sun 10am-5pm
Cards: Access, Visa

DIRECTIONS: A384 Kingsbridge to
Totnes, follow signs to Kingsbridge
on A381. Left at Slapton signpost
(after Stanborough Hundred Hotel)
then follow brown tourist cyder press
signposts.

2/116
● CERAMICS

Marianne De Trey
Shinners Bridge Pottery, Dartington,
Totnes, Devon TQ9 6JB
Tel: (01803) 862046

Hand-thrown decorative porcelain.
Open: By appointment only
Cards: No

DIRECTIONS: 2 miles west of Totnes
on A385. Access via Cider Press
Centre car park.

2/117
● WOOD

**Bill Hooper Wooden Bathroom
Furniture and Small Gifts**
Parford, Moretonhampstead, Newton
Abbot, Devon TQ13 8PU
Tel: (01647) 433472

Wooden bathroom furniture and gifts.
Open: Mon-Sat 8am-8pm
Cards: No

DIRECTIONS: A30 opposite turning
from Chagford, by Eastern Court
Hotel, Dunsford, about a mile on the
right.

2/118
■ FLOUR

Crowdy Mill
Bow Road, Harbertonford, Totnes,
Devon TQ9 7HU
Tel: (01803) 732340

Organic flour: wholemeal,
unbleached white, malted grain and
rye.
Open: 10.30am-5.30pm
Cards: No

DIRECTIONS: On A381 Totnes to
Kingsbridge Road. In Harbertonford
follow brown tourist signs.

2/119
● CERAMICS

**David Leach Lowerdown
Pottery**
Lowerdown Pottery, Bovey Tracey,
Devon TQ13 9LE
Tel/Fax: (01626) 833408

Stoneware and porcelain.

Open: Mon-Sun 9am-6pm,
appointment advised
Cards: No

DIRECTIONS: ½ mile out of Bovey
Tracey at Lowerdown Cross on
B3387, opposite Edgemoor Hotel.

2/120
■ DAIRY PRODUCE

Ticklemore Cheese
1 Ticklemore Street, Totnes,
Devon TQ9 5EJ
Tel: (01803) 865926

Cheese, ice-cream, apple juice,
chutnies, jams and honey.
Open: Mon-Fri 9am-5.30pm, Sat
9.15am-4.45pm. Closed bank hols
Cards: No

DIRECTIONS: In centre of Totnes,
located just off the plains.

2/121
● TOYS

David Plagerson
28 Bridgetown, Totnes, Devon TQ9 5AD
Tel: (01803) 866786

Handmade wooden Noah's Arks and
other carved toys.
Open: By appointment
Cards: No

DIRECTIONS: Just outside town
centre of Totnes.

2/122
● CERAMICS

Colin Kellam
The Lion Brewery, South Street, Totnes,
Devon TQ9 5DZ
Tel: (01803) 863150

Stoneware pottery.
Open: Mon-Fri 9am-5pm
Cards: Access, Amex, Diners, Visa

DIRECTIONS: At the centre of
Totnes Civic Square car park.

2/123
● WOOD

Rendle Crang Woodcraft
19-20 Burke Road, Industrial Estate,
Totnes, Devon TQ9 5JA
Tel: (01803) 865447

Hardwood woodturning, bowls,
lamps, balustrades.
Open: Mon-Fri 8.30am-5pm. Closed
bank hols and 2 weeks in August
Cards: No

DIRECTIONS: From Exeter A38 to
Dartbridge (Buckfastleigh) and follow
road signs to Totnes. Follow road to
Torquay over railway bridge, then
first left at roundabout into Babbage
Road, then second right into Burke
Road.

2/124
■ FARM PRODUCE

Riverford Farm Foods
Riverford Farm, Staverton, Totnes,
Devon TQ9 6AF
Tel: (01803) 762523
Fax: (01803) 762571

Home-cured bacon, sausages, beef,
lamb, poultry and English charcuterie.
Open: Mon-Sat 9am-6pm, Easter-
Christmas Sun 10am-4pm
Cards: Access, Switch, Visa

DIRECTIONS: On A384 Totnes to
Buckfastleigh road, 2 miles south of
A38 just north of Riverford Bridge.

2/125
● GLASS

House of Marbles & Teign
Valley Glass
The Old Pottery, Pottery Road, Bovey
Tracey, Devon TQ13 9DS
Tel: (01626) 835358
Fax: (01626) 835315

Glass-blowing and marbles.
Restaurant.
Open: Mon-Sun 9am-5pm,
Christmas-Easter closed Sun
Cards: Access, Visa

DIRECTIONS: Turn off the A38
between Exeter and Plymouth at the
Drum Bridges roundabout, then
follow the brown tourist signs.

2/126
● JEWELLERY

Rebecca Edmunds

Western Watch Centre, 7 Fore Street,
Bovey Tracey, Devon TQ13 9AD
Tel: (01626) 832943

Handmade precious metal jewellery.
Open: Mon-Sat 9am-5.15pm
Cards: Access, Visa

DIRECTIONS: Follow signs to Bovey
Tracey. 200 yards past bridge over
river Bovey, on right of High Street.

2/127
■ CIDER

Gray's Farm Cider

Halstow, Tedburn St Mary, Exeter,
Devon EX6 6AN
Tel: (01647) 61236

Cider from local apples.
Open: Mon-Sat 8am-6pm. Closed
bank hols
Cards: No

DIRECTIONS: Between Tedburn St
Mary and Dunsford, about 6 miles
west of Exeter.

2/128
■ CIDER

E & P Bromell

Lower Uppercott, Tedburn St Mary, Nr
Exeter, Devon EX6 6AZ
Tel: (01647) 61294

Cider, scrumpy and vegetables in
season.
Open: Mon-Fri 7am-7pm, summer
9pm
Cards: No

DIRECTIONS: From A30, 5 miles
from Exeter take Tedburn St Mary
road into village. Take first right into
Whitestone Road. 300 yards on the
right.

2/129
● FORGEWORK

John Churchill, Blacksmith

The New Forge, Capton Workshops,
Capton, Nr Dartmouth, Devon TQ6 0JE
Tel: (01803) 712535

Architectural and domestic
ironmongery.
Open: Mon-Fri 9am-1pm, 2-5pm,
some weekends
Cards: No

DIRECTIONS: Turn off B3207 4
miles before Dartmouth at
Sportsmans' Arms. Follow signs to
Capton. Follow road downhill
through village, bear left after
telephone kiosk. 300 yards on right.

2/130
▨ FRUIT/VEGETABLES

Dittisham Fruit Farm

Capton, Dartmouth, Devon TQ6 0JE
Tel: (01803) 712452

Soft fruit, fruit liqueurs, sloe gin,
herbs and vegetables.
Open: Mar-Oct daily 10am-5pm
Cards: No

DIRECTIONS: Signposted from
Sportmans' Arms pub in Capton, on
A3120 to Dartmouth.

2/131
▨ WINE

Sharpham Vineyard and Sharpham Creamery

Sharpham House, Ashprington, Totnes,
Devon TQ9 7UT
Tel: (01803) 732203
Fax: (01803) 732037

Wine and cheese.
Open: Mon-Fri 2-5pm, other times by
appointment
Cards: No

DIRECTIONS: From Totnes take the
A381 signposted Kingsbridge. Take
first left signposted Ashprington. In
the centre of Ashprington turn left at
the war memorial. Vineyard shop is
1½ miles down no through road.

2/132
■ WINE

Whitstone Vineyards
Bovey Tracey, Devon TQ13 9NA
Tel: (01626) 832280

Wines, and vineyard tours by
appointment.
Open: Mon-Fri 8am-12pm, other times
by appointment. Closed all holidays
Cards: No

DIRECTIONS: On old Bovey
Tracey/Moretonhampstead road just
after turn to Bovey Tracey hospital.

2/133
● PLANTS

Peveril Clematis Nursery
Christow, Nr Exeter, Devon EX6 7NG
Tel: (01647) 252937

Nursery specialising in clematis.
Open: Mon-Wed, Fri-Sat, 10am-1pm,
2-5.30pm
Cards: No

DIRECTIONS: 9 miles west of Exeter,
off B3193 Teign Valley Road. Situated
in centre of village, between school
and Artichoke Inn.

2/134
■ PRESERVES

Heaven Scent Herbs
Crediton Station, Station Yard, Crediton,
Devon EX7 3BY
Tel/Fax: (01363) 777754

Wholegrain herb and spice mustards.
Open: By appointment only
Cards: No

DIRECTIONS: In Crediton Station
buildings.

2/135
✳ MULTIPLE

Coombe Farm Gallery
Dittisham, Dartmouth, Devon TQ6 0JA
Tel/Fax: (01803) 722352

Jewellery and art.
Open: Mon-Sat 10am-5pm
Cards: No

DIRECTIONS: From Totnes take
Dartmouth road (about 7 miles). At
the Sportsman's Arms, turn left to
Dittisham (3 miles). Turn left to
Coombe, studio signposted.

2/136
■ ICE-CREAM

Pure Jersey Ice Cream
Rookbeare Farm, Cheriton Fitzpaine,
Crediton, Devon EX17 4BE
Tel: (01363) 866424

Ice-cream and Jersey cream.
Open: Mon-Sat 9am-6pm.
Recommended to telephone first
Cards: No

DIRECTIONS: Turn off A3072 to
Cheriton Fitzpaine, left through
village, right on leaving village and up
steep hill, first left and follow lane ¾
mile to farm.

2/137
● ART

Simon Drew Gallery
13 Foss Street, Dartmouth,
Devon TQ6 9DR
Tel: (01803) 832832
Fax: (01803) 833040

Prints, cards and originals.
Open: Mon-Sat 9am-5pm. Closed
Christmas and January
Cards: Access, Visa

DIRECTIONS: Leave A38 at
Buckfastleigh, towards Totnes. Foss
Street in centre of Dartmouth.

2/138
● ART

John Gillo Gallery
3 The Old Market, Dartmouth,
Devon TQ6 9QF
Tel/Fax: (01803) 833833

Prints, paintings and sculptures.
Open: Mon-Sat 9.30am-1pm, 2pm-
5.30pm
Cards: Access, Amex, Diners, Switch,
Visa

DIRECTIONS: Old Market Square is
opposite Woolworths.

2/139
■ ICE-CREAM

Langworthys Ice Cream Dairy
The Good Intent, 30 Lower Street,
Dartmouth, Devon TQ6 9AN
Tel: (01803) 832157

Ice-cream and clotted cream.
Open: Winter 7am-6pm, summer
7am-10pm
Cards: No

DIRECTIONS: In Dartmouth,
opposite Lower Ferry and historic
Bayards Cove.

2/140
● CERAMICS

Lotus Pottery
Stoke Gabriel, nr Totnes, Devon TQ9 6SL
Tel: (01803) 782303

Wide range of wood-fired pots.
Open: Mon-Fri 9am-12.30pm,
1.30pm-5.30pm, Sat 9am-12.30pm
Cards: No

DIRECTIONS: In Stoke Gabriel turn
right at T-junction, follow signs to
pottery.

2/141
■ CIDER

Churchward Cider
Yalberton Farm, Yalberton Road, Paignton,
Devon TQ4 7PE
Tel: (01803) 558157

Farmhouse cider, scrumpy dry,
Devon mix, medium and sweet.
Open: Winter Mon-Sat 9am-5.30pm,
Sun 12 noon-2pm, summer Mon-Sat
9am-9pm, Sun 12 noon-3pm, 7pm-
9pm
Cards: No

DIRECTIONS: Just off the Torbay
ring road. Turn right down Yalberton
road, ½ mile down by the stream.

2/142
● CERAMICS

Robert Tinnyunt Ceramics
The Pottery, 96 Exeter Road,
Kingsteignton, Devon TQ12 3LU
Tel: (01626) 61011

Hand-thrown stoneware pottery,
functional and individual.

Open: Mon-Fri 10am-5pm, Sat-Sun
by appointment
Cards: No

DIRECTIONS: A380 to Torbay,
turning on to B3195 for
Kingsteignton. Pottery on left approx
400 yards after passing Ten Tors Inn.

2/143
● WOOD

One Good Turn
Unit 15, Old Pottery Court, 8A Fore Street,
Chudleigh, Devon TQ13 0HX
Tel: (01626) 853453

Wood-turned articles and soft toys.
Open: Christmas to Easter Tue-Sat
9.30am-5pm, Easter to Christmas
Mon-Sat 9.30am-5pm
Cards: No

DIRECTIONS: Off A38 Exeter to
Plymouth road. In town, opposite war
memorial.

2/144
● PLANTS

Churchills Garden Nursery
Exeter Road, Chudleigh, Devon TQ13 0DD
Tel/Fax: (01626) 852585

Trees, shrubs, climbers and
herbaceous plants.
Open: Mid Mar-mid Oct Mon-Fri
2pm-5pm, Sat, Sun and bank hols
10am-5pm, other times by
appointment
Cards: No

DIRECTIONS: Take slip road off A38
to Chudleigh. Follow signposts on
Exeter road out of Chudleigh.

2/145
■ CHEESE

Quicke & Partners
Home Farm, Newton St Cyres, Exeter,
Devon EX5 5AY
Tel: (01392) 851222
Fax: (01392) 851382

Traditional cheeses, including
Cheddar.
Open: Mon-Sat 8.30am-5pm. Closed
bank hols
Cards: No

DIRECTIONS: On A377 Exeter to Crediton road, 3 miles from Exeter on right immediately after Newton St Cyres village.

2/146
● FURNITURE

Nicholas Chandler Furniture Maker
Woodpeckers, Rackenford, Tiverton, Devon EX16 8ER
Tel/Fax: (01884) 881380

Contemporary furniture, boxes, bowls, tables and chairs.
Open: Mon-Sun 9am-6pm
Cards: No

DIRECTIONS: From M5 J27 take A361 to Barnstaple. 7 miles on from Tiverton, turn right to Bickham and Woodburn. Continue 400 yards to signpost for house on right. Down drive, first right.

2/147
● SADDLERY GOODS

McCoy Saddlery & Leathercraft
High Street, Porlock, Minehead, Somerset TA24 8QD
Tel: (01643) 862518
Fax: (01643) 863088

Saddlery, bridlework, repairs, suede and leather riding chaps, brushing boots.
Open: Mon-Fri 9am-5.50pm, Sat 9am-5pm
Cards: Access, Amex, Switch, Visa

DIRECTIONS: On A39, 6 miles west of Minehead. At bottom of Porlock Hill by junction to Porlock Weir and Ship Inn.

2/148
■ COFFEE/TEA

D J Miles & Co Ltd
Vale Yard, High Street, Porlock, Somerset TA24 8PU
Tel: (01643) 862585
Fax: (01643) 863048

Tea and fresh-roasted coffee.
Open: Mon-Fri 8.30am-5pm. Closed Christmas, Easter and bank hols
Cards: No

DIRECTIONS: In small road immediately opposite post office.

2/149
■ CIDER

Reddaway's Farm Cider
Lower Rixdale Farm, Luton, Ideford, Newton Abbot, Devon TQ13 0BN
Tel: (01626) 775218

Traditional Devonshire farm cider or scrumpy.
Open: Mon-Sat all day
Cards: No

DIRECTIONS: Turn off the A380 Torbay to Exeter road where signposted to Ideford and Luton, go through Ideford into Luton. Turn left at telephone box and drive ½ mile to farm.

2/150
● ART

Anna Fraser Fine Art
Winsford Gallery, Winsford, Minehead, Exmoor, Somerset TA24 7JE
Tel: (01643) 851288

Animal and human portraits from life or photograph.
Open: Advisable to telephone first
Cards: No

DIRECTIONS: In centre of village, just across the Ford. Old Wesleyan Chapel with Gothic-style windows.

2/151
● KNITWEAR

Strands of Shaldon
24 Strand, Shaldon, Teignmouth, Devon TQ14 0DL
Tel: (01626) 873544

Knitwear in natural fibres.
Open: Mon-Sat 10am-5pm. Closed Christmas
Cards: Access, Visa

DIRECTIONS: Take A381 to Teignmouth from A380. Turn right at bridge into Shaldon, turn left into Fore Street, continue into Strand, on right.

2/152
■ FISH/SHELLFISH

River Exe Shellfish Farms
Lyson, Kenton, Exeter, Devon EX6 8EZ
Tel: (01626) 890133
Fax: (01626) 891789

Oysters, mussels and clams.
Open: Mon-Fri 9am-5pm, Sat-Sun by
appointment. Closed bank hols
Cards: Access, Visa

DIRECTIONS: Take A380 Exeter to
Torquay road. Turn left at café to
Starcross Kenton, through forest and
down hill for 1½ miles. Turn left at
crossroads to Lyson and Oxton, first
on left.

2/153
■ CIDER

Clark's Farm Cider
Shortridge Hill, Seven Crosses, Tiverton,
Devon EX16 8HH
Tel: (01884) 252632

Farmhouse cider from local apples.
Open: Please telephone for times
Cards: No

DIRECTIONS: J27 of M5 then A373
to Tiverton. From fire station take
Seven Crosses Road to Beckley, turn
right after 350 yards at Wormsland
Cross and the farm is first entrance on
the right.

2/154
■ BAKED GOODS

Mrs Gill's Country Cakes
Unit 4/5, Link House, Leat Street, Tiverton
Devon EX16 5LG
Tel: (01884) 242744
Fax: (01884) 257440

Fruit, Dundee and wedding cakes.
Open: Mon-Fri 9am-5pm, but
telephone in advance
Cards: No

DIRECTIONS: J27 of M5. At first
roundabout on A373 turn left, past
large school on right. At intersection
turn right into Kennedy Way, over
bridge, and follow road round to left.
First turning on right (signposted).

2/155
● FURNITURE

Sugan Chairs
Exeham Farm, Exebridge, Dulverton,
Somerset TA22 9AY
Tel: (01398) 323776

Celtic chairs, tables and dressers in
hardwoods.
Open: Telephone for appointment but
usually 10am-5pm
Cards: Access, Visa

DIRECTIONS: Between Bampton
and Dulverton. Find Anchor Inn,
cross bridge and turn immediately left
down farm track.

2/156
■ MEAT/POULTRY/GAME

Burrow Products
High Burrow Farm, Timberscombe,
Minehead, Somerset TA24 7UD
Tel: (01643) 841427

Gressingham duck.
Open: Daily 9am-5pm, telephone first
Cards: No

DIRECTIONS: Burrow is between
Timberscombe and Wootton
Courtenay off the Dunster to
Wheddon Cross road near Minehead.

2/157
● CERAMICS

Mill Pottery
Wootton Courtenay, Minehead,
Somerset TA24 8RB
Tel: (01643) 841297

Pots suitable for everyday use, and
specially decorated items.
Open: Mon-Sat 9.30am-1pm, 2-5pm,
Sun by appointment
Cards: Access, Visa

DIRECTIONS: 2 miles from Dunster
on A396, follow signs for Wootton
Courtenay and pottery. Also
signposted on A39, 2 miles west of
Minehead.

2/158
✱ MULTIPLE

Pulhams Mill Furniture & Crafts
Pulhams Mill, Brompton Regis, Dulverton, Exmoor, Somerset TA22 9NT
Tel: (01398) 371366

Solid timber furniture, handpainted china – country scenes and animals. Also local and countryside crafts.
Open: Easter to Sept Mon-Sat 10am-6pm. Oct-Easter Mon-Sat 10am-5pm. Sun in summer. Closed Jan-Feb
Cards: Access, Visa

DIRECTIONS: ½ a mile from centre of Brompton Regis on road to Wimbleball Reservoir.

2/159
■ WINE

Dunkery Vineyard
Wootton Courtenay, Nr Minehead, Somerset TA24 8RF
Tel/Fax: (01643) 841505

Wines.
Open: By appointment
Cards: No

DIRECTIONS: From A39 go south through Dunster, after 2 miles turn right to Wootton Courtenay.

2/160
● CERAMICS

The Exmoor Pottery
3 Parks Lane, Minehead, Somerset TA24 5NU
Tel: (01643) 706188

Pottery and sculpture, wild flowers, trees, scenes of Exmoor, figurines.
Open: Mon-Sat 9am-1pm, 2pm-5pm, variable holidays
Cards: No

DIRECTIONS: From Taunton, follow A39 through Minehead. Pass Wellington Square on left (the Wellington Hotel). Take next turn on right into Parks Lane. The studio is next to the launderette about 10 yards on right.

2/161
✱ MULTIPLE

The Craft Emporium
13 Friday Street, Minehead, Somerset TA24 5UB
Tel: (0643) 707006

Local crafts: pottery, woodwork, glass, textiles, jams, prints, floral work, doorstops and gifts using textiles.
Open: Mon-Sat 9.30am-4pm
Cards: No

DIRECTIONS: From seafront on main shopping street, ¾ way up Friday Street, on left just before Tourist Information.

2/162
● CERAMICS

Park Street Pottery
13A Park Street, Minehead, Somerset TA24 5NQ
Tel: (01643) 702753

Pottery (many items include 24-ct gold lustres), also hand-blown glass and sculptured wood.
Open: Mon-Fri 10am-1pm, 2pm-5pm, Sat 10am-1pm; Jan Mon-Fri 10am-12 noon, Sat 10am-1pm
Cards: Access, Visa

DIRECTIONS: Top end of Minehead, by pelican crossing.

2/163
● TOYS

Eric Horne Collectors Toys
The Studio, Farleys Court, Fore Street, Topsham, Exeter, Devon EX3 0HJ
Tel: (01392) 877600

Handmade collectors' toys aimed mainly at the adult market. Dutch dolls from 18in high.
Open: Mon-Fri 10am-1pm, 2pm-4.30pm, Sat 10am-12 noon, or by appointment
Cards: Access, Amex, Visa

DIRECTIONS: M5 J30 take A376 to Topsham, Farleys Court off Fore St, by estate agents.

2/164
● FORGEWORK

Bill Poirrier – Artist Blacksmith
Riverden Forge, Roadwater, Watchet,
Somerset TA23 0QA
Tel: (01984) 640648

Functional or sculptural metalwork.
Open: Daily 9am-5pm
Cards: No

DIRECTIONS: 3 miles south of
Washford on A39 between Williton
and Minehead. Signposted Cleave
Abbey, Roadwater. 400 yards up hill
from Valiant Soldier, fork right then
turn right.

2/165
● PETS ACCESSORIES

Comfy Pet Products
2-4 Parsonage Street, Bradninch, Exeter,
Devon EX5 4NW
Tel: (01392) 881285

Brushes, rugs, travelling hampers for
dogs and cats.
Open: Telephone for appointment
Cards: Access, Visa

DIRECTIONS: J28 of M5 into
Cullompton. Take Exeter road, follow
signs to Bradninch. At bottom of hill
turn left down Parsonage Street. First
house on left.

2/166
■ FLOUR

Dunster Working Water Mill
Mill Lane, Dunster, Minehead,
Somerset TA24 6SW
Tel: (01643) 821759

Stoneground flour and muesli.
Open: Apr-Oct daily, except Sat,
10am-5pm, July and Aug every day.
Closed Nov-Mar except first Fri/Sat
in Dec
Cards: No

DIRECTIONS: From A39 Williton to
Minehead road turn south on to A396
Tiverton road immediately on
entering Dunster village. Mill Lane is
left fork off A396 on south side of
Dunster.

2/167
■ MEAT/POULTRY/GAME

Pipers Farm
Langford, Cullompton, Devon EX15 1SD
Tel: (01392) 881380
Fax: (01392) 881600

Traditional and continental cuts, ham,
bacon, sausages and pâtés.
Open: Mon-Fri 9am-5pm, Sat 9am-
1pm. Closed Sun and bank hols
Cards: Access, Switch, Visa

DIRECTIONS: J28 of M5, 3½ miles
from Cullompton on B3181 towards
Broadclyst. Take 2nd left, signposted
Clyst Hydon. Pipers is a further 1¼
miles.

2/168
● PAPER PRODUCTS

Two Rivers Paper Company
Pitt Mill, Roadwater, Watchet ,
Somerset TA23 0QS
Tel: (01984) 641028
Fax: (01984) 640282

Rag handmade paper for watercolour
and other art forms.
Open: Mon-Sat 9am-6pm. Closed
bank hols
Cards: No

DIRECTIONS: 1¼ miles south-east of
Roadwater on the Old Mineral Line.

2/169
■ CIDER

Torre Cider Farm
Washford, Watchet, Somerset TA23 0LA
Tel: (01984) 640004

Working cider-farm with range of
traditional farmhouse ciders, apple
juice, country wines, cheeses, fruit
and vegetables, free-range eggs.
Open: Every day except 25 Dec. Apr-
end Oct 9am-8pm, Nov-end Mar
9am-5pm
Cards: No

DIRECTIONS: Between Bridgwater
and Minehead on A39. 1 mile down
Abbey Road from Washford.

2/170
● CERAMICS

Helen Maasz Porcelain
Whispers, Langley Marsh, Wiveliscombe,
Somerset TA4 2UL
Tel: (01984) 624414

Glazed porcelain.
Open: Telephone first, but normally
9.30am-5.30pm
Cards: No

DIRECTIONS: In Langley Marsh 200
yards before Three Horseshoes pub.

2/171
■ FARM PRODUCE

**Combe Sydenham Country
Park**
Monksilver, Taunton, Somerset TA4 4JG
Tel: (01984) 656284
Fax: (01984) 656273

Country park (with Monksmill foods
and Monksmill bakery). Shop stocks
estate trout, fresh, frozen smoked
venison, cheese, cheese and bakery
products. All from the estate's own
resources.
Open: Sun-Fri 10am-5pm all year, Sat
11am-2pm
Cards: Switch (pending)

DIRECTIONS: From Taunton,
Combe Sydenham Country Park is on
the B3188, between Wiveliscombe
and Watchet.

2/172
■ FLOUR

Otterton Mill
Budleigh Salterton, Devon EX9 7HG
Tel: (01395) 568521

Flour, breads, cakes and preserves.
Open: Daily 10.30am-5.30pm. Closed
3 days at Christmas
Cards: Access, Visa

DIRECTIONS: 20 minutes off M5
from Exeter turn-off. Take A3052 to
Newton Poppleford. Turn right for
Budleigh Salterton. Signposted left
after 4 miles.

2/173
● PLANTS

**J M Spiller Elworthy Cottage
Garden Plants**
Elworthy Cottage, Elworthy, Lydeard St
Lawrence, Taunton, Somerset TA4 3PX
Tel: (01984) 656427

Hardy plant nursery, perennials and
hardy geraniums.
Open: 14 Mar-19 Oct Thur 1.30-5pm,
April Sat, some Sun, Aug by
appointment. Closed 20 Oct-13 Mar
Cards: No

DIRECTIONS: 12 miles north-west of
Taunton, 5 miles north of
Wiveliscombe. Take A358 Minehead
road from Taunton and then B3224,
signposted Monksilver. On B3188 in
middle of Elworthy.

2/174
● FURNITURE

**Justin Williams and Jane Cleal
Furniture**
Unit C, South Road Workshops, Watchet,
Somerset TA23 0HF
Tel: (01984) 633123

Contemporary furniture.
Open: Mon-Fri 9am-5.30pm
Cards: No

DIRECTIONS: On B3191 from
Williton, avoid turning left over
railway bridge in centre of Watchet.
Take the next right into South Road.

2/175
● ART

Sona Bennett
Haddon House, Stogumber, nr Taunton,
Somerset TA4 3SX
Tel: (01984) 656219

Landscapes in water colours and
animals in oil pastels.
Open: By appointment only
Cards: No

DIRECTIONS: Take turning
signposted Stogumber off the A358
(Taunton to Minehead road). Haddon
House is on far side of village,
opposite turning to Monksilver.

2/176
● CERAMICS/SILK

Winkley & Wex
Vellow Pottery and Silks, Lower Vellow,
Williton, Taunton, Somerset TA4 4LS
Tel: (01984) 656458

Coloured hand-painted silks – scarves,
ties, pictures. Handmade porcelain
and stoneware pots.
Open: Mon-Sat 8.30am-6pm
Cards: No

DIRECTIONS: Follow signpost to
Vellow and Stogumber from A358 1½
miles south-east of Williton.

2/177
■ CIDER

E W Pearse
Burscombe Farm, Sidbury, Sidmouth,
Devon EX10 0QB
Tel: (01395) 597648

Farmhouse cider.
Open: Daily 8am-10pm
Cards: No

DIRECTIONS: Turn right just before
entering Sidford on Honiton to
Sidford road. Continue on country
lanes for 1¼ miles to reach the farm
in the valley.

2/178
● ART

Richard Pocock Printmaker
4 Higher Houses, Runnington, Wellington,
Somerset TA21 0QN
Tel: (01823) 666224

Etchings, woodcuts, linocuts and
wood engravings.
Open: By appointment only
Cards: No

DIRECTIONS: Small village between
Langford Budville and Wellington on
lane off B3187, signposted to
Runnington. Higher Houses are at
the fork in the lane.

2/179
● WOOD

Paul McHardy Woodworker
Little Snoring, Fore Street, Milverton,
Taunton, Somerset TA4 1JU
Tel: (01823) 400745

Wooden stools, coffee tables,
chopping boards, fruit and salad
bowls.
Open: Strictly by appointment
Cards: No

DIRECTIONS: In centre of village, 2
doors down from post office.

2/180
■ CHEESE

Exmoor Blue Cheese
Willett Farm, Lydeard St Lawrence,
Taunton, Somerset TA4 3QB
Tel: (01984) 667328

Blue cheeses made from milk from
cows, goats, and sheep.
Open: Mon-Fri 9am-5pm, Sat 9am-
12pm, dairy by appointment
Cards: No

DIRECTIONS: Take A358 towards
Minehead from Taunton, turn left on
B3224 after Bishop's Lydeard. Willett
Farm is signposted to the right off
B3224 after 5 miles.

2/181
● CERAMICS

Nicola Werner Pottery
Old Parsonage, Hemyock, nr Cullompton,
Devon EX15 3RG
Tel: (01823) 680957

Majolica pottery and tiles.
Open: By appointment only. Closed
Christmas Day
Cards: No

DIRECTIONS: 5 miles south of M5
J26. 10 miles from Taunton, Honiton,
Cullompton and Chard.

2/182
● LIME WASH

Liz Induni

Redlands, Lydeard St Lawrence, Taunton,
Somerset TA4 3SE
Tel: (01984) 667253

Paints, lime washes and distemper.
Open: 9.30am-5.30pm but telephone
for appointment first
Cards: No

DIRECTIONS: Take A358 from
Taunton to Minehead. Turn left
opposite Cedar Falls Health Farm.
Drive on for 2 miles and turn right
after Friendship Inn. In middle of
village, opposite village hall.

2/183
● ART

Marilyn Ewens

Hooks, Crowcombe, Taunton,
Somerset TA4 4AE
Tel: (01984) 618683

Paintings, cards and art objects.
Open: Advisable to telephone first
Cards: No

DIRECTIONS: Take A358 from
Taunton towards Minehead. 10 miles
north-west of Taunton turn right into .
Crowcombe. Signposted drive on
right after Carew Arms pub and
before post office.

2/184
■ CIDER AND PERRY

Bollhayes Cider

Bollhayes Park, Clayhidon,
Devon EX15 3PN
Tel: (01823) 680230
Fax: (01823) 680807

Bottle-fermented sparkling cider,
perry and draught cider.
Open: Mon-Fri 9am-5pm. Sat by
appointment. Closed Sun
Cards: Access, Visa

DIRECTIONS: 4½ miles south of
Wellington. Telephone for directions
as not easy to find.

2/185
● WOOD

Sunshine Designs

Newton Cottage, Fitzhead, Taunton,
Somerset TA4 3JW
Tel: (01823) 400367
Fax: (01580) 201093

Brightly painted wooden occasional
tables in unusual designs.
Open: Mon-Sat 10am-6pm
Cards: No

DIRECTIONS: On B3227 from
Taunton to Wiveliscombe. 2 miles
past Norton Fitzwarren take right
turn to Halse. Take left turn in Halse
to Fitzhead. 2nd house on right by
Fitzhead village sign.

2/186
■ WINE

Quantock Vineyards and Orchards

The Counting House, Doddington, Nether
Stowey, Somerset TA5 1LE
Tel: (01278) 733100

Somerset apple wines and grape wine.
Open: Variable, by appointment
Cards: No

DIRECTIONS: On A39 1 mile past
Nether Stowey. At minor crossroads
with triangle of grass, turn left to
Crowcombe.

2/187
● PLANTS

Perrie Hale Forest Nursery

Northcote Hill, Honiton, Devon EX14 8TH
Tel: (01404) 43344
Fax: (01404) 47163

Native forest trees and shrubs; plants
suitable for establishing native hedges.
Open: Mon-Fri 9am-4.30pm, Sat
9am-12.30pm, other times by
appointment
Cards: No

DIRECTIONS: A30 London to Exeter
road, take slip road into Honiton, at
top of slip road turn left (Cotleigh
Road). Follow road under railway
bridge, nursery is ⅓ mile up hill on
right.

2/188
■ CIDER

R J Sheppy & Son
Three Bridges, Bradford-on-Tone, Taunton,
Somerset TA4 1ER
Tel: (01823) 461233
Fax: (01823) 461712

Draught and bottled cider.
Open: Mon-Sat 6.30am-6pm, Sun
(Easter-Christmas) 12 noon-2pm.
Closed 25, 26 Dec
Cards: No

DIRECTIONS: On A38 between
Taunton and Wellington, follow
brown signs.

2/189
■ GARLIC

Somerset Garlic
Bradfields Farm, Bradford-on-Tone,
Taunton, Somerset TA4 1HR
Tel: (01823) 461260

Dried flowers and garlic.
Open: Aug-Dec Mon-Sat 2pm-6pm
Cards: No

DIRECTIONS: On Bradford-on-
Tone to Oake Road, 1st gate on left
from Bradford over railway bridge.

2/190
● CERAMICS

Quantock Pottery
Chapel Cottage, West Bagborough,
Taunton, Somerset TA4 3EF
Tel/Fax: (01823) 433057

Relief pattern stoneware, casseroles,
mugs, jugs, vases, lampbases, garden
pots.
Open: Mon-Fri 9.30am-5.30pm, Sat-
Sun 11am-5pm. Closed 23 Dec-9 Jan
Cards: Access, Visa

DIRECTIONS: 9 miles from Taunton
on A358. Follow signs to Bagborough
up to top of village. Pottery is past the
Rising Sun pub on left.

2/191
■ CHEESE

Cricket Malherbie Farms Ltd
Stowey Court Farm, Nether Stowey,
Bridgwater, Somerset TA5 1LL
Tel: (01278) 732084
Fax: (01278) 733131

Cheese, cream and butter.
Open: Winter Mon-Sat 8.30am-5pm,
summer Mon-Sun 8.30am-5pm
Cards: No

DIRECTIONS: On A39 Bridgwater to
Minehead. 8 miles south-west of
Bridgwater, opposite junction
signposted Nether Stowey.

2/192
● PLANTS

Broadleigh Gardens
Barr House, Bishops Hull, Taunton,
Somerset TA4 1AE
Tel: (01823) 286231
Fax: (01823) 323646

Unusual and dwarf bulbs, woodland
and foliage plants, gardens.
Open: Open Mon-Fri 9am-4pm to
view and order
Cards: Access, Visa

DIRECTIONS: North of A38
Taunton to Wellington road, just
outside Bishops Hull on way to
Bradford-on-Tone. Take lane marked
Barr.

2/193
● GLASS

Shakspeare Glassworks
Foundry Road, Riverside Place, Taunton,
Somerset TA1 1JJ
Tel/Fax: (01823) 333422

Hand-blown glassware, vases, bowls,
goblets and paperweights.
Open: Mon-Sat 9.30am-5.30pm
Cards: Access, Visa

DIRECTIONS: In centre of Taunton,
just off the Brewhouse Theatre car
park.

2/194
■ WINE

Staplecombe Vineyard
Burlands Farm, Staplegrove, Taunton,
Somerset TA2 6SN
Tel: (01823) 451217

Wine, vineyard tours.
Open: Apr-Oct Mon-Sat 2-5pm, other
times by appointment
Cards: No

DIRECTIONS: From M4, J25
signposted Staplegrove, turn right in
Staplegrove, past church, turn left into
Rectory Road. Through village for ½
mile to T-junction, left for vineyard.

2/195
● GLASS

Chinks Grylls
Smoke Tree Studio, The Tin Chapel,
Enmore, Somerset TA5 2DW
Tel: (01278) 671238

Stained and decorated glass.
Open: Mon-Fri 9am-5.30pm
Cards: No

DIRECTIONS: Follow Durleigh Road
out of Bridgwater. Follow signs to
Enmore. ½ mile on left after Enmore
Golf Club.

2/196
■ WINE

Oatley Vineyard
Cannington, Bridgwater,
Somerset TA5 2NL
Tel/Fax: (01278) 671340

English white wines.
Open: Varied, best to telephone first
Cards: No

DIRECTIONS: 1 mile west of
Cannington, turn north off A39 at
small crossroad by red post box.
Vineyard is ¾ mile down lane.

2/197
■ CIDER

Henry's Farmhouse Scrumpy
Tanpits Cider Farm, Dyers Lane, Bathpool,
Taunton, Somerset TA2 8BZ
Tel: (01823) 270663

Farmhouse scrumpy.

Open: Mon-Sat 8.30am-6pm. Closed
25 Dec and Good Friday
Cards: No

DIRECTIONS: On A361 Taunton to
Bridgwater road, approx 3 miles
north-east of Taunton.

2/198
● KNITWEAR

Jacob Spinners
Orchard Cottage, Bickenhall, Taunton,
Somerset TA3 6UF
Tel: (01823) 480663

Knitwear and fleeces from own
coloured sheep.
Open: Strictly by appointment. Closed
Sun
Cards: No

DIRECTIONS: At Five Dials pub in
Horton, taken Bickenhall road, 3
miles on left.

2/199
■ FRUIT/VEGETABLES

Charlton Orchards
Creech St Michael, Taunton,
Somerset TA3 5PF
Tel: (01823) 412979
Fax: (01823) 412959

Apples, pears, plums, gooseberries,
damsons and late raspberries in
season. Apple juices and preserves.
Open: Mon-Sat 10am-6pm, Sun 2pm-
5pm
Cards: No

DIRECTIONS: 3 miles north-east of
Taunton. 2 miles north of village
centre. Off A361 Glastonbury road, 1
mile down Charlton (no through)
road.

2/200
■ MEAT/POULTRY/GAME

Somerset Ducks
Greenway Farm, North Newton,
Bridgwater, Somerset TA7 0DS
Tel: (01278) 662656

Duck: stuffed, boned, sausages,
sauces, pâtés.
Open: Mon-Fri 9am-1pm. Closed
March to 10 Dec
Cards: No

DIRECTIONS: A38, through North Petherton towards Taunton. 2½ miles dual carriageway, turn left down Moon Lane, farm on right.

2/201
■ ICE-CREAM

Barnard & Gooding
Keward Farm, River Road, Pawlett, Bridgwater, Somerset TA6 4SE
Tel: (01278) 685173
Fax: (01278) 684664

Ice-cream, including goats' milk ice-cream.
Open: Mon-Fri 8.30am-4pm, Sat 8.30am-12pm
Cards: No

DIRECTIONS: From J23 of M5 take A38 north. After 1 mile turn into Pawlett at brow of hill. Left at post office, left at crossroads into River Road.

2/202
■ CIDER

Ashill Cider
Ashtons Farm, Ashill, Nr Ilminster, Somerset TA19 9NE
Tel: (01823) 480513

Scrumpy cider.
Open: Mon-Sat, all reasonable hours, Sun 12pm-3pm only. Closed 25 Dec, Good Friday
Cards: No

DIRECTIONS: On A358 Taunton to Ilminster road, follow signposts to Ashill village. Sign on verge for 'Real Scrumpy', follow arrow. Cider farm ½ mile on left.

2/203
● BASKETS

The Somerset Willow Company
Units 10-12, The Wireworks Estate, Bristol Rd, Bridgwater, Somerset TA6 4AP
Tel: (01278) 424003

Basketware and conservatory furniture.
Open: Mon-Fri 8.30am-5pm. Closed around Christmas
Cards: Access, Visa

DIRECTIONS: Off M5, J23 and south on to A38, workshops and showroom

just before the roundabout on left (slip road turning).

2/204
● BASKETS

And Beautiful Baskets
1 Drakes Way, Off Broad Street, Lyme Regis, Dorset DT7 3QP
Tel: (01297) 444714

Unusual and beautiful baskets.
Open: Summer Mon-Sun 10am-5pm. Closed Jan-Mar
Cards: No

DIRECTIONS: Central Lyme Regis, 100 yards from the sea, up Broad Street. Drakes Way is the courtyard on the right.

2/205
● BASKETS

Willow Wetlands Visitor Centre
Meare Green Court, Stoke St Gregory, Taunton, Somerset TA3 6HY
Tel: (01823) 490249
Fax: (01823) 490814

Willow furniture and baskets.
Open: Mon-Sat 9am-5pm. Closed 25-27 Dec
Cards: Access, Visa

DIRECTIONS: 6 miles east of Taunton, Stoke St. Gregory/North Curry road. Signposted (brown tourist) off A368 and A361.

2/206
● FOOTWEAR

Sedgemoor Shoes Ltd
River Lane, Dunwear, Nr Bridgwater, Somerset TA7 0AA
Tel: (01278) 427662

Made-to-measure footwear.
Open: Mon-Fri 10am-4pm. Closed 1 week at Christmas, Spring holiday, last week July, 1st week August
Cards: No

DIRECTIONS: Off A372. East side of Bridgwater, approximately 5 miles from J23 of M5.

2/207
● PLANTS

Mallet Court Nursery
Curry Mallet, Taunton, Somerset TA3 6SY
Tel: (01823) 480748
Fax: (01823) 481009

Rare and unusual plants, maples and oaks.
Open: Mon-Fri 9am-5pm, weekends by appointment
Cards: No

DIRECTIONS: On A358 turn left, signposted Hatch Beauchamp. Follow signs to Curry Mallet. Take first left past post office and Bell Inn. Nursery along on right.

2/208
■ CIDER

Rich's Somerset Farmhouse Cider
Mill Farm, Watchfield, Nr Highbridge, Somerset TA9 4RD
Tel: (01278) 783651

Farmhouse cider from West Country apples.
Open: Mon-Sat 9am-7pm, Sun 12 noon-3pm. Closed 25 Dec
Cards: No

DIRECTIONS: Take B3139 Highbridge to Wells road, Watchfield approximately 1½ miles. Barrels in yard entrance on left.

2/209
● PLANTS

YSJ Seeds, Kingsfield Conservation Nurseries
Broadenham Lane, Winsham, Chard, Somerset TA20 4JF
Tel/Fax: (01460) 30070

Native trees and shrubs, wildflower plants, bulbs, wildflower seed, some rare and endangered.
Open: Mon-Sun 8.30am-4pm. Closed 25 Dec, Easter
Cards: No

DIRECTIONS: In Winsham village on B3162 Chard to Bridport road. Approx 4 miles south of Chard.

2/210
● BASKETS

The Cane Workshop
The Gospel Hall, Westport, Langport, Somerset TA10 0BH
Tel: (01460) 281636

Cane, rush, seagrass, pre-woven cane, bamboo, baskets, cane and rush seating kits.
Open: Mon-Fri. Closed 20 Dec-5 Jan
Cards: No

DIRECTIONS: On the B3168 from Ilminster to Curry Rivel. 200 yards north of the Old Barn Owl Inn at Westport.

2/211
● FORGEWORK

The Forge
Cricket St Thomas Wildlife Park, Cricket St Thomas, Chard, Somerset TA20 4DA
Tel: (01460) 30502

Traditional and ornamental ironwork, from fences and fireplaces to hinges and artefacts.
Open: Summer Mon-Sun 10.30am-5pm, winter Mon-Sun 11am-4.30pm. Closed 25 Dec
Cards: Access, Visa

DIRECTIONS: On the A30 between Chard and Crewkerne.

2/212
■ FRUIT

Stawell Fruit Farm
Stawell, Nr Bridgwater, Somerset TA7 9AE
Tel: (01278) 722732

Apples, plums, strawberries, apple juice.
Open: Daily 11am-4pm, but advisable to telephone for details
Cards: No

DIRECTIONS: 1 mile off A39, 5 miles east of Bridgwater. Take J23 of M5.

2/213
■ CIDER AND PERRY

Coombes Cider
Japonica Farm, Mark Causeway, Mark, Nr
Highbridge, Somerset TA9 4QD
Tel: (01278) 641265

Cider, sparkling perry and pure apple
juice.
Open: Mon-Sat 9am-6pm, Sun
12 noon-2pm. Closed 25-26 Dec
Cards: No

DIRECTIONS: Off M5, J22, north on
to A38, 1st right at Fox and Goose
pub for 2 miles, right at crossroads,
signposted.

2/214
■ SMOKED PRODUCE

Brown & Forrest
The Smokery, Bowdens Farm, Hambridge,
Langport, Somerset TA10 0BP
Tel: (01458) 251520
Fax: (01458) 253475

Smoked eel, salmon, trout, duck.
Open: Mon, Tue, Thur 10am-1pm
Cards: Access, Visa

DIRECTIONS: From Curry Rivel take
Ilminster Road (B3168) to
Hambridge. 50 yards after village sign,
turn left up concrete farm track.
Follow to farm courtyard and
smokery.

2/215
■ WINE

Moorlynch Vineyard
Moorlynch, Bridgwater, Somerset TA7 9DD
Tel: (01458) 210393
Fax: (01458) 210247

White wine, still and sparkling,
brandy, cider, preserves.
Open: Tue-Sat 10.30am-5pm, Sun
12 noon-5pm, and bank hols
10.30am-5pm. Closed 25-26 Dec
Cards: Access, Visa

DIRECTIONS: Signposted off A39
Bridgwater to Glastonbury road, and
A361 Taunton to Glastonbury road.

2/216
■ BAKED GOODS

S Moores
The Biscuit Bakery, Morcombelake,
Bridport, Dorset DT6 6ES
Tel: (01297) 489253
Fax: (01297) 489753

Dorset knobs, shortbread, rich fruit
cake and 11 varieties of cookie.
Open: Mon-Fri 9am-5pm, summer
Sat 9am-1pm. Closed 10 days over
Christmas, public holidays
Cards: No

DIRECTIONS: On A35 in centre of
Morcombelake (between Bridport
and Lyme Regis).

2/217
● FURNITURE

Moobles Design
Higher Farm, Wayford, Crewkerne,
Somerset TA18 8QQ
Tel: (01460) 73166

Furniture in English hardwoods or
reclaimed timber.
Open: Mon-Sat 10am-7pm, Sun by
appointment
Cards: No

DIRECTIONS: Take B3165 to Lyme
Regis from Crewkerne, turn right at
Clapton Mill, 1st left into Wayford.
Through village, then right after
phone box and follow track for ⅓
mile.

2/218
● ART

John Morgan's Fantastica
The Laurels, Watergore, South Petherton,
Somerset TA13 5JQ
Tel: (01460) 240917

Fantasy paintings, produced as framed
and unframed prints, postcards and
greetings cards.
Open: By appointment only
Cards: No

DIRECTIONS: Next to Pot Shop on
old A303 at Watergore, between
Cemetery Cross roundabout and
Lopen Head.

2/219
● CERAMICS
Dennis China Works
Shepton Beauchamp, Ilminster,
Somerset TA19 0JT
Tel: (01460) 240347
Fax: (01460) 242009

Hand-thrown decorated pottery.
Open: Daily 9am-5pm. Closed 1 week
at Christmas
Cards: Access, Visa

DIRECTIONS: Off A303, 1 mile west
of South Petherton. Do not take
Ilminster bypass. Ask in Shepton
Beauchamp for directions.

2/220
● CERAMICS
Aller Pottery
The Pottery, Aller, Nr Langport,
Somerset TA10 0QN
Tel: (01458) 250244

Utilitarian and decorative pottery:
mugs, jugs, bowls, vases and
breadcrocks.
Open: Mon-Sat 9am-6pm, Sun by
appointment
Cards: Access, Visa

DIRECTIONS: On A372, 2 miles
north of Langport on Bridgwater
Road as you enter Aller.

2/221
■ WINE
La Mare Vineyard
St Mary, Jersey, Channel Islands JE3 3BA
Tel: (01534) 481491
Fax: (01534) 485210

Wines, jellies, jams, Jersey mustards
and horseradish.
Open: Mon-Sat 10am-5.30pm. Closed
mid Oct-Nov, 22 Dec-Apr
Cards: Access, Amex, Switch, Visa

DIRECTIONS: 7 miles north-west of
St Helier, ¼ mile before Devil's Hole
on C103. Well signposted.

2/222
● ROCKING-HORSES
Margaret Spencer & Co.
Goulds Nap, Chard Road, Crewkerne,
Somerset TA18 8BA
Tel: (01460) 72362

Wooden rocking-horses.
Open: Mon-Fri 9am-5pm, Sat-Sun by
appointment only. Closed 24 Dec-1
Jan
Cards: Access, Visa

DIRECTIONS: On A30 by end of
30mph limit sign, coming out of
Crewkerne towards Chard. Black and
white house on right.

2/223
■ CIDER
Somerset Cider Brandy Company and Burrow Hill Cider
Pass Vale Farm, Burrow Hill, Kingsbury
Episcopi, Martock, Somerset TA12 5BU
Tel/Fax: (01460) 240782

Cider brandy, cider.
Open: Mon-Sat 9am-5.30pm
Cards: Access, Visa

DIRECTIONS: Turn off A303 just
before Murtock. Follow signs to
Kingsbury Episcopi (3 miles). In the
village take the Hambridge road out,
past the Rusty Axe pub, 1 mile out of
the village, there are signs to help.

2/224
● CERAMICS
Muchelney Pottery
Muchelney, Langport, Somerset TA10 0DW
Tel: (01458) 250324

Handmade wood-fired stoneware.
Open: Mon-Fri 9am-1pm, 2pm-5pm,
Sat 9am-1pm, or by appointment
Cards: Access, Visa

DIRECTIONS: 15 miles east of
Taunton, take road south from
Langport, marked Crewkerne-
Muchelney. Follow tourist signs in
village. The pottery is thatched
building on the left.

2/225
● SILVERWARE

Silver Workshop
Bow Street, Langport, Somerset TA10 9PQ
Tel: (01458) 251122

Silver articles including chalices,
wedding rings, commemorative
boxes.
Open: Mon-Fri 9.30am-5.30pm. Sat
9.30am-1pm
Cards: No

DIRECTIONS: In main street of
Langport, on left, opposite layby.

2/226
● PLANTS

Kelways Limited
Barrymoor Farm, Langport,
Somerset TA10 9EZ
Tel: (01458) 250521
Fax: (01458) 253351

Peonies and irises.
Open: Mon-Fri 9am-5pm, Sat 10am-
5pm, Sun 9am-4pm. Closed 25-26 Dec
Cards: Access, Visa

DIRECTIONS: On B3153 Langport to
Somerton road, about ½ mile from
town centre on right.

2/227
● LEATHER GOODS

Mendip Leathercraft
Sidcot Lane, Winscombe, Avon BS25 1HH
Tel: (01934) 842783

Leather goods including travel
accessories, belts.
Open: Mon-Sat 9am-5pm. Closed
Wed and Sat pm
Cards: No

DIRECTIONS: Turn off A38 at Sidcot,
towards Winscombe and Weston-
Super-Mare, 300 yards on right.

2/228
■ CHEESE

Denhay Farms Ltd
Broadoak, Bridport, Dorset DT6 5NP
Tel: (01308) 422770
Fax: (01308) 424846

Cheddar cheese, air-dried ham,
sausages and dry-cured bacon.
Open: Mon-Thur 9am-4.30pm.
Closed bank hols
Cards: Access, Visa

DIRECTIONS: From Bridport take
B3162 north towards Broadwinter.
After 2 miles turn left at crossroads to
Broadoak. Take 2nd left in village
signposted Denhay only.

2/229
● WOOD

Somerset Creative Products
Tel: (01278) 641622
Fax: (01278) 641116

Wooden decorative accessories and
furniture.
Open: By appointment only
Cards: Access, Visa

DIRECTIONS: Details given on
arranging appointment.

2/230
● TOYS

Jean George Designs
Hunter's Vale, Salwayash, Bridport,
Dorset DT6 5HX
Tel: (01308) 488434

Toy theatres, puppets.
Open: Advisable to telephone first
Cards: No

DIRECTIONS: On B3162 2½ miles
north of Bridport on left in lane
opposite Fir Tree Close.

2/231
✳ MULTIPLE

Broadwindsor Craft Centre
Beaminster, Dorset DT8 3PX
Tel: (01308) 868362

Paintings, cabinets, decorated
ironwork, original knitwear, hats and
semi-stone jewellery. Café.
Open: 1 Mar-23 Dec daily 10am-5pm
Cards: Visa

DIRECTIONS: On Beaminster road
300 yards outside Broadwindsor.
Farm buildings.

2/232
● CERAMICS

Art Benattar Craft
31 Market Square, Crewkerne, Somerset
TA18 7LP
Tel: (01460) 73118

Handmade ceramics.
Open: Mon-Sat 10am-5.30pm
Cards: No

DIRECTIONS: Facing the Victoria
Hall in the centre of Crewkerne,
which is situated on the A30 between
Yeovil and Chard.

2/233
● PLANTS

Scotts Nurseries Merriott Ltd
Merriott, Somerset TA16 5PL
Tel: (01460) 72306
Fax: (01460) 77433

Fruit trees and roses, flowering trees
and hedge plants.
Open: Mon-Sat 9am-5pm, Sun
10.30am-4.30pm
Cards: Access, Switch, Visa

DIRECTIONS: In Merriott,
signposted off B3165.

2/234
● CERAMICS

D B Pottery
Highway Cottage, Church Street, Merriott,
Somerset TA16 5PR
Tel: (01460) 75655

Handmade pottery, functional,
sculptural.
Open: Mon-Sun 9.30am-dusk. Closed
Mon-Fri 1pm-2pm
Cards: No

DIRECTIONS: 2 miles north of
Crewkerne, take B356 towards Lopen
Head. At Lopen Head in Merriott
almost opposite Kings Head pub.

2/235
■ CIDER

**Wilkins and Son Farmhouse
Cider**
Lands End Farm, Mudgley, Wedmore,
Somerset BS28 4TU
Tel: (01934) 712385

Dry, medium or sweet cider, Cheddar
cheese.
Open: Mon-Sat 10am-8pm, Sun
10am-1pm
Cards: No

DIRECTIONS: On the Cheddar to
Glastonbury road, B3151, 2 miles
south of Wedmore go left on Mudgley
Hill. At end of Lands End Farm go to
No Through Road.

2/236
■ CIDER

Ashwood Cider
Ashwood Farm, Shipham Hill, Cheddar,
Somerset BS27 3DD
Tel: (01934) 742393

Traditional cider.
Open: Mon-Sat 9am-9pm, Sun 12-
3pm, 7pm-9pm
Cards: No

DIRECTIONS: Left by roundabout on
A371 just before Cheddar, signposted
to Shipham, ¼ mile up hill on right.

2/237
● CANDLES

Bridport Candlemakers
Bramfield, 10 Beaumont Avenue, Bridport,
Dorset DT6 3AU
Tel: (01308) 422176

Candlemakers, mainly beeswax,
furniture polish in beeswax and in
chosen colour.
Open: Mon-Sun, preferably by
appointment
Cards: Access, Visa

DIRECTIONS: Take Beaminster/
Yeovil road, turn north at eastern
roundabout then 1st left and right into
Coneygar Road. 2nd right to
Beaumont Avenue, then left.

2/238
■ SMOKED PRODUCE
Bridfish Ltd
Unit 1, Sea Road North, Bridport,
Dorset DT6 3BD
Tel/Fax: (01308) 456306

Smoked fish and meats.
Open: Mon-Fri 9am-5pm, Sat 9am-
4pm. Closed bank hols
Cards: Access, Visa

DIRECTIONS: From Dorchester,
turn right at first roundabout in
Bridport off A35. On to Beaminster
Road. About 200 yards on left on
small trading estate.

2/239
● FURNITURE
Parnham House
Beaminster, Dorset DT8 3NA
Tel: (01308) 862204
Fax: (01308) 863494

Furniture (contemporary) glass,
wood, textiles and ceramics.
Open: Apr-Oct Sun, Wed and bank
hols 10am-5pm
Cards: Access, Amex, Diners, Visa

DIRECTIONS: On A3066 5 miles
north of Bridport on Crewkerne road,
½ mile south of Beaminster.

2/240
● CERAMICS
Eeles Family Pottery
Mosterton, Beaminster, Dorset DT8 3HN
Tel: (01308) 868257

Handmade wood-fired stoneware and
porcelain.
Open: Mon-Sun 9am-6pm. Closed
Christmas
Cards: No

DIRECTIONS: On the A3066
between Beaminster, Dorset and
Crewkerne in Somerset.

2/241
● JEWELLERY
**Michael Burton Gold &
Silversmith**
Osborne Cottage, Hurst, Martock,
Somerset TA12 6JU
Tel: (01935) 822362
Fax: (01935) 822352

Jewellery, teapots, tableware.
Open: Mon-Sat 9am-5pm
Cards: No

DIRECTIONS: Off A303, between
Yeovil and South Petherton
roundabout, opposite Yandles
woodyard.

2/242
● WOOD
Yandle & Sons Ltd
Hurst Works, Martock, Somerset TA12 6JU
Tel: (01935) 822207
Fax: (01935) 824484

Woodturning and carving: tools and
finishing products. Also dolls' houses
and furniture.
Open: Mon-Fri 9am-1pm, 2pm-5pm.
Sat 9am-5pm, Sun 9am-1pm. Closed
bank hols
Cards: Access, Switch, Visa

DIRECTIONS: 9 miles north-west of
Yeovil, 1 mile north of A303. Between
Martock and Bower Hinton on
B3165.

2/243
■ CHEESE
Times Past Cheese Dairy
Westfield Lane, Draycott, Cheddar,
Somerset BS27 3TP
Tel: (01934) 743465
Fax: (01278) 445544

Unpasteurised Cheddar, Red
Leicester, Double Gloucester and
Caerphilly cheeses.
Open: Mon-Fri 9am-1pm
Cards: No

DIRECTIONS: Take A341 Cheddar to
Wells road. Turn opposite Red
Dragon pub in Draycott down Back
Lane. Take third turning on right.
Dairy at end of lane on right.

2/244
● CERAMICS
Sara Parsons
Chestnut Farm, Kent Street, Cheddar,
Somerset BS27 3LG
Tel: (01934) 743297

Ceramic sculptures and pots.
Open: Advisable to telephone for
appointment
Cards: No

DIRECTIONS: In village approaching
from Bristol or Weston-super-Mare,
left off B3035. Up Upper North
Street, turn left at King's Head pub,
50 yards on left.

2/245
■ CIDER
Derrick's Cider
Cheddar Valley Cheese Depot, The Gorge,
Cheddar, Somerset BS27 3QE
Tel: (01934) 743113
Fax: (01934) 744449

Ciders, jams, honey, pickles, 60
different country wines, brandies,
meads and English teapots.
Open: Mar-Nov Mon-Sun 9am-5pm,
Nov-Dec, Sat-Sun only
Cards: Access, Switch, Visa

DIRECTIONS: Enter Cheddar village,
follow signs to Gorge and Caves on
B3135. Shop on right between Cox's
Cave and Goughs Cave.

2/246
● FOOTWEAR
Adams & Jones
White Cottage Courtyard, Magdalene
Street, Glastonbury, Somerset BA6 9EH
Tel: (01458) 834356
Fax: (01458) 834868

Made-to-measure footwear.
Open: Mon-Fri 9am-5pm, Sat 10am-
4pm
Cards: Access, Visa

DIRECTIONS: Take A39 from J23 of
M5 to Glastonbury. Opposite Abbey
ruins, lane next to Market House Inn.

2/247
■ CHEESE
Ashley Chase Estate
Parks Farm Cheese Unit, Litton Cheney,
Dorchester, Dorset DT2 9AZ
Tel: (01308) 482580
Fax: (01308) 482608

Cheddar, blue and soft cheeses,
butter.
Open: Mon-Sat 9am-12pm
Cards: No

DIRECTIONS: From A35 turn to
Litton Cheney through village, left at
White Horse, then 2nd right.
Signposted Ashley Chase Cheese
Dairy.

2/248
■ CIDER
Whitehead Cider
Tootle Bridge Farm, Barton St David,
Somerton, Somerset TA11 6DF
Tel: (01458) 50220

Somerset farmhouse cider.
Open: Telephone in advance
Cards: No

DIRECTIONS: 5 miles south-east of
Glastonbury. Take the A361 towards
Shepton Mallet, turn south towards
Baltonsborough, head towards Barton
St David alongside river Brue. The
farm is next to Tootle Bridge.

2/249
■ FRUIT/VEGETABLES
West Bradley Orchards
Glastonbury, Somerset BA6 8LT
Tel: (01458) 50227
Fax: (01458) 51008

15 varieties of apples and pears.
Open: Daily 10am-5pm
Cards: No

DIRECTIONS: 3 miles east of
Glastonbury and Street. Either turn
south off A361 (Glastonbury/Shepton
Mallet road) at West Pennard road, or
east off A37 (Yeovil/Shepton Mallet
road).

2/250
● PLANTS

Otters' Court Heathers
Back Street, West Camel, Yeovil,
Somerset BA22 7QF
Tel: (01935) 850285

Lime-tolerant heathers.
Open: Wed-Sun 9am-5.30pm
Cards: No

DIRECTIONS: In West Camel 300
yards along Back Street from village
shop.

2/251
■ WINE

Wootton Vineyard
North Wootton, Shepton Mallet,
Somerset BA4 4AG
Tel: (01749) 890359

Eau de vie (white brandy) from
English grapes.
Open: Mon-Sat 10am-1pm, 2pm-5pm
Cards: No

DIRECTIONS: Signposted on A39, 1
mile south of Wells and on A361, 4
miles south of Shepton Mallet. About
3 miles from each main road.

2/252
● CERAMICS

Chapel Yard Pottery
1 Market Street, Abbotsbury,
Dorset DT3 4JC
Tel: (01305) 871663

Coloured, decorated domestic ware,
stoneware and earthenware, plant
pots.
Open: Winter Tue-Sat 9am-5.30pm,
occasional Sun
Cards: No

DIRECTIONS: Enter Abbotsbury via
coast road, 50 yards past post office on
the left.

2/253
● WOOD

Dansel Gallery
Rodden Row, Abbotsbury, Weymouth,
Dorset DT3 4JL
Tel: (01305) 871515
Fax: (01305) 871518

Wooden items from furniture to toys.
Open: Oct-Easter 10am-5pm, April-
July 10am-5.30pm, July-Sept 9.30am-
6pm. Closed Christmas
Cards: Access, Switch, Visa

DIRECTIONS: On B3157 between
Weymouth and Bridport. On main
road in village.

2/254
● FORGEWORK

Michael Malleson
Trent Smithy, Rigg Lane, Trent, Sherborne,
Dorset DT9 4SS
Tel: (01935) 850957

Sculptural, decorative and functional
hot-forged ironwork.
Open: Mon-Fri 9am-5pm, Sat by
appointment
Cards: No

DIRECTIONS: Trent is between
Yeovil, Sherborne and Marston
Magna, off A30 or B3148. Rigg Lane
is opposite the telephone box in
Trent.

2/255
■ WINE

Pilton Manor Vineyard
Pilton, Shepton Mallet, Somerset BA4 4BE
Tel: (01749) 890325
Fax: (01749) 890262

Wines, still, sparkling and dessert.
Open: July-mid Sept, Wed-Sat 11am-
5pm, Sun 11am-3pm, mid Sept-June
Mon-Fri 9am-4.30pm
Cards: Access, Visa

DIRECTIONS: On A361 between
Shepton Mallet and Glastonbury, on
the Glastonbury side of the village of
Pilton.

2/256
● SCULPTURE
Sukey Erland
The Malthouse, Pilton, Shepton Mallet,
Somerset BA4 4EA
Tel: (01749) 890341

Figurative sculpture in bronze.
Open: By appointment only
Cards: No

DIRECTIONS: Opposite car park of
Crown Inn in Pilton, on A361 between
Shepton Mallet and Glastonbury.

2/257
● CERAMICS
Ridge Pottery
The Pottery, High Street, Queen Camel, Nr
Yeovil, Somerset BA22 7NF
Tel: (01935) 850753

Decorated stoneware, wood-fired
from local clays.
Open: Mon-Sat 9am-6pm
Cards: No

DIRECTIONS: 7 miles north of
Yeovil on the A359, 1 mile from the
A303 on village high street.

2/258
● FURNITURE
Robinsons
High Street, Queen Camel, Nr Yeovil,
Somerset BA22 7NH
Tel: (01935) 850609

Period furniture from reclaimed
timber.
Open: Mon-Fri 9am-6pm, Sat by
appointment
Cards: No

DIRECTIONS: On A359 7 miles
north of Yeovil, 1 mile south of A303
at Sparkford. In centre of village.

2/259
■ MEAT/POULTRY/GAME
Barrow Boar
Fosters Farm, South Barrow, Yeovil,
Somerset BA22 7LN
Tel: (01963) 440315
Fax: (01963) 440901

Unusual meats including Barrow
boar, sausages, bison, kid, peacock,
venison, kangaroo, alligator.

Open: Mon-Fri 8.30am-5.30pm
Cards: Access, Visa

DIRECTIONS: In village of South
Barrow, 1½ miles from Sparkford on
A303. Turn right after church, 200
yards on right.

2/260
■ WINE
Bagborough Vineyard
Pylle, Shepton Mallet, Somerset BA4 6SX
Tel: (01749) 831146

Wines and ciders.
Open: Mon-Sun 9am-7pm
Cards: No

DIRECTIONS: From Shepton Mallet
go south towards Yeovil and Exeter on
the A37. 3 miles south of the town,
turn left into Bagborough Lane. First
on the left, 300 yards from the main
road.

2/261
■ CHEESE
Chewton Cheese Dairy
Priory Farm, Chewton Mendip, Bath,
Somerset BA3 4NT
Tel: (01761) 241666
Fax: (01761) 241202

Cheddar cheese and other dairy
products.
Open: Mon-Sun 9am-4.30pm. Closed
25-26 Dec, 1 Jan
Cards: No

DIRECTIONS: On the A39, 6 miles
north of Wells on the road towards
Bristol and Bath, just before entering
the village of Chewton Mendip.

2/262
● ART
Jim Woods
Garden Cottage, South Street, Castle Cary,
Somerset BA7 7ET
Tel: (01963) 351039

Watercolour paintings.
Open: 10am-4pm, but telephone for
appointment first. Closed bank hols
Cards: No

DIRECTIONS: At South Cary end of Castle Cary behind South Court House on South Street.

2/263
■ BEER

Oakhill Brewery
High Street, Oakhill, Bath,
Somerset BA3 5AS
Tel: (01749) 840134
Fax: (01749) 840531

Real ales: Oakhill Best Bitter, Yeoman 1767 and Black Magic Stout.
Open: Mon-Fri 8am-5pm, Sat 9am-12pm
Cards: No

DIRECTIONS: In centre of Oakhill village on A467. 4 miles north of Shepton Mallet.

2/264
■ FISH/SHELLFISH

Abbotsbury Oysters Ltd
Ferrybridge, Weymouth, Dorset DT4 9YU
Tel: (01305) 788867
Fax: (01305) 760776

Oysters and seafood.
Open: Mon-Fri 8am-6pm, Sat-Sun (Summer only) 9am-6pm. Closed Easter day and 25 Dec
Cards: Access, Visa

DIRECTIONS: Turn right off road to Portland at Ferrybridge pub, just before bridge.

2/265
■ CHEESE

J A and E Montgomery Ltd
Manor Farm, North Cadbury, Yeovil,
Somerset BA22 7DW
Tel: (01963) 440243

Unpasteurised, mature Cheddar cheese.
Open: Mon, Tue, Thur, Fri 8.30am-6pm, Wed 8.30am-1pm, Sat 9am-1pm, Sun 9.30am-12pm
Cards: No

DIRECTIONS: Take A303 from Wincanton and turn left to Cadbury.

2/266
■ WINE

Castle Cary Vineyard
Honeywick House, Castle Cary,
Somerset BA7 7LP
Tel: (01963) 350323

White wine.
Open: Mon-Sat 9am-5pm, Sun 12 noon-3pm
Cards: No

DIRECTIONS: Turn right off A371 Wincanton to Shepton Mallet road at Waggon and Horses pub. Vineyard is on left at bottom of hill, ½ mile on road to Cole.

2/267
● FORGEWORK

Cerne Valley Forge
Mill Lane, Cerne Abbas, Nr Dorchester,
Dorset DT2 7LA
Tel/Fax: (01300) 341298

Ornamental ironwork in wrought iron and mild steel. From paper knives to large gates.
Open: Mon-Fri 8.30am-4.30pm, Sat 9am-4.30pm. Evenings by appointment
Cards: No

DIRECTIONS: From A532 go into Cerne Abbas, take Duck Street, opposite the New Inn and turn right into Mill Lane. The forge is the first turning on the right.

2/268
● CERAMICS

Abbey Pottery
Cerne Abbas, Dorchester, Dorset DT2 7JQ
Tel: (01300) 341865

Stoneware pottery for oven and table, porcelain.
Open: Tue-Sun 10am-6pm. Closed 25-26 Dec
Cards: Access, Visa

DIRECTIONS: Off A352 Dorchester to Sherbourne road, follow tourist sign for pottery, down lane off Duck Street.

2/269
● TEXTILES

Dianne Davies Designs

2 Bratton House, Higher Bratton Seymour,
Wincanton, Somerset BA9 8DA
Tel: (01963) 34670

Hand-printed and painted textiles,
wallhangings.
Open: Wed 10am-4pm, other times by
appointment
Cards: No

DIRECTIONS: From the A303
London to Penzance road, take the
A371 towards Castle Cary. Between
Holbrooke Hotel and Hadspen
House.

2/270
● HERBS

R T Herbs

Orange Farm, Kilmersdon, Bath,
Somerset BA3 5TD
Tel: (01761) 435470

Culinary, aromatic, medicinal plants,
wild flowers, cottage garden plants
and shrubs. Display garden.
Open: Daily 9am-6pm inc bank hols.
Closed Christmas
Cards: No

DIRECTIONS: B3139 east of A367
Radstock to Shepton Mallet. Behind
Kilmersdon Garage.

2/271
● CERAMICS

Christine-Ann Richards
Ceramicist

Chapel House, High Street, Wanstrow,
Shepton Mallet, Somerset BA4 4TE
Tel: (01749) 850208

Porcelain vessels for conservatories,
gardens and water-gardens.
Open: By appointment
Cards: No

DIRECTIONS: Turn left at main
crossroads in Wanstrow. Studio in
schoolroom behind old Methodist
Chapel.

2/272
● CERAMICS

Stephen Morgan

Jericho, Mells Down, Mells, Frome,
Somerset BA11 2RL
Tel: (01373) 813242

Garden terracotta, floor tiles and
glazed wall tiles.
Open: By appointment only
Cards: No

DIRECTIONS: Take A362 from
Frome towards Radstock. After 2
miles, turn left at Charlton's
Sawmills. At bottom of hill turn left
(private road). 500 yards, left-hand
fork, 500 yards to Jericho.

2/273
■ HERBS

Coach House Herbs

Lewell Yard, Lewell Lodgen, West
Knighton, Dorchester, Dorset DT2 8PD
Tel: (01305) 853779

Fresh culinary herbs, unusual oriental
and salad leaves.
Open: All day. Closed Christmas
Cards: No

DIRECTIONS: 3½ miles south-east of
Dorchester, north of A352. In north-
west corner of village, unmarked
drive.

2/274
■ WINE

Whatley Vineyard and Herb
Garden

Whatley, Frome, Somerset BA11 3LA
Tel: (01373) 836467
Fax: (01373) 836579

White wines, herb plants.
Open: Wed-Sat and bank hols 10am-
1pm, 2pm-6pm, Sun 12 noon-5pm,
Oct-March by appointment only
Cards: No

DIRECTIONS: 2 miles west of Frome
on the old Wells road and signposted
from A361 at Holwell.

2/275
■ CIDER

Mill House Cider

33 Moreton Road, Owermoigne,
Dorchester, Dorset DT2 8HZ
Tel: (01305) 852220

Cider, cider brandy, cider vinegar,
shop and museum.
Open: Mon-Fri 9am-5pm. Closed 25-
28 Dec, 1 Jan
Cards: No

DIRECTIONS: Follow brown signs to
cider museum.

2/276
● LEATHER GOODS

Blackmore Vale Saddlery

Four Winds, West Bourton, Gillingham,
Dorset SP8 5PE
Tel: (01747) 840741

Saddler, bellows and leather goods.
Open: All reasonable hours
Cards: Access, Visa

DIRECTIONS: 3 miles north-west of
Gillingham on Wincanton road
(B3081), ½ mile south of West
Bourton.

2/277
✳ MULTIPLE

The Black Swan Guild

2 Bridge Street, Frome,
Somerset BA11 1BB
Tel: (01373) 473980

Painted silk, baskets, picture-framing,
jewellery, ceramics and papier mâché.
Open: Mon-Sat 10am-5pm. Closed
Sun and bank hols
Cards: Access, Visa

DIRECTIONS: In Frome town centre
close to library and next to main car
park.

2/278
■ MEAT/POULTRY/GAME

Norwood

Bath Road, Norton St Philip, Bath, Avon
BA3 6LP
Tel: (0373) 834356
Fax: (0373) 834765

Organic farm, breeding rare and
traditional farm animals; producing
quality organic beef, lamb and pork.
Farm shop open all year. Visitor
Centre open spring and summer
Open: 24 Mar-24 Sept daily 10.30am-
6pm
Cards: No

DIRECTIONS: Six miles south of
Bath on the B3110.

2/279
● FORGEWORK

Newton Forge

Stalbridge Lane, Sturminster Newton,
Dorset DT10 2JQ
Tel: (01258) 472407
Fax: (01258) 471111

Hand-forged ironwork, gates, railings,
curtain poles, lighting, fireplaces.
Open: Mon-Fri 9am-5pm, Sat 9am-
4pm by appointment. Closed daily
1pm-2pm, and 25 Dec-1 Jan
Cards: Access, Visa

DIRECTIONS: On A357 9 miles west
of Blandford. Travel west 100 yards
past old mill, turn right into
Stalbridge Lane, 500 yards to Newton
Forge.

2/280
■ FISH/SHELLFISH

Whistley Crayfish

Whistley Waters, Milton on Stour,
Gillingham, Dorset SP8 5PT
Tel/Fax: (01747) 840666

Freshwater crayfish.
Open: 8am-8pm. Closed Nov-May
Cards: No

DIRECTIONS: At Milton on Stour
post office take road to Wyke. Second
right after 500 yards. First left after 1½
miles, signposted.

2/281
● CERAMICS

Foxdale Pottery
The Old Bakery, Child Okeford, Blandford,
Dorset DT11 8EF
Tel: (01258) 860039

Handmade pottery, domestic pots,
house nameplates, garden pots.
Open: Mon-Sun 10am-5.30pm,
telephone first
Cards: No

DIRECTIONS: Centre of Child
Okeford.

2/282
● MUSICAL INSTRUMENTS

Michael Johnson Harpsichords
St Andrew's Studio, Woodbridge Lane,
Bedchester, Shaftesbury, Dorset SP7 0JU
Tel: (01747) 811455
Fax: (01747) 811061

Harpsichords, design, manufacture
and restoration.
Open: Mon-Fri 8am-5pm
Cards: No

DIRECTIONS: 1 mile west towards
Sturminster Newton from Fontmell
Magna, which is 4 miles south of
Shaftesbury on the A350.

MAP 3

3/283
■ BAKED GOODS
Marshfield Bakery
Westend Farm, Marshfield, Chippenham,
Wiltshire SN14 8JH
Tel: (01225) 891709
Fax: (01225) 891141

Shortbreads, flapjacks, fruit cakes.
Open: Mon-Fri 8am-5pm
Cards: No

DIRECTIONS: On A420
Chippenham to Bristol road. Just
outside Marshfield village. 3 miles
from J18 of M4.

3/284
■ FISH/SHELLFISH
Mere Fish Farm
Ivymead Mere, Warminster,
Wiltshire BA12 6EN
Tel/Fax: (01747) 860461

Fresh trout, cold and hot smoked
trout and terrine.
Open: Mon-Fri 9am-5pm, Sat 9am-
1pm. Closed bank hols
Cards: No

DIRECTIONS: Turn into Water
Street by Yapps wine merchant. 1st
left is Ivymead. 50 yards straight ahead
take lane by lake and car park.

3/285
■ DAIRY PRODUCE
Bere Marsh Farm Shop
Shillingstone, Blandford Forum,
Dorset DT11 0QY
Tel: (01258) 860284

Ice-cream and real fruit ices. Also
fresh pasta and sauces.
Open: Thur-Sat 10am-4pm
Cards: No

DIRECTIONS: Take A357 from
Blandford Forum towards
Sturminster Newton. After
Shillingstone turn right to Child
Okeford. Pass under railway bridge
and turn immediately left into farm.

3/286
■ WINE
Elms Cross Vineyard
Bradford-on-Avon, Wiltshire BA15 2AL
Tel/Fax: (01225) 866917

Grapes and wines.
Open: Fri, Sat, Mon 9.30am-5.30pm
Cards: No

DIRECTIONS: From centre of
Bradford-on-Avon take B3109 to
Frome. Cross Kennet and Avon canal,
after ¼ mile take right to Westwood.
Vineyard 200 yards on left.

3/287
■ VEGETABLES
Gold Hill Organic Farm
Child Okeford, Nr Blandford Forum,
Dorset DT11 8HB
Tel: (01258) 860293

Organic salad and winter vegetables.
Open: Wed-Sun 8am-6pm. Closed
Mar-Apr
Cards: No

DIRECTIONS: Take A350 to
Shaftesbury. 2 miles after Stourpaine
turn left to Child Okeford. Through
village, and farm is on right 50 yards
before Saxon Inn.

3/288
● JEWELLERY
Paws Jewellery (David Watts) Workshop
Southbrook Workshop, Bere Regis,
Nr Wareham, Dorset BH20 7LN
Tel: (01202) 631966
Fax: (01202) 625262

Jewellery workshop, diamond and
stone setters.
Open: Please always telephone first
Cards: No

DIRECTIONS: Opposite watercress
farm in Bere Regis.

3/289
● FURNITURE

R E Hogg Upholsterer
82a West Street, Bere Regis, Wareham,
Dorset BH20 7HL
Tel: (01929) 471603

Upholstered furniture. Traditional
materials.
Open: Mon-Fri 9am-6pm. Sat 9am-
1pm. Closed: 1 week at Christmas
and bank hols
Cards: No

DIRECTIONS: Centre of Bere Regis.
2 doors from post office. On junction
of A31 and A35.

3/290
● FORGEWORK

Wing & Staples
Motcombe Forge, Motcombe, Nr
Shaftesbury, Dorset SP7 9PE
Tel: (01747) 853104

Hand-forged decorative and practical
ironwork, showroom.
Open: Mon-Fri 8am-5pm, Sat 8am-
12pm
Cards: No

DIRECTIONS: A350, Motcombe turn
off. Motcombe Forge is 2 miles north
of Shaftesbury and 2 miles from
Gillingham.

3/291
● FURNITURE

Southern Crafts Ltd
The Old Brewery, Durweston, Blandford
Forum, Dorset DT11 0QE
Tel: (01258) 453987
Fax: (01258) 480201

Furniture in hard and soft woods.
Open: Mon-Fri 8am-5pm, Sat 9am-
12pm
Cards: No

DIRECTIONS: From traffic lights and
bridge over river Stour where A357
meets A350 travel ½ mile west
through Durweston. Last building on
right.

3/292
● SILVERWARE

Chris Murphy Craft Studio
4 Gold Hill Parade, Shaftesbury,
Dorset SP7 8LY
Tel: (01747) 854067

Handmade jewellery and silverware.
Open: Mon-Tue, Thur-Sat, 9.30am-
12.30pm, 1.30pm-5pm. Closed bank
hols
Cards: Access, Amex, Visa

DIRECTIONS: In the centre of
Shaftesbury, in the town hall cellars,
facing Gold Hill, opposite the
museum.

3/293
● CERAMICS

The White Horse Pottery
Newtown, Westbury, Wiltshire BA13 3EE
Tel: (01373) 864772

Glazed domestic pottery, architectural
and horticultural ware.
Open: Mon-Sat 10am-5pm, closed
bank hols
Cards: No

DIRECTIONS: At junction of B3098
Bratton Road and Newtown, the road
leading to the Westbury White Horse
and Bratton Castle.

3/294
● KNITWEAR

Knowlton Knitwear
Horsehill Cottage, Donhead St Mary,
Shaftesbury, Dorset SP7 9DS
Tel: (01747) 828495

Jacob wool knitwear from own sheep.
Open: 9am-5pm by appointment
Cards: No

DIRECTIONS: Off A30, out of
Ludwell towards Shaftesbury.

3/295
■ FARM PRODUCE

Keyneston Mill
Tarrant Keyneston Fruit Farm, Tarrant
Keyneston, Blandford, Dorset DT11 9HZ
Tel: (01258) 452596

Sparkling and table wine. Farm shop.

Open: Daily 10am-5pm. Restaurant closed October to February
Cards: Access, Visa

DIRECTIONS: From Wimborne on the B3082 road to Blandford turn left at the True Lovers Knot pub, through Tarrant-Keyneston and the entrance is straight ahead at the T-junction.

3/296
● CERAMICS

Lacock Pottery
1 The Tanyard, Church Street, Lacock, Chippenham, Wiltshire SN15 2LB
Tel: (01249) 730266

Porcelain and stoneware.
Open: Mon-Tue, Thur-Sun 10am-5pm
Cards: No

DIRECTIONS: On the A350 between Chippenham and Melksham. In the centre of Lacock, adjacent to the village church.

3/297
● FURNITURE

Belinda Ballantine School of Painted Furniture
The Abbey Brewery, Market Cross, Malmesbury, Wiltshire SN16 9AS
Tel: (01666) 822047
Fax: (01666) 822293

Painted furniture, decorative paint effects.
Open: Mon-Fri 10am-5pm, but telephone first
Cards: Access, Visa

DIRECTIONS: Top of High Street in Malmesbury. Straight over Market Cross at end of lane on right.

3/298
● PAPER PRODUCTS

Compton Marbling
Lower Lawn Barns, Tisbury, Salisbury, Wiltshire SP3 6SG
Tel: (01747) 871147
Fax: (01747) 871265

Hand-marbled paper, stationery, books, lighting and decorative accessories.
Open: Mon-Fri 9am-5pm

Cards: Access, Visa

DIRECTIONS: On A303 turn left to Tisbury and Forthill. In Forthill take right at T-junction and first left through arch and Forthill park. At crossroads with Beckford Arms pub go straight over, ½ mile on left.

3/299
■ MEAT PRODUCTS

Sandridge Farmhouse Bacon
Sandridge Farm, Bromham, Nr Chippenham, Wiltshire SN15 2JL
Tel: (01380) 850304

Wiltshire and oak-smoked bacons, dry-cured hams, farmhouse sausages.
Open: Mon-Sat 9am-5pm
Cards: No

DIRECTIONS: Off A3102, take turning to Bromham. Between Calne and Melksham. From M4 leave at J16.

3/300
● STONE

Tony Viney
Sandy Hill Workshops, Corfe Castle, Wareham, Dorset BH20 5JF
Tel/Fax: (01929) 480977

Polished Purbeck stone plates and bowls revealing fossil shells.
Open: Daily 10am-6pm
Cards: No

DIRECTIONS: Take second left on entering Corfe Castle from Wareham. Go under railway bridge and turn immediately right. Workshop is opposite railway station.

3/301
● PLANTS

Naked Cross Nurseries
Waterloo Road, Corfe Mullen, Wimbourne, Dorset BH21 3SR
Tel: (01202) 693256

Heather specialist, small garden centre and nursery.
Open: Mon-Sat 9am-5.30pm, Sun 9.30am-5pm. Closed 25 Dec-1 Jan
Cards: Access, Amex, Visa

DIRECTIONS: At Wimborne bypass on A31 head for Corfe Mullen south.

Go straight on over 3 small roundabouts. At bottom of hill, nursery is on the right opposite Beacon Hill.

3/302
● DOLLS' HOUSES
Honeychurch Toys Ltd
2 Old Swan Yard, High Street, Devizes, Wiltshire SN10 1AT
Tel: (01380) 727170

Wooden dolls' houses and dolls' house furniture.
Open: Mon-Sat 9.30am-5pm. Closed Wed pm and first 2 weeks in Feb
Cards: Visa

DIRECTIONS: In centre of Devizes. Opposite the Dolcipani Bakery.

3/303
● CERAMICS
Poole Pottery Limited
The Quay, Poole, Dorset BH15 1RF
Tel: (01202) 666200
Fax: (01202) 682894

Pottery.
Open: Mon-Fri 9am-5pm. Sun and bank hols 10am-5pm. July-Aug 9am-9.30pm. Closed 25, 26 Dec
Cards: Access, Switch, Visa

DIRECTIONS: On Poole Quay. Follow signs from Ringwood on A31.

3/304
● CERAMICS
The Owl Pottery
108 High Street, Swanage, Dorset BH19 2NY
Tel: (01929) 425850

Pottery featuring owls and wildlife. Hand-decorated tiles, ceramic jewellery, animal sculptures.
Open: Reasonable hours, closed Sun and Thur pm
Cards: No

DIRECTIONS: A351 to Swanage. Up High Street past the library and the town hall, near the mill pond and parish church.

3/305
● PAINTS
Farrow & Ball Ltd
33 Uddens Trading Estate, Wimborne, Dorset BH21 7NL
Tel: (01202) 876141
Fax: (01202) 873793

National Trust and Jane Churchill paint ranges.
Open: Mon-Fri 9am-5pm. Closed bank hols
Cards: Access, Switch, Visa

DIRECTIONS: Off A31 between Ferndown and Wimborne.

3/306
■ WINE
Horton Estate Vineyard
Horton, Wimborne, Dorset BH21 7JG
Tel: (01258) 840258

Wine.
Open: Sat 10am-4pm; also Thur-Fri 10am-4pm July-Aug
Cards: No

DIRECTIONS: Horton village is 7 miles from the Ashley Heath roundabout near Ringwood on the A31. Vineyard is next to the red phone box, 50 yards east of the village.

3/307
■ MEAT PRODUCTS
The Sausage Shop
Wigbeth Farm, Horton, Wimborne, Dorset BH21 7JJ
Tel: (01258) 840723

20 varieties of sausages, cured bacon, home-made faggots, *boerewors*.
Open: 9.30am-5pm. Closed Wed, Sun
Cards: No

DIRECTIONS: A35 to Ringwood, at Ashley Heath roundabout turn left to Horton. Shop 7 miles on left.

3/308
● CERAMICS
Tarka & Jane King Ceramics
Pentridge House, Pentridge, Salisbury,
Wiltshire SP5 5QX
Tel: (01725) 552231
Fax: (01725) 552252

Decorated white slip cast earthenware.
Open: By appointment only between
9am-5pm
Cards: No

DIRECTIONS: On A354 between
Salisbury and Blandford. Signposted
to village of Pentridge.

3/309
● SMOKING PIPES
Tilshead Pipe Co Ltd
19 Candown Road, Tilshead, Nr Salisbury,
Wiltshire SP3 4SJ
Tel: (01980) 620679
Fax: (01980) 620500

Briar smoking pipes.
Open: Mon-Fri 8.30am-5.30pm.
Closed Christmas and New Year
Cards: No

DIRECTIONS: On A360 14 miles
north of Salisbury. Take first right
after Tilshead post office.

3/310   ● PLANTS
Knoll Gardens
Stapehill Road, Hampreston, Nr Wimborne,
Dorset BH21 7ND
Tel: (01202) 873931
Fax: (01202) 870842

Ceanothus and phygelius. Informal
garden and water gardens, tearoom.
Open: Mar-Nov 10am-5.30pm,
limited winter opening, please
telephone
Cards: Access, Switch, Visa

DIRECTIONS: Between Wimborne
and Ferndown, off B3073 Ham Lane.
Exit A31 at Canford Bottom
roundabout (signposted 1½ miles)

3/311
● PLANTS
Trehane Nursery
Stapehill Road, Hampreston, Nr Wimborne,
Dorset BH21 7NE
Tel/Fax: (01202) 873490

Camellia nursery and blueberry
specialists, 400 varieties.
Open: Mon-Sun 10am-4.30pm, Feb-
Oct Sat-Sun 10am-4.30pm. Closed 25
Dec-1 Jan
Cards: Access, Visa

DIRECTIONS: From the roundabout
on the A31 linking Ferndown and
Wimborne by-passes, take the B3073.
At the crossroads after 1½ miles, turn
left up Stapehill Road. The nursery is
just before Knoll Gardens.

3/312
■ DAIRY PRODUCE
Woodlands Park Dairy
Woodlands, Wimborne, Dorset BH21 8LX
Tel: (01202) 822687
Fax: (01202) 826051

Yoghurt from sheep's and goats' milk,
also cheese and ice-cream.
Open: Mon-Fri 8am-5pm. Closed 24
Dec-2 Jan
Cards: No

DIRECTIONS: 1 mile north of
Verwood on B3081. Turn left after
Crawe Valley Golf Club. Sign on left,
dairy is 400 yards down track on left.

3/313
● CERAMICS
The Edmondsham Pottery
Smallbridge Farmhouse, Edmondsham,
Nr Cranborne, Wimborne,
Dorset BH21 5RH
Tel: (01725) 517251

Stoneware and terracotta pottery.
Open: Mon-Sun 9am-6pm. Closed 25
Dec
Cards: No

DIRECTIONS: From Ringwood to
Verwood crossroads turn right down
Edmondsham road for 2 miles. Turn
left to pottery ½ mile on left.

3/314
● FORGEWORK

Saxon Forge
Verwood Road, Three Legged Cross,
Wimborne, Dorset BH21 6RR
Tel: (01202) 826375

Blacksmith, ornamental ironwork,
gates, railings, items for the home.
Open: Mon-Sat 8am-5.30pm
Cards: No

DIRECTIONS: From the A31
Ringwood to Ashley Heath road, turn
right at the roundabout to Three
Legged Cross. Take the road opposite
the garage to Verwood, the forge is
1 mile on the right.

3/315
● CERAMICS

Hare Lane Pottery
Cranborne, Wimborne, Dorset BH21 5QT
Tel: (01725) 517700

Terracotta and glazed domestic
pottery.
Open: Telephone in advance
Cards: No

DIRECTIONS: 2 miles east of Fleur
de Lys pub in Cranborne towards
Alderholt. Or half-way between
Alderholt and Cranborne, 2 miles
north of Verwood.

3/316
● CERAMICS

Bowled Over
Manor Farmhouse, Patney, Devizes,
Wiltshire SN10 3RB
Tel: (01380) 840501
Fax: (01380) 848189

Hand-painted pottery, pudding
basins, jugs and mugs.
Open: By appointment only
Cards: No

DIRECTIONS: Leave A342 at
Chirton. Through village and on to
Patney. First right, last house on left.

3/317
■ PRESERVES

Olives Et Al
4 Castle Lane, Wilton, Salisbury,
Wiltshire SP2 0HG
Tel: (01722) 744559

Olives, pesto, tapenade, olive oils and
more.
Open: By appointment only
Cards: Access, Visa

DIRECTIONS: A36 Wilton to
Warminster road, into Wilton town
centre, right at traffic lights, up North
Street, 300 yards up on left, located in
Castle Lane.

3/318
● FURNITURE

Trannon Furniture Ltd
Chilhampton Farm, Wilton, Salisbury,
Wiltshire SP2 0AB
Tel/Fax: (01722) 744577

Solid ash chairs, recliners, tables,
desks and settees.
Open: Mon-Fri 9am-5pm. Sat by
appointment
Cards: No

DIRECTIONS: 1 mile west of Wilton
House on A36 towards Warminster.
Brick flint farm buildings on left of
road.

3/319
■ BAKED GOODS

Cookie Craft
Michaelmas, Common Platt, Purton,
Wiltshire SN5 9LB
Tel: (01793) 770250

Scrumpy cider cakes, wine cakes,
traybakes and cookies.
Open: Mon-Fri 8.30am-5pm. Closed
20 Dec-20 Jan
Cards: No

DIRECTIONS: 3 miles north of J16
M4 take road to Swindon, then
Purton and Lyddiard Millicent. Turn
right into Tewkesbury Way. On apex
of bend to left turn right to Common
Platt. Follow sign.

3/320
● CERAMICS
E. Baggaley Ltd
Branksome China Works, Shaftesbury
Street, Fordingbridge, Hampshire SP6 1JF
Tel: (01425) 652010

Porcelain tableware and factory tours.
Open: Mon-Sat 9.30am-4.30pm.
Closed bank hols
Cards: No

DIRECTIONS: Between Salisbury and
Ringwood, off A338. In
Fordingbridge bear right at end of
High Street. On left.

3/321
● FISHING
Cain Rod Co
Meadow Barn, Lower Woodford, Salisbury,
Wiltshire SP4 6NQ
Tel: (01722) 782602
Fax: (01722) 782300

Fly-fishing centre including custom
fly rods and fishing accessories.
Open: Mon-Fri 8.30am-6.30pm, Sat
9am-1pm. Closed Christmas
Cards: Access, Amex, Switch, Visa

DIRECTIONS: On Woodford Valley
road 4 miles south of Amesbury (off
A345) and 3 miles north of Salisbury.
Opposite Wheatsheaf Inn.

3/322
■ FLOUR
Rushall Farms
Littlecott Farmhouse, Enford, Pewsey,
Wiltshire SN9 6EB
Tel: (01980) 630335

Flour, bread, cakes, eggs, honey.
Open: Tue, Fri 8am-5pm
Cards: No

DIRECTIONS: A342 Devizes road
south-east of Devizes. Mill has large
sign outside.

3/323
● CERAMICS
Braybrooke Pottery
Andover Road, Upavon, Pewsey,
Wiltshire SN9 6AB
Tel: (01980) 630466

Domestic, decorative and
commemorative stoneware and
earthenware thrown pots.
Open: Telephone in advance
Cards: No

DIRECTIONS: On A342 Andover to
Devizes, 100 yards east of bridge over
river Avon, and east of A342 and A345
(Salisbury to Marlborough)
crossroads.

3/324
● FURNITURE
The Walnut Tree Workshop
The Old Dairy, Station Approach,
Breamore, Fordingbridge,
Hampshire SP6 2AB
Tel: (01725) 512165

Furniture.
Open: Mon-Fri 8am-6pm, Sat by
appointment. Variable holidays in
summer
Cards: No

DIRECTIONS: From the A338 to
Breamore, go past the Bat and Ball
pub on the left, 150 yards on the left is
a road, take the track next to it on the
right.

3/325
● ROCKING-HORSES
Robert Mullis Rocking Horse Maker
55 Berkeley Road, Wroughton, Swindon,
Wiltshire SN4 9BN
Tel/Fax: (01793) 813583

Wooden rocking-horses and
collection of rocking animals.
Open: By appointment
Cards: Access, Visa

DIRECTIONS: From J15 of M4 take
A346 towards Marlborough. At top of
hill, turn right. Follow Wroughton
sign. From Three Tuns pub follow
Swindon sign. Berkeley Road is 2nd
turning on left.

3/326
■ DAIRY PRODUCE

Berkeley Farm Dairy
Berkeley Farm, Wroughton, Swindon,
Wiltshire SN4 9AQ
Tel: (01793) 812228

Guernsey cream, butter and milk.
Open: 9am-3pm
Cards: No

DIRECTIONS: A4361 Devizes to
Swindon road. 1 mile south of
Swindon.

3/327
● PLANTS

**Macpenny Nurseries and
Woodland Garden**
154 Burley Road, Bransgore, Christchurch,
Dorset BH23 8DB
Tel: (01425) 672348

Nursery and woodland garden,
composted New Forest bracken.
Open: Mon-Sat 9am-5pm, Sun 2pm-
5pm. Closed 25 Dec and 1 Jan
Cards: Access, Visa

DIRECTIONS: Off A35 from
Christchurch to Lyndhurst, right at
Cat and Fiddle pub, on to crossroads
by the Crown Inn, turn right towards
Burley and Thorney Hill. ½ mile on
the right.

3/328
■ EGGS

Martin Pitt
Levetts Farm, Clench Common,
Marlborough, Wiltshire SN8 4DS
Tel: (01672) 512035
Fax: (01672) 514976

Free-range eggs and handmade
mayonnaise.
Open: Daily 9am-3pm
Cards: No

DIRECTIONS: 2 miles south of
Marlborough on A345 to Pewsey.

3/329
■ CIDER

New Forest Cider
Littlemead, Pound Lane, Burley, Ringwood,
Hampshire BM24 4ED
Tel: (01425) 403589

Traditional farmhouse cider sold in
draught straight from the barrel
(sample before purchase). Also apple
juice, local preserves and small
craftware.
Open: All year 9am-7pm, Christmas-
end of January limited opening,
telephone first
Cards: No

DIRECTIONS: 3 miles south of A31.
Turn right at village war memorial on
to the Bransgore road. 300 yards from
the village centre on the left by the
Forest Tea House & Restaurant (look
for the barrel sign by the road).

3/330
● TOYS

Hill Top Toys
Manor Cottage, Ben Lane, Farley,
Salisbury, Wiltshire SP5 1AF
Tel: (01722) 712265

Traditional mohair teddy bears and
other soft toys including hand
puppets.
Open: By appointment only
Cards: No

DIRECTIONS: 4 miles east of
Salisbury along A30, then 4 miles
south of A30 on edge of village next to
Farley road sign.

3/331
■ SMOKED PRODUCE

Fjordling Smokehouses
Dunstable Farm, Pitton Road, West
Winterslow, Salisbury, Wiltshire SP5 1SA
Tel: (01980) 862689
Fax: (01980) 863944

Norwegian oakwood smokehouse:
fish, meat and poultry.
Open: Fri 2pm-7pm. Sat 9.30am-1pm.
Closed bank hols
Cards: Access, Visa

DIRECTIONS: Take A30 Salisbury to
London road. 5 miles from Salisbury

turn left to Firsdown and the
Winterslow. After 1 mile turn right at
crossroads, and after further ¼ mile
smokehouse is on left.

3/332
● BELLOWS

John Jones Fire Bellows
35 Milton Lilbourne, Pewsey,
Wiltshire SN9 5LQ
Tel: (01672) 62696

Fire bellows in traditional shapes.
Open: 10am-5pm but telephone first
Cards: No

DIRECTIONS: On road between
Pewsey and Burbage. In passage
opposite village hall, 75 yards from
road.

3/333
■ MEAT/POULTRY/GAME

S W Pickles & Sons
3 Fernhill Lane, New Milton,
Hampshire BH25 5JN
Tel: (01425) 614577

Venison, game and sausages.
Open: Mon, Wed 8am-1pm, Tue,
Thur-Sat 8am-1pm, 2pm-5.30pm
Cards: No

DIRECTIONS: Southern edge of New
Forest. 200 yards north of railway
station.

3/334
■ MEAT/POULTRY/GAME

Eastbrook Farm Organic Meats
50 High Street, Shrivenham, Swindon,
Oxfordshire SN6 8AA
Tel: (01793) 790460
Fax: (01793) 791239

Organic beef, pork, lamb, chicken,
home-cured bacon and oven-ready
specialities.
Open: Tue-Fri 9am-5pm, Sat 8am-
2pm
Cards: Access, Visa

DIRECTIONS: M4, J15. Take A419
for 1½ miles to A420. Road to Oxford
for 3 miles. Turn right under railway
to Shrivenham. Shop on left with red
and white canopy.

3/335
■ SAUSAGES

K A Gardner
16 High Street, Ludgershall, Andover,
Hampshire SP11 8PZ
Tel: (01264) 790318

Sausages, bacon and pies.
Open: Tue-Fri 8.30am-5.30pm, Sat
8am-4pm. Closed Sun and Mon, and
bank hols
Cards: No

DIRECTIONS: On A346 Andover to
Marlborough Road, 9 miles north-
west of Andover. Turn right at
monument in village. 100 yards
further on the right opposite the
Crown pub.

3/336
● STONE

Lloyd of Bedwyn
91 Church Street, Great Bedwyn,
Marlborough, Wiltshire SN8 3PF
Tel: (01672) 870234

Marble granite stone.
Open: Mon-Fri 8am-5pm. Closed
Christmas
Cards: No

DIRECTIONS: M4, J14. Take A338 to
Hungerford. Turn right along A4 for
3 miles, turn left to Little and Great
Bedwyn. In centre of village.

3/337
● PLANTS

Apple Court Nursery
Hordle Lane, Hordle, Lymington,
Hampshire SO41 0HU
Tel/Fax: (01590) 642130

Unusual plants, including hostas,
ferns and grasses, day lilies. Gardens
open.
Open: Thur-Mon 9.30am-1pm, 2pm-
5.30pm. Closed Dec-Jan
Cards: No

DIRECTIONS: From the A337
between Lymington and New Milton
turn north into Hordle Lane at the
Royal Oak, at Downton crossroads.

3/338
● PLANTS

Steven Bailey Ltd
Silver Street, Sway, Lymington,
Hampshire SO41 6ZA
Tel: (01590) 682227
Fax: (01590) 683765

Garden pinks, carnations and
alstroemeria, geraniums, cyclamen,
winter pansies and primroses.
Open: All year Mon-Fri 8am-4.30pm,
Mar-Dec Sat 9am-4.30pm, Mar-July
Sun 10am-4pm
Cards: Access, Visa

DIRECTIONS: On the Lymington/
Hordle road and not in Sway village
itself.

3/339
● WOOD

Mike Bradley, Craftsman Woodturner
Unit 4, Regal Way, Faringdon,
Oxfordshire SN7 7BX
Tel/Fax: (01367) 242316

Wood-turning for domestic and trade,
large columns, spinning wheels to
furniture.
Open: Mon-Fri 9am-5pm. Closed
bank hols and over Christmas
Cards: No

DIRECTIONS: On A420 Swindon to
Oxford road, 12 miles north-east of
Swindon, follow industrial signs into
Faringdon Park Road. Turn right into
Regal Way, bear left through security
gates.

3/340
● GLASS

Alum Bay Glass Ltd
The Glassworks, Alum Bay,
Isle of Wight PO39 0JD
Tel: (01983) 753473
Fax: (01983) 756263

Glasswork.
Open: Mon-Sun 9.30am-5.30pm.
Closed Christmas to New Year
Cards: Access, Amex, Diners, Switch,
Visa

DIRECTIONS: Drive west until end
of road.

3/341
■ WINE

New Forest Wine
Hollybush Vineyard, Setley, Brockenhurst,
Hampshire SO42 7UF
Tel: (01590) 623054 and 622246

Wine baskets, jams, honey. 6-acre
vineyard open to the public.
Open: 1 Apr-24 Dec, Tue-Sat 10am-
12.30pm, 2pm-5.30pm, Sun 12-5pm
Cards: No

DIRECTIONS: On A337 1 mile south
of level crossing at Brockenhurst.

3/342
● CERAMICS

Angels Farm Pottery
Angels Farm, Pinkney Lane, Lyndhurst,
Hampshire SO43 7FE
Tel: (01703) 284079

Pottery workshop and showroom.
Open: Mon-Sat 9am-5pm. Closed 25-
28 Dec
Cards: No

DIRECTIONS: Take A35 around
Lyndhurst, follow signs to
Bournemouth on one-way system,
branching left into Chapel Lane after
Goose Green. Pottery signposted on
left.

3/343
● WOOD

Nether Wallop Trading Company
Maltings, Nether Wallop,
Hampshire SO20 8EW
Tel/Fax: (01264) 781734

Chopping-, carving- and serving-
boards.
Open: 9am-5pm by appointment only
Cards: No

DIRECTIONS: From Stockbridge is
first thatched cottage on left in Nether
Wallop.

3/344
● CERAMICS

Burley Pottery
8 Southampton Road, Lymington,
Hampshire SO41 9GG
Tel: (01590) 671076

Hand-thrown stoneware pottery,
ceramic figures, clowns, caricatures.
Open: Mon-Sun 10am-5pm. Closed
25-26 Dec
Cards: No

DIRECTIONS: Turn off M27 at
Cadnam on to A337. In Lymington
opposite Safeways.

3/345
● PLANTS

Spinners
Boldre, Lymington, Hampshire SO41 5QE
Tel: (01590) 673347

Hardy plants and shrubs, garden
open.
Open: Tue-Sat 10am-5pm. Closed 25-
26 Dec
Cards: No

DIRECTIONS: Signposted off the
A337 between Brockenhurst and
Lymington, and also off the
Lymington/Beaulieu road (ignore
signs to Boldre Church).

3/346
● GARDEN FURNITURE

Heritage Woodcraft
Unit 5, Shelley Farm, Ower, Nr Romsey,
Hampshire SO51 6AS
Tel: (01703) 814145

Handmade traditional wooden
wheelbarrows and hardwood garden
furniture.
Open: Mon-Fri 8am-5pm, or by
appointment. Closed bank hols
Cards: Access, Visa

DIRECTIONS: At Ower off A36,
close to J2 of M27.

3/347
■ FLOUR

Doves Farm Foods
Salisbury Road, Hungerford,
Berkshire RG17 0RF
Tel: (01488) 684880
Fax: (01488) 685235

Flour millers, organic and specialist,
including rye spelt, gram, malthouse,
brown rice.
Open: Mon-Fri 9am-5pm. Closed
bank hols
Cards: No

DIRECTIONS: 3 miles south of
Hungerford on A338, entrance on left
50 yards past Wiltshire county border
sign.

3/348
■ FARM PRODUCE

Kimbridge Farm Shop
Kimbridge, Romsey, Hampshire SO51 0LE
Tel: (01794) 340777
Fax: (01794) 341295

Rainbow trout, smoked trout and
other smoked items, 40 British
cheeses, fresh pasta and sauces.
Open: Daily 9am-5pm. Closed 4 days
over Christmas and Easter
Cards: No

DIRECTIONS: Off A3057 Romsey to
Stockbridge road. 3½ miles north of
Romsey, turning opposite Bear &
Ragged Staff pub.

3/349
■ MEAT/POULTRY/GAME

Sutherland's of Eldon
Upper Eldon Farm, King's Somborne,
Stockbridge, Hampshire SO20 6QN
Tel/Fax: (01794) 368158

Sausages, cured ham and fresh pork
from own wild boar cross.
Open: Mon-Sat 10am-6pm, but
telephone first
Cards: No

DIRECTIONS: Take A3057
Stockbridge to Romsey road. Turn
left at church in King's Somborne,
then 2nd right (Eldon Road). Go 2
miles along single track road. Go past

bungalow on right, is the next house on left.

3/350
● PLANTS

Longstock Park Garden Nursery
Longstock, Stockbridge,
Hampshire SO20 6EH
Tel: (01264) 810894
Fax: (01264) 810439

Hardy and tender nursery stock.
Open: Mon-Sat 8.30am-4.30pm. Also Sun Apr-Sept 2pm-5pm
Cards: No

DIRECTIONS: From Stockbridge take A30 towards Salisbury, turn right for Longstock and go through village. Continue up hill, turn right at farmyard. Nursery is on left about 400 yards along wooded track.

3/351
● BASKETS

John Hayward
Cane and Woodcraft Centre, 57 High Street, Beaulieu, Hampshire SO42 7YA
Tel: (01590) 612211

Baskets and furniture in cane, willow and rush.
Open: Wed-Sat 10am-1pm, 2pm-5pm, Sun 12 noon-5pm
Cards: Access, Visa

DIRECTIONS: Opposite the garden centre.

3/352
■ WINE

The Beaulieu Gift Shop
Montagu Ventures Ltd, John Montagu Building, Beaulieu, Brockenhurst
Hampshire SO42 7ZN
Tel: (01590) 612345
Fax: (01590) 612624

Wine and confectionery.
Open: Daily 10am-6pm. Closed 25 Dec
Cards: Access, Amex, Diners, Switch, Visa

DIRECTIONS: From Southampton take A35 to the west, then the A326, and then B3056 to Beaulieu.

3/353
■ CONFECTIONERY

Beaulieu Chocolates
High Street, Beaulieu, Brockenhurst, Hampshire SO42 7YA
Tel: (01590) 612279
Fax: (01590) 612624

Handmade chocolates.
Open: Easter-Nov 10am-5.30pm. Dec-Easter 10am-5pm. Closed 25, 26 Dec
Cards: Access, Amex, Diners, Visa

DIRECTIONS: In High Street on one-way system.

3/354
● CERAMICS

High Street Pottery
24 High Street, Kintbury, Newbury, Berkshire RG15 0TW
Tel: (01488) 657388

Brightly coloured stoneware, decorative and domestic ware, tiles to order.
Open: Tue-Sat 9am-5.30pm. Closed bank hols
Cards: Access, Visa

DIRECTIONS: Take A4 west from Newbury. After 5 miles turn left to Kintbury village. Situated 50 yards on left past crossroads in centre of village.

3/355
■ DAIRY PRODUCE

Calbourne Classics
Three Gates Farm, Shalfleet, Isle of Wight PO30 4NA
Tel/Fax: (01983) 531204

Clotted cream, ice-cream and frozen dairy desserts.
Open: Mon-Fri 9am-5pm, Sat-Sun 2pm-5pm. Oct-Apr Mon-Fri mornings only
Cards: No

DIRECTIONS: 4 miles west of Newport on Forest road, towards Yarmouth. Pass Trumour Feeds on left, farm is first on right after double bend.

3/356
● PLANTS

Hollington Nurseries
Woolton Hill, Newbury,
Berkshire RG20 9XT
Tel: (01635) 253908
Fax: (01635) 254990

Herbs, scented plants, climbers, old roses and hedging plants.
Open: Mar-Sept Mon-Sat 10am-5.30pm, Sun and bank hols 11am-5pm, Oct-Dec 10am-4pm. Closed 24 Dec-5 Jan
Cards: No

DIRECTIONS: Off A343, 4 miles south of Newbury. Follow signs.

3/357
● PLANTS

Exbury Gardens Ltd
The Estate Office, Exbury, Southampton,
Hampshire SO45 1AZ
Tel: (01703) 891203
Fax: (01703) 243380

Plant centre, tearooms, garden open.
Open: Mon-Sun 10am-5.30pm or dusk if earlier. Closed Nov-last week in Feb
Cards: Access, Mastercard, Switch, Visa

DIRECTIONS: 15 miles south-west of Southampton, 2 miles south of Beaulieu off B3054.

3/358
■ COFFEE

Quetzal Coffee Company
10 New Barn Farm Cottages, Crawley,
Nr Winchester, Hampshire SO21 2PP
Tel/Fax: (01962) 776608

Roasted, unblended arabica coffee from Central and South America.
Open: 9am-5pm but telephone in advance
Cards: No

DIRECTIONS: From Winchester through Littletown into Crawley. Approximately ½ mile the other side of Crawley.

3/359
● CERAMICS

Ardington Pottery
15 Home Farm, School Road, Ardington,
Nr Wantage, Oxfordshire OX12 8PN
Tel: (01235) 833302

Stoneware pottery, tableware, kitchenware and giftware.
Open: Mon-Sat 10am-5pm, Sun 11.30am-5pm. Closed 25 Dec-8 Jan
Cards: No

DIRECTIONS: In the village of Ardington. 1½ miles east of Wantage. Look for the Home Farm Craft Workshop sign, then follow for Home Farm.

3/360
■ WINE

Bothy Vineyard
Frilford Heath, Abingdon,
Oxfordshire OX13 6QW
Tel: (01491) 681484

Wine and grapes, honey and fresh asparagus in season.
Open: Weekends and most weekdays 10am-dusk
Cards: No

DIRECTIONS: From A34 Abingdon junction take A415 towards Witney. Take first right to Tubney and follow road for 2 miles. Vineyard is ¼ mile before A338 crossroads.

3/361
● SILK

Whitchurch Silk Mill
28 Winchester Street, Whitchurch,
Hampshire RG28 7AL
Tel: (01256) 893882

Silk products, ties, scarves, gifts, tours.
Open: Tue-Sun and bank hols, 10.30am-5pm. Closed 25 Dec-1 Jan
Cards: Access, Amex, Switch, Visa

DIRECTIONS: On A34 midway between Newbury and Winchester and on B3400, 7 miles east of Andover and 12 miles west of Basingstoke, in centre of Whitchurch.

3/362
● SILVERWARE

Geoffrey Harding
31 The Green, Steventon, Abingdon,
Oxfordshire OX13 6RR
Tel: (01235) 831371

Gold and silversmith, mainly
commissions.
Open: All reasonable times, telephone
in advance
Cards: No

DIRECTIONS: In centre of
Steventon, on B4017, 4 miles south of
Abingdon.

3/363
● JARDINIERES

Carolyn Sheffield Designs
Spring Pond, Laverstoke, Whitchurch,
Hampshire RG28 7PD
Tel: (01256) 895115
Fax: (01256) 895114

Hand-glazed, lacquered jardinières,
lamps, pots, candlesticks.
Open: 9am-4pm
Cards: No

DIRECTIONS: 1½ miles off B3400
along Laverstoke Lane towards M3.
2½ miles west of Overton. 2½ miles
east of Whitchurch.

3/364
■ SAUSAGES

A B Bosley & Son
13 Oxford Road, Abingdon,
Oxfordshire OX14 2ED
Tel: (01235) 520258

Pork sausages and cooked meats.
Open: Mon-Fri 8am-1pm, 2pm-5pm,
Sat 7am-1pm. Closed Christmas and
bank hols
Cards: Access, Amex, Switch, Visa

DIRECTIONS: North side of
Abingdon, ½ mile from town centre.

3/365
● LIME WASH

The Lime Centre
Long Barn, Morestead, Winchester,
Hampshire SO21 1LZ
Tel: (01962) 713636
Fax: (01962) 715350

Mature lime putty, mortar, render and
lime wash for conservation of historic
architecture.
Open: By appointment between
8.30am-5pm. Closed 24 Dec-3 Jan
Cards: No

DIRECTIONS: 3 miles south of
Winchester. At crossroads by pond
take turning to Twyford. Entrance 85
yards on left.

3/366
■ CIDER

Godshill Farmhouse Cider
The Cider Barn, High Street, Godshill,
Isle of Wight PO38 3HZ
Tel/Fax: (01983) 840680

Cider, vinegars and herb oils.
Open: Mon-Sat 10am-6pm, Sun
12 noon-3pm. Summer school
holidays Mon-Sat 10am-9pm. Closed
Jan-Feb
Cards: Access, Switch, Visa

DIRECTIONS: Situated 30 yards from
main car park in the High Street.

3/367
■ WINE

Barton Manor Gardens and
Vineyards
East Cowes, Isle of Wight PO32 6LB
Tel: (01983) 292835
Fax: (01983) 293923

Wines, gardens open.
Open: April-mid Oct 10.30am-5.30pm
Cards: Access, Visa

DIRECTIONS: On the East Cowes
Road A3021, next to Osborne House.

3/368
● WOOD

Chrisken
26 Cedar Drive, Kingsclere, Newbury,
Berkshire RG15 8TD
Tel: (01635) 297957

Inlaid wooden items for lacemakers,
boxes, small frames and thimble
stands.
Open: Telephone for appointment
Cards: No

DIRECTIONS: On A339 midway
between Newbury and Basingstoke.
Take roundabout to village centre,
then second left.

3/369
● JEWELLERY

Vivian Pare
Scottalls End, Hampstead Norreys,
Newbury, Berkshire RG16 0RT
Tel: (01635) 201206

Gold and silver jewellery.
Open: 10am-4pm, but telephone in
advance
Cards: No

DIRECTIONS: Near mini-
roundabout on B4009.

3/370
● BRASS RUBBING

Island Brass Rubbing Centre
The Coach House, St George's Church,
Arreton, Isle of Wight PO36 8BA
Tel: (01983) 402066

Brass rubbings.
Open: Easter-Oct Mon-Sat 10am-
6pm, evenings by arrangement.
Closed Nov-early Mar
Cards: No

DIRECTIONS: On the main
Sandown to Newport road, behind
the White Lion pub and adjacent to St
George's church at Arreton. Footpaths
connect to Arreton Manor and
Country Craft Centre.

3/371
✳ MULTIPLE

The Old Granary Art & Craft Centre
Bank Street, Bishop's Waltham,
Hampshire SO32 1AE
Tel: (01489) 894595

Calligraphy, dried flowers,
enamelling, glass engraving, jewellery,
plaques, pottery, prints, sculpture.
Open: Tue-Sat 10am-4pm. Closed 2
weeks after Christmas
Cards: No

From Bishop's Waltham bypass enter
town from the Crown pub and follow
one-way system. Above Tony's
Brasserie.

3/372
■ WINE

Wickham Vineyards
Botley Road, Shedfield,
Hampshire SO32 2HL
Tel: (01329) 834042
Fax: (01329) 834907

English wines, tours of the vineyard
and winery.
Open: Mon-Sat 10.30am-6pm, Sun
11.30am-5.30pm. Closed 1-15 Jan
Cards: Access, Visa

DIRECTIONS: Halfway between
Botley and Wickham on the A334.
Exit J7 or 10 from the M27, follow
brown tourism signs.

3/373
● CERAMICS

Tichborne Pottery
Tichborne, Nr Alresford,
Hampshire SO24 0NE
Tel: (01962) 732825

Stoneware pottery including teapots,
jugs, bowls, plates and vases in variety
of glazes.
Open: Advisable to telephone in
advance
Cards: No

DIRECTIONS: Between Cheriton and
Alresford. Pottery is signposted off the
village road that runs through
Tichborne.

3/374
■ FRUIT/VEGETABLES
West Lea Farm Shop
West Lea, Ladycroft, Alresford,
Hampshire SO24 0QP
Tel: (01962) 732476
Fax: (01962) 732710

Watercress and watercress soup.
Open: Mon-Sat 9.30am-4.30pm.
Closed 25, 26 Dec, and Easter
Cards: No

DIRECTIONS: Take B3047 from
Alresford after 1 mile. Take first right
towards Kingsworthy. Shop beside
watercress beds.

3/375
● CERAMICS
Sidney Hardwick
Cedarwood, Stream Road, Upton, Didcot,
Oxfordshire OX11 9JG
Tel: (01235) 850263

Stoneware and porcelain pottery,
domestic ware, wash-hand basins,
mirrors, vases, candlesticks, bowls.
Open: Mon-Sun 9am-5pm, best to
telephone in advance
Cards: No

DIRECTIONS: South of Oxford off
A34, East of Wantage on A417. In
Upton turn into Station Road, 2nd
right down Pound Lane, 1st left on to
Stream Road, house and pottery on
the right.

3/376
■ WINE
Meon Valley Vineyard
Hill Grove, Swanmore, Southampton,
Hampshire SO32 2PZ
Tel/Fax: (01489) 877435

Red, white and sparkling wines.
Open: Mar-Dec Tue-Sun 10.30am-
5.30pm
Cards: No

DIRECTIONS: Between Rising Sun
and Hunters Inn on road from
Shirrell Heath to Droxford.

3/377
● PLANTS
Blackthorn Nursery
Kilmeston, Alresford,
Hampshire SO24 ONL
Tel: (01962) 771796

Alpines, perennials and rare shrubs,
epimediums, daphnes and hellebores.
Open: Mar-Sept Fri-Sat 9am-5pm
Cards: No

DIRECTIONS: At Cheriton on the
A272 Winchester to Petersfield road,
turn south at crossroads by Shell
garage to Kilmeston.

3/378
● FURNITURE
John Nixon Fine Furniture
15 The Street, Aldermaston, Nr Reading,
Berkshire RG7 4LN
Tel/Fax: (01734) 713875

Furniture.
Open: Mon-Fri 9am-5pm by
appointment. Closed 25 Dec-1 Jan
Cards: No

DIRECTIONS: 1¾ miles from A4 on
A340 in centre of village opposite
Hind's Head pub.

3/379
● FURNITURE
Jim Crockatt Furniture
Pococks Cottage, Mariners Lane, Bradfield,
Berkshire RG7 6HX
Tel: (01734) 744728

Furniture using native hardwoods.
Open: Mon-Sat 9am-5pm. Closed
Aug
Cards: No

DIRECTIONS: Turn left up the hill
out of Thatcham, by Antique Shop
Chapel. Go through Bucklebury,
Southend and Bradfield. Second left
past Queens Head pub. Third house
on right on the hill.

3/380
● TEXTILES

Daffodil
4 Warren Farm Cottages, Rectory Road,
Streatley, Berkshire RG8 9QG
Tel: (01491) 872148

Handwoven rugs and wall hangings,
some handspun and hand-dyed
articles.
Open: Tue 10.30am-4pm, otherwise
by appointment. Closed 25-26 Dec
Cards: No

DIRECTIONS: On A417 Wantage
road out of Streatley, take Rectory
Road, 1½ miles on left.

3/381
● CERAMICS

Elizabeth Gale Ceramics
Taplands Farm Cottage, Taplands Corner,
Soberton, Hampshire SO32 3PY
Tel/Fax: (01705) 632686

High-fired domestic ceramic ware.
Open: By appointment
Cards: Access, Visa

DIRECTIONS: Off M27 at J7. Go to
Botley, then Wickham. Take A32
Alton, almost opposite Roebuck Inn,
turn right to Soberton. Take third
right off (Chapel Lane). At bottom
turn left, 2nd house.

3/382
● BOOKBINDING

The Bindery
Wolverton, West Meon, Petersfield,
Hampshire GU32 1LQ
Tel/Fax: (01730) 829267

Bookbinding in paper, cloth and
leather, book restoration and repairs.
Calligraphy.
Open: By appointment only
Cards: No

DIRECTIONS: Coming from Alton
on A32 the first house on the right as
you enter West Meon. It has a
wooden fence and is opposite a bus
lay-by.

3/383
● JEWELLERY

Elisabeth Napier-Munn
1 Duchess Close, Whitchurch-on-Thames,
Pangbourne, Reading, Oxfordshire RG8 7EN
Tel: (01734) 842181

Precious jewellery.
Open: By appointment only
Cards: No

DIRECTIONS: J12 of M4. Take A340
to Pangbourne, across Toll Bridge.
High Street Whitchurch B471, on
right after Greyhound pub. Old house
with wistaria.

3/384
● CERAMICS

Blenheim Pots & Plaques
Blenheim Farm, Nr Wallingford,
Oxfordshire OX10 6PR
Tel: (01491) 839707

Hand-thrown slip-decorated ceramic
pots and plaques, oven-to-tableware.
Open: Wed-Sat 10am-5pm, Sun, Mon
by appointment only. Closed
Christmas-mid Jan, 1st 2 weeks July
Cards: No

DIRECTIONS: East from Wallingford
town centre on A4130 (Henley road).
After 1¾ miles turn right on minor
road signposted Hailey. Pottery ¼
mile on left.

3/385
● MUSICAL INSTRUMENTS

Malcolm Combes
54 Harvest Road, Denmead, Waterlooville,
Hampshire PO7 6LL
Tel: (01705) 250174

Violins, violas and cellos using
traditional materials and methods.
Open: By appointment
Cards: No

DIRECTIONS: Denmead is 3 miles
north-west of Waterlooville on B2150.
Take Denmead to Southwick road,
Harvest Road is 3rd right.

3/386
■ WINE

Boze Down Vineyard
Hardwick Road, Whitchurch, Reading,
Oxfordshire RG8 7QS
Tel: (01734) 844031

Wines.
Open: Sat 11am-6pm, Sun noon-5pm
else by appointment. Mar-April, Sept
by appointment
Cards: No

DIRECTIONS: From Pangbourne (4
miles from J12 on M4) turn north at
George Hotel, go over Thames toll
bridge, after ½ mile turn right into
Hardwick Road.

3/387
● PLANTS

Hayward's Carnations
The Chace Gardens, Stakes Road,
Purbrook, Waterlooville,
Hampshire PO7 5PL
Tel: (01705) 263047

Nursery, carnations and pinks.
Open: Mon-Fri 9.30am-4.30pm, Sat
am. Closed 3 weeks over Christmas
and first 2 weeks in August
Cards: No

DIRECTIONS: From A3 Portsmouth
to London road, 5 miles outside
Portsmouth take Waterlooville
junction, follow signs to Purbrook, by
Purbrook junction at Stokes Garden.

3/388
● WOOD

Pendennis Crafts
175 Frogmore Lane, Lovedean,
Waterlooville, Hampshire PO8 9RD
Tel: (01705) 595919

Wooden rocking-horses, dolls' houses
and wooden wheelbarrows.
Open: By appointment only
Cards: No

DIRECTIONS: Leave A3M south of
Petersfield at B2149. Follow signs to
Cowplain. Straight on at roundabout
down Catherington Lane, across next
roundabout then next left on Crouch
Lane leading to Frogmore Lane.

3/389
● CERAMICS

Clanfield Pottery
131 Chalton Lane, Clanfield, Waterlooville,
Hampshire PO8 0RG
Tel: (01705) 595144

Hand-thrown ceramics.
Open: Mon-Tue, Thur-Fri 10.30am-
5pm, Wed 10.30am-12.30pm, Sat-Sun
10.30am-4pm. Closed Aug and
Christmas
Cards: Access, Visa

DIRECTIONS: Off the A3, 7 miles
south of Petersfield. Take the
Clanfield/ East Meon turn-off just
south of Queen Elizabeth forest. Next
to the village pond in the centre of the
village.

3/390
● SCALE MODELS

D R Designs
12 The Close, Langrish, Petersfield,
Hampshire GU32 1RH
Tel: (01730) 261040

Scale model period homes in wood,
model aircraft, cars, butter churns,
wood-turning, furniture.
Open: Mon-Fri 9.30am-4pm, Sat
9.30am-12.30pm, otherwise by
appointment. Closed 25 Dec
Cards: Access, Diners, Visa

DIRECTIONS: Go 3½ miles through
Stroud into Langrish on A272, take
first turn left marked East Meon. 400
yards downhill, turn right into The
Close, directly opposite white
thatched cottage on left.

3/391
● GARDEN FURNITURE

Gaze Burvill
Plain Farm Old Dairy, East Tisted,
Hampshire GU34 3RT
Tel: (01420) 587467
Fax: (01420) 587354

Garden furniture made of steam-bent
English oak. Seats, benches, tables.
Open: Mon-Fri 8.30am-5.30pm. Sat-
Sun by appointment
Cards: No

DIRECTIONS: South on A32 from
Alton. Take 1st right after East Tisted
Village. Then first left into Plain Farm
and workshop is at top of hill.

3/392
■ WINE
Cane End Vineyard
Cane End Farm, Cane End, Reading,
Berkshire RG4 9HG
Tel/Fax: (01734) 722114

White and rosé wines.
Open: Mon-Sun 12 noon-5pm
Cards: Access, Switch, Visa

DIRECTIONS: 5 miles north of
Reading on A4074 Reading to
Wallingford road, just past Fox pub on
left-hand side.

3/393
● CLOTHES
Rose Glennie Smocks
The Old Mill House, Clanfield,
Waterlooville, Hampshire PO8 0RP
Tel: (01705) 593789

Classic hand-smocked clothing.
Open: By appointment only
Cards: Access, Visa

DIRECTIONS: 6 miles south of
Petersfield turn left off A3 to
Clanfield (1½ miles). Old Mill House
is on right next to Rising Sun pub.

3/394
■ SAUSAGES
David Bowtell
Home Farm Shop, East Tisted, Alton,
Hampshire GU34 3QP
Tel: (01420) 588418

Additive-free meat and sausages (18
varieties).
Open: Thur-Sat 10am-5pm. Sun
10am-1pm
Cards: Access, Visa

DIRECTIONS: 4 miles south of Alton
on A32. Turn left signposted to
Selborne. Also sign to David Bowtell
Farm Shop. 400 yards up hill on right.

3/395
■ FLOUR
Mapledurham Watermill
Mapledurham Estate, Mapledurham,
Reading, Berkshire RG4 7TR
Tel: (01734) 723350
Fax: (01734) 724016

Wholemeal flour and its by-products.
Open: Telephone for appointment
Cards: No

DIRECTIONS: 4 miles north-west of
Reading off A4074. On north bank of
river Thames.

3/396
● FORGEWORK
Robert Smith
The Forge, Gosport Road, Farringdon,
Alton, Hampshire GU34 3DL
Tel: (01420) 587233

Traditional and modern ironwork,
restoration, general blacksmithing.
Open: 8am-5pm, telephone first
Cards: No

DIRECTIONS: 2 miles south of Alton
on A32. From A31 Alton, take A32,
the Forge is 100 yards past Royal Oak
pub on right before crossroads.

3/397
● CERAMICS
Farmhouse Ceramics
Hartley Cottage, Hartley Wespall,
Basingstoke, Hampshire RG27 0BB
Tel/Fax: (01256) 882487

Hand-painted dinnerware and
ornamental ceramics.
Open: By appointment only
Cards: No

DIRECTIONS: Between Basingstoke
and Reading on A33. Take Hartley
Wespall and Rotherwick sign. Take
first left. Second house on left.

3/398
● CERAMICS

Coldpiece Pottery
Coldpiece Farm, Mattingley, Basingstoke,
Hampshire RG27 8LQ
Tel: (01734) 326540
Fax: (01734) 326578

Terracotta pots and scented candles.
Open: Mon-Fri 9.30am-5.30pm by
appointment. Closed bank hols
Cards: No

DIRECTIONS: On B349 between
Reading and Basingstoke. Opposite
Whitewater Nursery.

3/399
■ DAIRY PRODUCE

Wellington Dairy Products
The Wellington Office, Stratfield Saye,
Reading, Berkshire RG7 2BT
Tel: (01256) 882882
Fax: (01256) 882345

Dairy ice-cream from Guernsey milk,
cheese.
Open: Mon-Sun 10am-5pm, closed
Mon-Fri Jan-Feb
Cards: No

DIRECTIONS: On the
Hampshire/Berkshire border just off
the A33, 7 miles from Reading and 6
miles from Basingstoke.

3/400
● CERAMICS

Selborne Pottery
The Plestor, Selborne, Alton,
Hampshire GU34 3JQ
Tel: (01420) 511413
Fax: (01420) 511233

Glazed stoneware.
Open: Mon-Fri 9am-6pm. Weekends
by appointment
Cards: No

DIRECTIONS: Take B3006 south of
Alton towards A3. Opposite the
Wakes (Gilbert White Museum) and
behind Selborne Gallery.

3/401
● GYPSY CRAFT

**Romany Folklore Museum &
Workshop**
Limes End Yard, Selbourne, Nr Alton,
Hampshire GU34 3JW
Tel: (01420) 511486

Caravan workshop for restoration and
decoration. Traditional gypsy crafts,
and canal boat ware.
Open: By appointment only
Cards: No

DIRECTIONS: 4 miles south of Alton
on B3006.

3/402
● FURNITURE

Screens Gallery
The Malthouse, Bridgefoot Path, Emsworth,
Hampshire PO10 7EB
Tel/Fax: (01243) 377334

Carved and painted wooden room
screens, wall panels, paintings and
furniture
Open: Mon-Fri 10am-4pm, best to
telephone in advance. Closed bank
hols, Easter, Christmas
Cards: No

DIRECTIONS: Between Portsmouth
and Chichester on the old A27 coast
road. Bridgefoot Path is on the east
side of the Western Mill pond.

3/403
■ FRUIT/VEGETABLES

Blackmoor Apple Shop
Blackmoor, Liss, Hampshire GU33 6BS
Tel: (01420) 473782
Fax: (01420) 487813

12 varieties of English apple. Also
cakes and savouries.
Open: Mon-Sat 9am-5pm. Closed
bank hols
Cards: No

DIRECTIONS: Turn left off A325
between Petersfield and Farnham.
Signposted Blackmoor, just past
church.

3/404
● GLASS
Jonathan Andersson
Dean Farm Studios, Kingsley,
Hampshire GU35 1NY
Tel: (01420) 477502
Fax: (01420) 87155

Art glass: created in glass and metal.
Open: Mon-Fri by appointment only
Cards: Access, Switch, Visa

DIRECTIONS: Follow signs for
Birdworld. Turn right at New Inn
Pub. Directly behind Rapid Rovers
garage opposite golf course.

3/405
■ MEAT/POULTRY/GAME
Gabriel Machin
7 Market Place, Henley-on-Thames,
Oxfordshire RG9 2AA
Tel: (01491) 574377

Butcher and fishmonger – pies, glazed
hams, bacon, smoked salmon.
Open: Mon-Sat 8.30am-5.30pm.
Closed bank hols and 3 days at
Christmas
Cards: No

DIRECTIONS: 8 miles on A4130
from M4 Maidenhead junction. In
centre at traffic lights.

3/406
● TEXTILES
Geraldine St Aubyn Hubbard
Rosebrook, Farm Lane, Nutbourne,
Chichester, West Sussex PO18 8SA
Tel: (01243) 377372

Handwoven silk and wool. Items
include ties, waistcoats, scarves,
shawls and jackets.
Open: Telephone for appointment
Cards: Visa

DIRECTIONS: 6 miles west of
Chichester, 2 miles east of Emsworth.
Take A259 between Southbourne and
Chidham. Take farm lane south near
Elf garage towards creek. Rosebrook
on right at end of tarmac.

3/407
■ MEAT/POULTRY/GAME
Hampshire Game Ltd
The Game Centre, 1 Petersfield Road,
Greatham, Liss, Hampshire GU33 6AA
Tel/Fax: (01420) 538162

Oven-ready game and venison.
Open: Mon-Fri 8am-5pm, Sat 9am-
1pm, Sun 9am-12pm
Cards: No

DIRECTIONS: Leave A3 London to
Portsmouth road at roundabout on
main A325. In village of Greatham, 8
miles south of Farnham.

3/408
● PLANTS
Blackmoor Nurseries
Blackmoor, Liss, Hampshire GU33 6BS
Tel: (01420) 473576
Fax: (01420) 487813

Wide range of fruit plants.
Open: Nov-Mar Sat 9am-12.30pm.
Orders can be collected during
weekday office hours
Cards: No

DIRECTIONS: One mile off A325
between Bordon and Liss. Follow
signs to Blackmoor Apple Shop.

3/409
■ MEAT/POULTRY/GAME
Goldesborough Quail
Clements Farm, Wheatley, Bordon,
Hampshire GU35 9PA
Tel: (01420) 22485

Eggs, quail eggs, game and fish.
Open: Mon-Sat 8am-12noon. Closed
bank hols
Cards: No

DIRECTIONS: Take B3004 off the
A325. Farm in middle of Wheatley
village.

3/410
● CERAMICS

Rupert Spira Ceramics
Froyle Pottery, Lower Froyle, Nr Alton,
Hampshire GU34 4LL
Tel: (01420) 23693
Fax: (01420) 22797

Pottery, domestic ware and tiles.
Open: Mon-Fri 9am-5pm, weekends
by appointment
Cards: No

DIRECTIONS: A31 between Farnham
and Alton, signposted Lower Froyle.
50 yards past Prince of Wales pub on
the left.

3/411
● PLANTS

Peter Trenear Nurseries
Chequers Lane, Eversley Cross,
Basingstoke, Hampshire RG27 0NX
Tel: (01734) 732300

Tree and shrub nursery, slow-grown
trees for bonsai training, pines and
herbs.
Open: Mon-Sat 9am-4.30pm. Closed
bank hols, by appointment in June.
Cards: No

DIRECTIONS: On the B3272, turn
down lane by Chequers Inn, 500
yards on left.

3/412
■ MEAT/POULTRY/GAME

Brunning Hams Farm Shop
Heath Ride, Finchhampstead, Wokingham,
Berkshire RG11 3QJ
Tel: (01734) 733287

Home-produced fresh meat, sausages,
bacon, ham. Cakes, meringues and
gateaux.
Open: Fri-Sun 10am-1pm, otherwise
by appointment. Closed 25-26 Dec
Cards: No

DIRECTIONS: A321 from
Wokingham, right fork at Gowrings
Garage, first left into Kiln Ride, cross
main road into Kiln Ride which
becomes Heath Ride.

3/413
■ WINE

Thames Valley Vineyard
Stanlake Park, Twyford, Reading,
Berkshire RG10 0BN
Tel: (01734) 340176
Fax: (01734) 320914

Wine and cider.
Open: Mon-Sat 10am-5pm, Sun
12 noon-5pm. Closed 25 Dec-1 Jan,
and weekends in Jan
Cards: Access, Visa

DIRECTIONS: From traffic lights in
centre of Twyford, ¾ mile south-east
on B3918 Twyford to Bracknell road.
Entrance on left.

3/414
● KNITWEAR

Alison Ellen Knitwear
Jeffreys Cottage, Bealeswood Lane,
Dockenfield, Farnham, Surrey GU10 4HS
Tel: (01252) 792442

Hand-knitted jumpers, jackets,
waistcoats and hats using hand-dyed
natural yarns.
Open: By appointment
Cards: Access, Visa

DIRECTIONS: 5 miles south of
Farnham, in Dockenfield village,
Bealeswood Lane is almost opposite
church and phone box, second house
on left.

3/415
■ ICE-CREAM

Blackburne & Haynes
Meadow Cottage Farm, Churt Road,
Headley, Bordon, Hampshire GU35 8SS
Tel: (01428) 712155
Fax: (01428) 714001

Dairy ice-cream, fruit sorbet and
reduced-calorie dairy ice-cream. Farm
shop.
Open: Daily, dawn to dusk. Closed 25
Dec
Cards: No

DIRECTIONS: On lane between
Churt and Headley between B3002
and A287.

3/416
● CERAMICS
Grayshott Pottery
School Road, Grayshott, Hindhead,
Surrey GU26 6LR
Tel: (01428) 604404
Fax: (01428) 604944

Pottery and coffee shop.
Open: Mon-Fri 9am-5.30pm. Closed
bank hols
Cards: Access, Switch, Visa

DIRECTIONS: A3, 15 miles south of
Guildford, 300 yards through
Hindhead traffic lights take the B3002
on the right just past a garage. Follow
the road to Grayshott village, then
signposted.

3/417
● PLANTS
Millais Nurseries
Crosswater Farm, Churt, Farnham,
Surrey GU10 2JN
Tel: (01252) 792698
Fax: (01252) 792526

Rhododendrons and azaleas, gardens
open in May.
Open: Tue-Fri 10am-1pm, 2pm-5pm.
Sat Mar-Apr and Oct-Nov, Mon-Sun
in May
Cards: Access, Amex, Visa

DIRECTIONS: From A287
(Farnham-Haslemere) turn east into
Jumps Road ½ mile north of Churt
village. After ¼ mile turn left into
Crosswater Lane and follow nursery
signs.

3/418
✴ MULTIPLE
Manor Farm Craft Centre
Wood Lane, Seale, Nr Farnham,
Surrey GU10 1HR
Tel: (01483) 810208

Dried flowers, jewellery, knitwear,
pottery, soft furnishings, stone letter
carving.
Open: Tue-Sat 11am-5pm, Sun 2pm-
5pm. Closed Mon and 25 Dec-1 Jan
Cards: No

DIRECTIONS: Midway between
Guildford and Farnham just off A31

Hogs Back. Take signs to Seale and
follow tourist signs to village.

3/419
■ BEER
The Gribble Brewery
The Gribble Inn, Gribble Lane, Oving, Nr
Chichester, West Sussex PO20 6BP
Tel: (01243) 786893

Traditional real ales.
Open: Mon-Sat 11am-2.30pm, 6pm-
11pm, Sun 12noon-3pm, 7pm-
10.30pm
Cards: Access, Amex, Visa

DIRECTIONS: Off the A259
Chichester to Bognor Regis road,
approx 2 miles south, signposted
Oving. Turn right after level crossing,
first left in village.

3/420
■ SAUSAGES
Macey's
Rose Cottage, Lower Road, Cookham Rise,
Berkshire SL6 9EH
Tel: (01628) 521128
Fax: (01628) 419170

Sausages.
Open: Tue-Fri 7.30am-5.30pm. Sat
7am-4pm. Sun 9am-1.30pm
Cards: Access, Amex, Switch, Visa

DIRECTIONS: Past Cookham Rise
station – 300 yards. Between Pindar
Hall and Medical Centre.

3/421
● PLANTS
Butterfields Nursery
Harvest Hill, Bourne End,
Buckinghamshire SL8 5JJ
Tel: (01628) 525455

Pleiones (hardy orchids), dahlias and
chrysanthemums.
Open: 22 Apr-11 Jun Mon-Sun 9am-
1pm, 2pm-5pm, Mid Aug-Oct Mon-
Sun 9am-1pm, 2pm-5pm but
advisable to telephone first
Cards: No

DIRECTIONS: Off the B476 between
Cores End and the National Trust
property Cliveden.

3/422
■ CHEESE

Gospel Green
Gospel Green Cottage, Gospel Green, Nr
Haslemere, Surrey GU27 3BH
Tel: (01428) 654120

Unpasteurised cow's milk cheese,
cloth-bound and vegetarian.
Champagne-method cider.
Open: By appointment
Cards: No

DIRECTIONS: Heading south on
A283 from Chiddingfold, 3½ miles
cross Surrey/Sussex border, down hill,
right at crossroads, signposted to
Gospel Green. The only house there.

3/423
■ SMOKED PRODUCE

Dalton's Natural Food Centre
Barnham Road, Eastergate, West
Sussex PO20 6RP
Tel: (01243) 543543

Venison and game. Smoked fish and
meats. Ham and bacon.
Open: Mon-Fri 8.30am-5pm. Sat
8.30am-12.30pm
Cards: No

DIRECTIONS: Turn on to A29 from
A27 Chichester to Worthing road
towards Bognor Regis. Go south on
A29 past racecourse. Turn left at war
memorial and then 50 yards on right.

3/424
■ FRUIT/VEGETABLES

C R & B M Upton
The Lodge, 4 Top Road, Slindon, Arundel,
West Sussex BN18 0RP
Tel: (01243) 814219

Pumpkins, squash and ornamental
gourds.
Open: Daily 10am-dusk. Closed late
July to Nov
Cards: No

DIRECTIONS: Between Chichester
and Arundel off A27 and A29, about a
mile north-east of Fontwell
Racecourse.

3/425
■ FRUIT/VEGETABLES

Secretts Farm and Flower Shop
Hurst Farm, Chapel Lane, Milford,
Godalming, Surrey GU8 5HU
Tel: (01483) 426655
Fax: (01483) 861703

Vegetables, fruit and flowers.
Open: Mon-Thur 9am-5.30pm. Fri
9am-6pm. Sat 9am-4.30pm. Sun
10am-4pm. Closed Christmas, New
Year, Easter
Cards: Access, Switch, Visa

DIRECTIONS: Opposite village hall
and post office. (There is a private
road linking farm shop with Garden
Centre.)

3/426
● FORGEWORK

David Wright Blacksmith
The Forge, The Green, Chiddingfold,
Godalming, Surrey GU8 4TU
Tel: (01428) 684902

Wrought ironwork, traditional tools,
fire irons, fire baskets, gates, railings.
Open: Mon-Sat 9am-5pm, variable
holidays
Cards: No

DIRECTIONS: In the centre of
Chiddingfold village on the A283, 4
miles south of the A3 junction at
Milford.

3/427
● PLANTS

Secretts Garden Centre
Old Portsmouth Road, Milford, Godalming,
Surrey GU8 5HL
Tel: (01483) 426633
Fax: (01483) 426855

Plants from own farm and nursery.
Tools, containers and sundries.
Open: Mon-Sat 9am-5.30pm. Sun
10.30am-4.30pm. Closed 25, 26 Dec,
1 Jan
Cards: Access, Switch, Visa

DIRECTIONS: On outskirts of
Milford on left on road to Godalming
(Old Portsmouth Road).

3/428
● CERAMICS
Mary Wondrausch – The Pottery
Brickfields, Compton, Nr Guildford,
Surrey GU3 1HZ
Tel: (01483) 416961

Earthenware plates, jugs, bowls.
Open: Mon-Fri 9am-1pm, 2pm-5pm,
Sat-Sun 2pm-5pm. Closed 25 Dec
Cards: No

DIRECTIONS: On the A3 for
Portsmouth, take the 2nd exit past
Guildford, signposted to Compton
(B3000). Through village, take 2nd
turning on right – bumpy track and
pottery sign.

3/429
● PLANTS
Knaphill Garden Centre
Barrs Lane, Knaphill, Woking,
Surrey GU21 2JW
Tel: (01483) 481212
Fax: (01483) 797261

Rhododendrons, azaleas, plants, trees
and shrubs.
Open: Mon-Sat 9am-5pm, 6pm in
summer, most Sun. Closed 25 Dec-1
Jan
Cards: Access, Visa

DIRECTIONS: 6 miles from
Guildford via A322 and 2½ miles
from Woking to Lower Knaphill.

3/430
■ FARM PRODUCE
Loseley Park Farms
Loseley Park, Guildford, Surrey GU3 1HS
Tel: (01483) 304440
Fax: (01483) 302036

Bakery including quiche, cakes and
other sundries. Yoghurts, ice-cream.
Open: Mon-Fri 9am-5.30pm. Closed
bank hols
Cards: No

DIRECTIONS: Follow signs for
Loseley House off A3 at Compton.
From Godalming take B3000 and
follow signs.

3/431
● PLANTS
Morehavens Camomile Nurseries
28 Denham Lane, Chalfont St Peter,
Gerrards Cross, Buckinghamshire SL9 0EX
Tel: (01494) 871563

Camomile for lawns, paths and
edging.
Open: By appointment
Cards: No

DIRECTIONS: Off A423 at large
roundabout by Greyhound pub, on to
Joiners Lane. Turn left at T-junction
at top of hill into Denham Lane.

3/432
● CERAMICS
Josse Davis (Arundel Pottery)
84 Maltravers Street, Arundel,
West Sussex BN18 9DS
Tel: (01903) 883447

Raku and stoneware ceramics.
Open: By appointment only
Cards: No

DIRECTIONS: On A27 between
Worthing and Chichester. Next to
roundabout.

3/433
■ WINE
Arundel Vineyards
Church Lane, Lyminster,
West Sussex BN17 7QF
Tel: (01903) 883393

Wines, vineyard tours.
Open: Tue-Sun 12pm-5pm, tours by
arrangement
Cards: No

DIRECTIONS: Situated 1½ miles
south of Arundel. From A27 turn
south on to A284 Lyminster to
Littlehampton road. 1 mile on
signposted on the right.

3/434
✳ MULTIPLE

Smithbrook Kilns

The Estate Office, 85 Smithbrook Kilns,
Cranleigh, Surrey GU6 8JJ
Tel: (01483) 276455
Fax: (01483) 275426

Soft furnishings, silver jewellery,
model boats, sculptures, clothes,
stonemason, knitwear, models,
paintings.
Open: 9.30am-5.30pm
Cards: No

DIRECTIONS: On A281 Guildford to
Horsham road, 7 miles south of
Guildford. 200 yards past Leathern
Bottle pub just before junction with
Cranleigh-Godalming B2130.

3/435
■ CHEESE

Old Scotland Farmhouse Cheese

Old Scotland Farm, Staple Lane, Shere,
Guildford, Surrey GU5 9TE
Tel: (01483) 222526

Cheddar-type farmhouse cheese.
Open: Daily 2pm-6pm. Closed 25, 26
Dec
Cards: No

DIRECTIONS: From Guildford take
A246 towards Leatherhead. After 5
miles turn right signposted to Shere.
Follow road for ½ mile up the hill.

3/436
● ROCKING-HORSES

Clive Green Rocking Horses

The Lychgate, 20 Broadmark Lane,
Rustington, West Sussex BN16 2HJ
Tel: (01903) 786639

Carved wooden rocking-horses.
Open: By appointment only
Cards: No

DIRECTIONS: On A259 2 miles east
of Littlehampton. Broadmark Lane
runs from the sea to Rustington
Shopping Centre. Halfway between
sea and shops.

3/437
● PLANTS

Coombland Gardens

Coneyhurst, Billingshurst,
West Sussex RH15 9DY
Tel: (01403) 741549
Fax: (01403) 741079

Herbaceous plants including roses and
hardy geraniums.
Open: Mar-Oct Mon-Fri 2pm-4pm.
Bank hols and other times by
appointment only
Cards: No

DIRECTIONS: In Billingshurst turn
off A29 on to A272 to Haywards
Heath; approximately 2 miles into
Coneyhurst, turn south for ¾ mile.

3/438
■ CIDER

John Friar

Woolvens Farm, Billingshurst Road,
Ashington, West Sussex RH20 3BB
Tel: (01903) 892273

Cider from local apples.
Open: Mon-Sun 8am-6pm
Cards: No

DIRECTIONS: 1 mile west of
Ashington (A24) on Billinghurst road
B2133. Farm gate is back from the
road on the right.

3/439
● CUSHIONS

Fun Cushions

Toat Hill House, Slinfold, Horsham,
West Sussex RH13 7RL
Tel/Fax: (01403) 790264

Embroidered cushions with messages.
Open: By appointment
Cards: No

DIRECTIONS: On A264 between
Horsham and Billingshurst. 400 yards
up hill on right after Toat Hill garage
heading towards Billingshurst.

3/440
■ MEAT/POULTRY/GAME

Collins Butchers
5 Church Street, Warnham, Nr Horsham,
West Sussex RH12 3QP
Tel: (01403) 210666
Fax: (01403) 731197

Sausages and oven-ready dishes.
Cured, smoked and cooked meats and
poultry. In-store bakery.
Open: Mon-Fri 8am-6pm. Sat 8am-
5pm. Closed bank hols
Cards: No

DIRECTIONS: 2 miles north-east of
Horsham. Signposted off A24/A29
and A281. 50 yards from church and
next door to post office.

3/441
■ WINE

Thorncroft Vineyard
Thorncroft Drive, Leatherhead,
Surrey KT22 8JD
Tel: (01372) 372406
Fax: (01372) 363074

White wines, dessert wines.
Open: Mon-Sun, 9am-5pm, advisable
to telephone first
Cards: Access, Visa

DIRECTIONS: From A24 turn off for
Leatherhead at Gibons Grove
roundabout, ½ mile later, 1st left and
then 200 yards.

MAP 4

4/442
● TOYS
Sue Godber Crafts
The Old Vicarage, Lynwick Street,
Rudgwick, Nr Horsham, West
Sussex RH12 3DJ
Tel: (01403) 822749
Fax: (01403) 823388

Hand-knitted dolls dressed in
sweaters and school uniforms.
Open: Telephone for appointment
Cards: No

DIRECTIONS: In Rudgwick village,
off A281 Guildford to Horsham road.
7 miles west of Horsham turn into
Church Street. Turn left into
Lynwick Street at top of village. 100
yards on left.

4/443
● PLANTS
Holly Gate Nursery & Cactus Garden
Billingshurst Road, Ashington,
West Sussex RH20 3BA
Tel: (01903) 892930

Cactus nursery.
Open: Daily 9am-5pm
Cards: No

DIRECTIONS: Halfway between
Worthing and Horsham on A24,
½ mile from Ashington on B2133.

4/444
■ MEAT/POULTRY/GAME
The Game Larder
Rushett Farm, Leatherhead Road,
Chessington, Surrey KT9 2NQ
Tel: (01372) 749000

Game and smoked foods.
Open: Tue-Sat 10am-6pm, Sun 11am-
4pm
Cards: No

DIRECTIONS: M25 J9 towards
Chessington World of Adventures.
Off A243.

4/445
● PAPER PRODUCTS
Bridge House Design
Lemsford, Hertfordshire AL8 7TN
Tel: (01707) 323741
Fax: (01707) 332536

Water colours, greetings cards and
prints. Also children's cards and
merchandise.
Open: Daily 10am-5.30pm. Closed
Christmas/New Year and bank hols
Cards: Access, Visa

DIRECTIONS: Leave A1(M) at J4
towards Wheathampstead. Take B653,
turn right at Lemsford Church. On
right.

4/446
■ DAIRY PRODUCE
Bowmans Farm Shop
Bowmansgreen Farm, Coursers Road,
London Colney, St Albans,
Hertfordshire AL2 1BB
Tel: (01727) 821253
Fax: (01727) 826406

Ice-cream, milk, yoghurt, meat,
vegetables, cheese.
Open: All week 9am-5.30pm. Closed
25, 26 Dec
Cards: Delta, Mastercard, Switch, Visa

DIRECTIONS: J22 of M25. Third exit
from one or two roundabouts
(depending on direction). 500 metres
from 2nd roundabout on left.

4/447
■ WINE
Downers Vineyard
Clappers Lane, Fulking, Henfield,
West Sussex BN5 9NH
Tel: (01273) 857484
Fax: (01273) 857068

Wines.
Open: By appointment only
Cards: No

DIRECTIONS: 3 miles south of
Henfield on the A281 turn south into
Clappers Lane. In 1 mile turn right
into vineyard.

4/448
● DOLLS

Recollect Doll Studios
The Old School, London Road, Sayers
Common, West Sussex BN6 9HX
Tel: (01273) 833314

Dolls and dolls' hospital.
Open: Tue–Fri 10am-5pm, Sat 10am-
2pm
Cards: Access, Visa

DIRECTIONS: In between Albourne
and Hickstead on B2118. Turn off
A23 towards Hurstpierpoint and
Albourne.

4/449
● FORGEWORK

Wyvern Smithy
The Old Forge, Quick's Yard, High Street,
Handcross, West Sussex RH17 6BJ
Tel: (01444) 400491
Fax: (01403) 711792

Decorative ironwork, fire baskets and
irons, boot scrapers, weather-vanes,
candlesticks, lights.
Open: Tue, Thur-Sat 9am-5pm
telephone in advance, variable
holidays
Cards: No

DIRECTIONS: Northbound on the
A23 take the slip road for Handcross,
go right at the mini-roundabout, over
the bridge, left at the T-junction by
the Red Lion pub. By the Spar shop
go down the alleyway to the green
stable doors.

4/450
● PLANTS

Rupert Bowlby
The Bulb Nursery, Rocky Lane, Gatton,
Reigate, Surrey RH2 0TA
Tel/Fax: (01737) 642221

Alliums and unusual bulbs for the
garden and conservatory.
Open: Sept, Oct, Mar, Sat 10am-5pm,
Sun 2pm-5pm, other times by
appointment
Cards: No

DIRECTIONS: From J8 M25, 100
yards south turn left towards
Merstham, after 1 mile right into

Rocky Lane. Or north up Rocky Lane
from A23 north of Redhill.

4/451
● PLANTS

Allwood Bros
Mill Nursery, London Road, Hassocks,
West Sussex BN6 9NB
Tel: (01273) 844229

Allwoodii pinks and carnations.
Open: Mon-Fri 9am-4pm, but
telephone in advance
Cards: No

DIRECTIONS: On A273, Burgess
Hill side of Hassocks, from Hassocks
continue on A273 past Friar's Oak
pub, turn left on bend in road, signed
Mill Nursery and farm produce.

4/452
◼ WINE

Howe Green House Vineyards
Howe Green, Hertford,
Hertfordshire SG13 8LH
Tel: (01707) 261377
Fax: (01707) 268679

White wine.
Open: Mon-Sun 10am-6pm,
telephone in advance
Cards: No

DIRECTIONS: On Howe Green Lane
off B158 from Hertford to Essendon
(B158 about 3 miles from A1 at
Hatfield).

4/453
● CERAMICS

Jill Pryke Pottery
8 High Street, Ditchling,
East Sussex BN6 8TA
Tel: (01273) 845246

Earthenware pottery, mugs and plates.
Open: Mon-Sat 10am-1pm, 2pm-
5pm. Closed Wed and Sun and
Christmas week
Cards: No

DIRECTIONS: Situated in Ditchling
High Street next to the Bull Hotel, on
B2112 road from Haywards Heath to
Brighton.

4/454
■ MEAT/POULTRY/GAME

Burstye Soays

Burstye Farm, Lindfield, Nr Haywards
Heath, West Sussex RH16 2QY
Tel: (01444) 483376

Soay lamb and sheepskins.
Open: By appointment
Cards: No

DIRECTIONS: Between Lindfield and
Ardingly on west side of B2028.
Shared entrance, signs also for
Buxshalls, Hill House Farm and
Caravan Club Site.

4/455
■ WINE

Rock Lodge Vineyard

Lewes Lane, Scaynes Hill, Nr Haywards
Heath, West Sussex RH17 7NG
Tel/Fax: (01444) 831567

Wines.
Open: Mon-Sat 11am-5pm. Closed
bank hols, 25 Dec-1 Jan
Cards: Access, Visa

DIRECTIONS: On A272 3 miles east
of Haywards Heath.

4/456
■ WINE

Godstone Vineyards

Quarry Road, Godstone, Surrey RH9 8ZA
Tel: (01883) 744590
Fax: (01883) 744443

Wines, vineyard shop and restaurant.
Open: Mon-Sun 10am-5.30pm, closed
25-26 Dec
Cards: Access, Delta, Visa

DIRECTIONS: Off the A22
Caterham-Godstone road, ½ mile
north of J6 M25, signposted.

4/457
● PLANTS

Priorswood Clematis Nursery

Priorswood, Widbury Hill, Ware,
Hertfordshire SG12 7QH
Tel/Fax: (01920) 461543

Clematis and other climbers,
honeysuckles, grapes, Virginia
creepers.

Open: Tue-Sun 8am-4.30pm and
bank hols. Closed 25 Dec
Cards: Mastercard, Visa

DIRECTIONS: 1 mile from Ware on
the B1004 Much Hadham road.

4/458
● PLANTS

W E Th Ingwersen Ltd

Birch Farm Nursery, Gravetye, East
Grinstead, West Sussex RH19 4LE
Tel: (01342) 810236

Alpines, hardy rock plants, shrubs,
conifers and rock garden bulbs.
Open: Mar-Sept Mon-Sun 9am-1pm,
1.30pm-4pm. Oct-Feb Mon-Fri 9am-
1pm, 1.30pm-4pm. Closed Christmas
fortnight
Cards: No

DIRECTIONS: Off B2110 East
Grinstead to Turners Hill Road, in
Vowels Lane between Gravetye
Manor and Kingscote Station.
Signposted turning opposite letterbox
via Forestry Commission road.

4/459
✱ MULTIPLE

Star Brewery Pottery

Castle Ditch Lane, Lewes,
East Sussex BN7 1YJ
Tel: (01273) 483295

Bookbinding, ceramics, glass-blowing,
picture-framing, pottery, illustrations.
Open: Mon-Sat 11am-5.30pm.
Advisable to telephone first
Cards: No

DIRECTIONS: Castle Ditch Lane
runs parallel to Fisher Street, near
Lewes Castle.

4/460
■ WINE

Breaky Bottom Vineyard

Breaky Bottom, Rodmell, Lewes,
East Sussex BN7 3
Tel: (01273) 476427

Dry white wine.
Open: Mon-Sat 10am-6pm or dusk.
Closed 25 Dec and Easter
Cards: No

DIRECTIONS: Take Rodmell road from Lewes, passing Iford village on left after 3 miles, and taking next turn right into Northease farm. Breaky Bottom is 1¼ miles down a farm track, accessible but very isolated.

4/461
● LEATHER GOODS
Jane Hopkinson
Whitegate Cottage (Studio), Spithurst, Barcombe, Lewes, East Sussex BN8 5EE
Tel: (01273) 400448

Leather bags and belts, evening and casual bags, and document cases.
Open: Mon-Fri 10am-5pm, but telephone in advance
Cards: No

DIRECTIONS: 1 mile north-east of Barcombe before church.

4/462
■ MEAT/POULTRY/GAME
Old Spot Farm Shop
Piltdown, Uckfield, East Sussex TN22 3XN
Tel: (01825) 722894
Fax: (01825) 723623

Sausages, bacon, ham, quiche, pâté, cheese, cakes.
Open: All week 8.30am-5.30pm. Closed 25, 26 Dec, 1 Jan
Cards: Access, Visa

DIRECTIONS: On A272 at Piltdown. 3 miles from Uckfield, 1 mile from Newick. Large board on north side of road.

4/463
● PLANTS
Starborough Nursery
Starborough Road, Marsh Green, Edenbridge, Kent TN8 5RB
Tel: (01732) 865614
Fax: (01732) 862166

Rare and unusual trees and shrubs, specialists in rhododendrons and azaleas.
Open: Mon, Thur-Sun 10am-4.30pm
Cards: Access, Visa

DIRECTIONS: On the B2028 between Lingfield and Edenbridge.

4/464
✳ MULTIPLE
Andrew Crace
Bourne Lane, Much Hadham, Hertfordshire SG10 6ER
Tel: (01279) 842685
Fax: (01279) 843646

Garden furniture, bronze sculptures, engraving, organic vegetables and herbs.
Open: Mon-Fri 9.30am-4pm, but telephone in advance
Cards: Access, Visa

DIRECTIONS: Bourne Lane is east off B1004, north of Widford and south of Much Hadham. Signposted to St Elizabeth's Home, Perry Green and Green Tye.

4/465
● PLANTS
Hopleys Plants Ltd
High Street, Much Hadham, Hertfordshire SG10 6BU
Tel: (01279) 842509
Fax: (01279) 843784

Shrubs, perennials and rockery plants.
Open: Mon, Wed-Sat 9am-5pm, Sun 2pm-5pm, bank hols 9am-5pm. Closed Jan
Cards: Access, Visa

DIRECTIONS: On B1004 Bishop's Stortford to Ware road, 50 yards north of the Bull pub.

4/466
■ CHEESE
Willowdown Dairy Goats
Humphreys Farm, Nutley, Uckfield, East Sussex TN22 3LS
Tel: (01825) 712432

Milk, yoghurt, soft and hard cheeses.
Open: Any time, preferably by appointment
Cards: No

DIRECTIONS: On A22 East Grinstead to Uckfield Road, 1 mile south of Nutley village. Large blue and white 'Goats Milk' sign on right hand side.

4/467
■ DAIRY PRODUCE

The Basing Herd
Lower Basing Farm, Furnace Lane,
Cowden, Kent TN8 7JU
Tel: (01342) 850251
Fax: (01352) 850022

Milk, cheese, yoghurt, ice-cream and
meat.
Open: Mon-Sun 9am-8pm
Cards: No

DIRECTIONS: M25 J6, A22 to East
Grinstead. A264 towards Tunbridge
Wells. After about 3 miles at
Hammerwood, turn left towards
Lingfield, take first lane right, farm
first on right.

4/468
✷ MULTIPLE

Middle Farm Shop & Craft Workshops
Middle Farm, Firle, Lewes,
East Sussex BN8 6LJ
Tel: (01323) 811411

Farm shop, ironwork, picture-
framing, wood carving, furniture,
painting, stained glass, spinning and
weaving.
Open: Mon-Fri 9.30am-6pm, Sat, Sun
and bank hols 9.30am-5pm
Cards: Access, Amex, Visa

DIRECTIONS: Four miles east of
Lewes on A27 between Firle and
Selmeston.

4/469
■ WINE

Barnsgate Manor Vineyard
Heron's Ghyll, Nr Uckfield,
East Sussex TN22 4DB
Tel: (01825) 713366
Fax: (01825) 713543

Wines, tearoom and restaurant.
Open: Mon-Fri 10am-5pm
Cards: Access, Visa

DIRECTIONS: On the A26, 4 miles
north of Uckfield.

4/470
■ CHEESE

Sussex High Weald Dairy Sheep Products
Putlands Farm, Duddleswell, Nr Uckfield,
East Sussex TN22 3BJ
Tel: (01825) 712647

Sheep's milk cheeses, yoghurts,
fromage frais.
Open: Daily
Cards: No

DIRECTIONS: On B2026, between
Fairwarp and Duddleswell tearooms.

4/471
● PLANTS

Perryhill Nurseries
Hartfield, East Sussex TN7 4JP
Tel: (01892) 770377
Fax: (01892) 770929

Nursery.
Open: Mar-Oct Mon-Fri 9am-5pm,
Nov-Feb 9am-4.30pm. Closed 25-26
Dec
Cards: Access, Switch, Visa

DIRECTIONS: 1 mile north of
Hartfield on the B2026.

4/472
● BATIK

Mary Potter
Hunters Wood, Shortgate Lane, Laughton,
Lewes, East Sussex BN8 6DE
Tel: (01825) 840438

Batik pictures and collages, scarves
and cards.
Open: Normal shop hours but best to
telephone in advance
Cards: No

DIRECTIONS: From A22 turn west
towards Lewes at Halland
roundabout. After 1 mile turn left,
towards Laughton. In approx ¾ mile
look for sign.

4/473
■ WINE

Penshurst Vineyards
Grove Road, Penshurst, Tonbridge,
Kent TN11 8DU
Tel/Fax: (01892) 870255

Wines, apple wine and apple juice.
Open: Sept-May Mon-Sun 10am-
5pm, June-Aug Mon-Sun 10am-6pm.
Closed 25 Dec and 1 Jan, Jan-Feb
weekends
Cards: Access, Visa

DIRECTIONS: 1 mile from Penshurst
off B2188.

4/474
■ CHEESE

Neals Yard Creamery Ltd
Everlands Estate, Ide Hill, Sevenoaks,
Kent TN14 6HU
Tel/Fax: (01732) 461020

Cheeses, yoghurts and *crème fraîche*.
Open: Mon-Thur 9am-3pm. Closed
Christmas week
Cards: No

DIRECTIONS: From Ide Hill turn
left. After 1 mile turn right into drive
(marked Everlands) on left hand bend.
Down 3 hairpins into courtyard.

4/475
● JEWELLERY

The Gowan Gallery
3 Bell Street, Sawbridgeworth,
Hertfordshire CM21 9AR
Tel: (01279) 600004

Precious jewellery. Also ceramics,
glass, wood and metalwork.
Open: Tue-Sat 10am-5pm. Closed 25
Dec to 1 Jan
Cards: Access, Visa

DIRECTIONS: Off A1184 between
Harlow and Bishop's Stortford (close
to M11). Opposite White Lion pub.

4/476
■ WINE

Chiddingstone Vineyards Ltd
Vexour Farm, Chiddingstone, Edenbridge,
Kent TN8 7BB
Tel: (01892) 870277
Fax: (01892) 870878

The second largest vineyard in Britain,
selling wine by the case only (red and
white). All wines are estate bottled.
Open: Always open
Cards: No

DIRECTIONS: From the B2027
(Tonbridge to Edenbridge road)
½ mile west of Chiddingstone
Causeway village follow sign to
Chiddingstone and Vexour Farm.

4/477
■ MEAT/POULTRY/GAME

Thrushes Bush Poultry Farm
Thrushes Bush, High Laver, Nr Harlow,
Essex CM17 0NS
Tel: (0279) 422673
Fax: (0279) 444055

Poultry farm – free-range eggs and
chickens for breeding or table. Breeds:
White Leghorns, Rhode Island Reds
and crosses. Hatching: April. Table
cockerels fresh: October. Organic
vegetables.
Open: Always
Cards: No

DIRECTIONS: From M11/A414
interchange take Harlow road then
turn right five times, signposted
Threshers Bush.

4/478
● KNITWEAR

The Mohair Centre
Brickfield Farm, Laughton Road,
Chiddingly, Lewes, East Sussex BN8 6JG
Tel/Fax: (01825) 872457

Home-produced mohair knitwear,
yarn and fleece. Spinning and weaving
supplies.
Open: Daily 10am-5pm. Closed 25-26
Dec
Cards: Access, Amex, Visa

DIRECTIONS: On B2124, Ringmer to Hailsham Road, 100 yards from junction with A22.

4/479
● GARDEN FURNITURE
Sarah Burgoyne Revivals
Whyly, East Hoathly, East Sussex BN8 6EL
Tel: (01825) 840738

Garden furniture.
Open: By appointment
Cards: Access, Visa

DIRECTIONS: Directions given on arrangement of appointment.

4/480
● CLOTHES
Specially for You
Warnham Cottage, East Hoathly, Lewes, East Sussex BN8 6DP
Tel: (01825) 840397

Since going to press this establishment has closed

4/481
■ FRUIT/VEGETABLES
Sepham Farm
Filston Lane, Shoreham, Sevenoaks, Kent TN14 5JT
Tel: (01959) 522774/523626
Fax: (01959) 525040

Farm shop and pick your own. Chalk grassland nature reserve.
Open: Tue-Sun 9am-5pm
Cards: No

DIRECTIONS: From Otford duck pond roundabout go west along High Street. Turn right past Fry's Garage and Twitton Lane. Turn right at T-junction. Farm entrance is first on right.

4/482
● SILK
David Evans Mill Shop
Bourne Road, Crayford, Kent DA1 4BP
Tel: (01322) 559401
Fax: (01322) 550476

Silk, and silk ties, scarves and other silk items.

Open: Mon-Fri 9.30am-5pm. Sat 9.30am-4.30pm. Closed Sun and bank hols
Cards: Access, Switch, Visa

DIRECTIONS: From M25 J2, take A2 towards London. Exit Black Prince Interchange for Bexley/Bexleyheath. On A223 Bourne Industrial Park at junction of London road and Bourne Road.

4/483
■ WINE
Hadlow Down Vineyard
The Brooms, Tinkers Lane, Hadlow Down, Nr Uckfield, East Sussex TN22 4ET
Tel: (01825) 830420

Wines, vineyard tours.
Open: Wed-Sun 11am-5.30pm or by arrangement
Cards: Visa

DIRECTIONS: A272 Maresfield to Hadlow Down road, go through village past derestriction sign and turn right into Tinkers Lane. 100 yards on left.

4/484
● DRIED FLOWERS
The Hop Shop
Castle Farm, Shoreham, Sevenoaks, Kent TN14 7UB
Tel: (01959) 523219
Fax: (01959) 524220

Dried flowers.
Open: Mon-Fri 1pm-5pm. Sat 10am-5pm
Cards: No

DIRECTIONS: Castle Farm is a few miles from J3 or J4 of M25. Signposted off the A225, halfway between Shoreham and Eynsford.

4/485
■ CHEESE
K W and A M Blunt
Greenacres Farm, Whitesmith, East Sussex BN8 6JA
Tel: (01825) 872380

Goats' and sheep's milk cheeses, soft, mould ripened.
Open: Mon-Sun 8am-8pm

Cards: No

DIRECTIONS: On A22 at Golden Cross, 10 miles north of Eastbourne, opposite B2124 to Ringmer and Laughton.

4/486
■ DAIRY PRODUCE

Ladywell Dairy Sheep Products
Cobblers Yard Farm, Leggs Lane, Langton Green, Tunbridge Wells, Kent TN3 0RQ
Tel: (01892) 863448

Yoghurt, ice-cream, soft cheese and milk.
Open: Daily 9am-6pm but advisable to telephone first at weekends and bank hols
Cards: No

DIRECTIONS: Take A264 west from Tunbridge Wells to Langton Green. Turn right at The Hare public house to Speldhurst and after ¼ mile turn left to Fordcombe. Farm entrance is ¼ mile on left.

4/487
■ WINE

St George's Vineyard
Waldron Village, Heathfield, East Sussex TN21 0RA
Tel: (01435) 812156
Fax: (01435) 813185

Wines, vineyard tours, cheeses and crafts, restaurant.
Open: April-Oct Wed-Sun 11am-5pm, Mar and Nov Sat-Sun 11am-5pm, Dec Mon-Sun 11am-5pm, Closed Jan and Feb
Cards: Access, Visa in restaurant

DIRECTIONS: 3 miles off A22 at East Hoathly, and 3 miles off A267 (Tunbridge Wells to Heathfield) turn off at Cross in Hand.

4/488
● PLANTS

Crown Point Nursery
Sevenoaks Road, Ightham, Sevenoaks, Kent TN15 0BH
Tel: (01732) 810694
Fax: (01732) 862166

Rhododendrons and azaleas. Also unusual trees and shrubs.

Open: Mon-Sat 10am-4.30pm
Cards: Access, Visa

DIRECTIONS: Next to Crown Point Inn on A25.

4/489
● PLANTS

County Park Nursery
Essex Gardens, Hornchurch, Essex RM11 3BU
Tel: (01708) 445205

Hebe, pittosporum, coprosma, unusual plants.
Open: Mar-Oct Mon-Sat 9am-6pm or dusk, Sun 10am-5pm. Closed Wed. Nov-Feb by appointment
Cards: No

DIRECTIONS: From J29 of M25 take A127 towards London. After 2½ miles pass Little Chef and turn left into Wingletye Lane then left to Essex Gardens. Small entrance between shops and petrol garage.

4/490
● DRIED FLOWERS

Norpar Dried Flowers
Navestock Hall, Romford, Essex RM4 1HA
Tel: (01277) 374968
Fax: (01277) 372562

Dried flowers and silk, parchment flowers, fruit and berries, candles and florists' sundries.
Open: Mon-Sat 9am-5pm. Closed bank hols
Cards: No

DIRECTIONS: Off A113 directly to Navestock, by church.

4/491
■ ICE-CREAM

Knightsbridge Farm Dairy Ice Cream
Knightsbridge Farm, Grovebridge, Hellingly, East Sussex BN27 4HT
Tel: (01435) 812574

Dairy ice-cream and untreated Jersey cream.
Open: Every day
Cards: No

DIRECTIONS: 3 miles south of
Horam on road to Hailsham that runs
parallel to A267 Hellingly Hospital
road.

4/492
● KNITWEAR

Diamond Fibres Ltd
Diamonds Farm, Horam, Heathfield,
East Sussex TN21 0HF
Tel: (01435) 812414

Knitwear and carded wool.
Open: By appointment
Cards: No

DIRECTIONS: Vines Cross Road –
½ mile on right from junction with
B2203.

4/493
■ WINE

Hidden Spring Vineyard
Vines Cross Road, Horam, Nr Heathfield,
East Sussex TN21 0HF
Tel/Fax: (01435) 812640

Wines. Free tour and tastings.
Open: Weekends and bank hols;
during week telephone in advance
Cards: Access, Visa

DIRECTIONS: On A267 from
Tunbridge Wells to Eastbourne in
Horam turn left into village, take road
to Vine Cross, vineyard on left-hand
side.

4/494
● PLANTS

Oakdene Alpine Nursery
Street End Lane, Broad Oak, Heathfield,
East Sussex TN21 8TU
Tel: (01435) 864382

Alpines.
Open: Wed-Sat 9am-5pm, other times
and bank hols by appointment
Cards: No

DIRECTIONS: On A265 Heathfield
to Burwash road, 15 miles south of
Tunbridge Wells. Past village shops,
turn north for ½ mile towards
Mayfield.

4/495
● BASKETS

The Truggery
Coopers Croft, Herstmonceux, Hailsham,
East Sussex BN27 1QL
Tel: (01323) 832314

Trug baskets from locally grown
coppiced wood.
Open: Mon-Sat 10am-5.30pm, also
bank hols and Sun June to Aug.
Closed 25 Dec-1 Jan
Cards: Access, Visa

DIRECTIONS: On A271 approx
1 mile west of Herstmonceux
village towards Hailsham.

4/496
■ FLOUR

Bartley Mill
Frant, Sussex TN3 8BH
Tel: (01892) 890372
Fax: (01892) 890101

Flour, farm shop, fresh trout, tea-
room, working watermill.
Open: Mar-Sept 10am-6pm. Oct-Feb
Sat and Sun 10am-6pm. Closed
Christmas and New Year
Cards: Access, Visa

DIRECTIONS: Off B2169
Lamberhurst to Tunbridge Wells
Road. Signposted 2 miles east of Bells
Yew Green.

4/497
● GLASS

Nicola Kantorowicz
Contemporary Stained Glass
8 Wyatt Close, Borough Green, Sevenoaks,
Kent TN15 8RP
Tel: (01732) 780376

Stained glass windows.
Open: By appointment only
Cards: No

DIRECTIONS: J2 off M20. 1½ miles
to Borough Green. Wyatt Close is
south of village off Quarry Hill Road.

4/498
● BASKETS

Sussex Trugs Limited
Thomas Smith's Trug Shop,
Hailsham Road, Herstmonceux,
East Sussex BN27 4LH
Tel: (01323) 832137
Fax: (01323) 833801

Craft goods, trug baskets.
Open: Mon-Fri 8am-5pm, Sat 9am-
7pm, closed some lunchtimes and
bank hols, also 25 Dec-1st week in Jan
Cards: Access, Visa

DIRECTIONS: On A271 road right in
centre of Herstmonceux village next
to Drummers Pine Shop.

4/499
● CERAMICS

Peter Phillips Pottery
Ivy Cottage, Taylors Lane, Trottiscliffe,
Kent ME19 5DS
Tel: (01732) 822901

Reduced stoneware, domestic ware,
casseroles, mugs, jugs, bowls and
decorative items.
Open: By appointment
Cards: No

DIRECTIONS: Junction A20 and A25,
Maidstone direction, turn left to
Trottiscliffe. Take School Lane by the
George pub and then Taylors Lane to
Ivy Cottage.

4/500
● FORGEWORK

Geo Carford Ltd
Ingatestone Forge, 3a High Street,
Ingatestone, Essex CM4 9ED
Tel: (01277) 353026
Fax: (01277) 355804

Ornamental ironwork.
Open: Mon-Fri 8.30am-5pm. Closed
25 Dec-1 Jan
Cards: No

DIRECTIONS: Off A12 between
Brentwood and Chelmsford.
Chelmsford end of High Street
behind Roses sweet shop.

4/501
● FURNITURE

Barry Michael Murphy
Dormer's Farmhouse, Windmill Hill,
Herstmonceux, Hailsham,
East Sussex BN27 4RY
Tel: (01323) 832388

Hand-made Windsor chairs and
settles.
Open: By appointment only
Cards: No

DIRECTIONS: On the A271, 1 mile
east of Herstmonceux, across from
the Horse Shoe Inn and next door to
Windmill Hill garage.

4/502
● CERAMICS

Hook Green Pottery
Hook Green, Nr Lamberhurst, Tunbridge
Wells, Kent TN3 8LR
Tel: (01892) 890504

Handmade ceramics, stoneware and
porcelain.
Open: Daily 9.30am-6pm,
appointments preferred
Cards: No

DIRECTIONS: On B2169 1 mile west
of Lamberhurst, 6 miles east of
Tunbridge Wells. On north-east
corner of Hook Green crossroads
opposite Elephants Head pub.

4/503
■ CIDER

Owlet Apple Juice and Cider
Owl House Fruit Farm, Mount Pleasant
Lane, Lamberhurst, Kent TN3 8LY
Tel: (01892) 890553

Apple juices and ciders, cherries and
apples in season.
Open: Mon-Fri 8am-5pm, by
appointment at other times
Cards: No

DIRECTIONS: Just south of A21 and
1 mile west of Lamberhurst. Take A21
south. Before Lamberhurst turn right
(marked to Hook Green) by Swan
Farm Shop and follow signs to Owl
House Gardens.

4/504
● PLANTS

Uplands Nursery
Hooe, Nr Battle, East Sussex TN33 9HD
Tel: (01424) 844846

Fuchsias.
Open: Mon-Sun 9am-5pm, dusk in
winter. Closed 25 Dec-1 Jan
Cards: Access, Visa

DIRECTIONS: 3 miles south of
Ninfield on the B2095 (fork right at
Hooe Common).

4/505
■ WINE

Lamberhurst Vineyards
Ridge Farm, Lamberhurst, Kent TN3 8ER
Tel: (01892) 890286
Fax: (01892) 890493

Wines, liqueurs and brandy, tours.
Open: Summer Mon-Sat 9am-6pm,
Sun 10am-6pm, winter Mon-Sat
9am-5pm, Sun 10am-5pm. Closed
25-26 Dec, 1 Jan
Cards: Access, Switch, Visa

DIRECTIONS: ½ mile off A21 south
of Tunbridge Wells, signposted with
brown tourist signs.

4/506
■ SMOKED PRODUCE

The Weald Smokery
Mount Farm, Flimwell,
East Sussex TN5 7QL
Tel: (01580) 879601
Fax: (01580) 879564

Oak-smoked food.
Open: Winter Mon-Sat 9am-5.30pm,
summer Mon-Sun 9am-5.30pm
Cards: No

DIRECTIONS: Flimwell is on A21.
Turn on to Hawkhurst road at traffic
lights. Farm is first property on left.

4/507
● CRICKET BATS

John Newbery Ltd
Station Road, Robertsbridge,
East Sussex TN32 5DG
Tel: (01580) 881104
Fax: (01580) 881244

Handmade English willow cricket
bats.
Open: Mon-Fri 9am-5pm
Cards: Access, Visa

DIRECTIONS: Off A21 London to
Hastings road, 10 miles north of
Hastings. Off High Street, above
Garden Machine Centre.

4/508
● PLANTS

Brenda Hyatt Auriculas
1 Toddington Crescent, Blue Bell Hill,
Chatham, Kent ME5 9QT
Tel: (01634) 863251

Auriculas.
Open: By appointment only
Cards: No

DIRECTIONS: In Blue Bell Hill
village off A229 between M2 and
M20.

4/509
■ WINE

Leeford Vineyards
Whatlington, Battle, Sussex TN33 0NQ
Tel: (01424) 773183

Five varieties of English wine.
Open: Jan-Easter, Mon-Fri 10am-
5.30pm, Sat-Sun by appointment.
Easter-24 Dec, Mon-Sat 10am-5pm,
Sun 12 noon-5.30pm
Cards: No

DIRECTIONS: On A21 to
Whatlington, turn right at Royal Oak
pub, signposted Battle, ½ mile on left.
From Battle town centre take Mount
Street, 2½ miles to vineyard.

4/510
✳ MULTIPLE

Kent Garden Vineyard
Yew Tree House, Upper Street, Leeds
Village, Nr Maidstone, Kent ME17 1SD
Tel/Fax: (01622) 861638

Country wines and costume dolls.
Open: Thur-Sun and bank hols 10am-
4pm. Closed Mon-Wed and 25 and 26
Dec
Cards: No

DIRECTIONS: From M20 follow
signs for Leeds Castle. Through
village and look out for brown on
white approach signs. A274 from
Maidstone to Langley turn left on to
B2163. Follow sign for Castle. Tourist
sign just past 10 Bells pub on right.

4/511
● PLANTS

Iden Croft Herbs
Frittenden Road, Staplehurst,
Kent TN12 0DH
Tel: (01580) 891432
Fax: (01580) 892416

Herbs, alpines, wild flowers.
Open: All year Mon-Sat 9am-5pm.
Additional opening Sun and bank hols
from Mar-Sep 11am-5pm. Closed 25
and 26 Dec
Cards: Access, Visa

DIRECTIONS: Turning into
Frittenden Road from A229, between
church and Elf garage, Iden Croft
Herbs sign ¼ mile on right of
Frittenden Road.

4/512
■ WINE

Carr Taylor Vineyards
Westfield, Hastings, East Sussex TN35 4SG
Tel: (01424) 752501
Fax: (01424) 751716

English sparkling wines, still white
and rosé wines, apple wine, Battle
vintage cider.
Open: Mon-Sun 10am-5pm. Closed
Sun 25 Dec-Easter and 25 Dec-2 Jan
Cards: Access, Visa

DIRECTIONS: 2 miles along the A28
after leaving the A21 (London-

Hastings). Turn left by New Inn pub
in centre of village. ¾ mile on brow of
hill on left-hand side.

4/513
■ WINE

Sculdown Vineyard & Orchard
Chitcombe Road, Broad Oak, Nr Rye,
East Sussex TN31 6EX
Tel/Fax: (01797) 252055

Wines, honey, preserves, flowers,
plants, fleeces for hand-spinners,
vines, fruit bushes and fruit.
Open: Fri-Sun 10am-5pm
Cards: No

DIRECTIONS: On B2089 between
Cripps Corner and Broadoak.

4/514
■ WINE

Sandhurst Vineyards
Hoads Farm, Crouch Lane, Sandhurst,
Cranbrook, Kent TN18 5PA
Tel/Fax: (01580) 850296

Wines and vineyard tours.
Open: Mon-Fri 2pm-5.50pm, Sat
11am-5.30pm, Sun 12 noon-3pm.
Closed Jan-Easter
Cards: Access, Diners, Visa

DIRECTIONS: From A268 travelling
from Hawkhurst towards Rye, take
first turning left ½ mile after
Sandhurst. Signposted on road,
½ mile on right at bottom of hill.

4/515
● PLANTS

Coghurst Nursery
Ivy House Lane, Nr Three Oaks, Hastings,
East Sussex TN35 4NP
Tel: (01424) 756228

Camellias, rhododendrons.
Open: Mon-Fri 12 noon-4.30pm. Sun
10am-4.30pm. Closed Sat
Cards: No

DIRECTIONS: 3 miles north of
Hastings take A28 to Westfield, turn
right at crossroads signposted Three
Oaks, then turn right after 1½ miles.

4/516
● GLASS

John Sambrook – Fanlight Maker
Park House, Ewhurst Lane, Northiam,
East Sussex TN31 6PA
Tel: (01797) 252615

Fanlight windows.
Open: Strictly by appointment
Cards: No

DIRECTIONS: 12 miles north of
Hastings in centre of Northiam.
Follow signs to 'Great Dixter' historic
house. On corner of Dixter Road,
opposite veterinary surgery.

4/517
● PLANTS

Great Dixter Nurseries
Northiam, Rye, East Sussex TN31 6PH
Tel: (01797) 253107
Fax: (01797) 252879

Clematis and unusual plant nursery.
Open: Mon-Fri 9am-12.30pm,
1.30pm-5pm, Sat 9am-12 noon, other
times by appointment
Cards: No

DIRECTIONS: On A28 Canterbury to
Hastings road, situated ½ mile north
of Northiam. Turn off A28 at post
office and follow signposted route
from village.

4/518
■ WINE

Rowenden Vineyard
Sandhurst Lane, Rolvenden, Cranbrook,
Kent TN17 4PQ
Tel: (01580) 241255

White wines.
Open: Tue-Sun 10am-6pm. Closed
25 Dec
Cards: No

DIRECTIONS: To Rolvenden on
A28, take B2086 signposted
Cranbrook, 200 yards after windmill
(on left) take first turn left signposted
Sandhurst. Vineyard is 1 mile down
lane on left.

4/519
■ DAIRY PRODUCE

S E Lane
White House Farm, Biddenden, Ashford,
Kent TN27 8LN
Tel: (01580) 291289

Jersey cream, milk, yoghurt, butter,
ice-cream.
Open: All week 8am-6pm. Closed 25
Dec
Cards: No

DIRECTIONS: Take A262 from
Biddenden towards Sissinghurst.
After 1½ miles turn right by Three
Chimneys pub. Keep right, 400 yards
on left.

4/520
■ WINE

Bearsted Vineyard
24 Caring Lane, Bearsted, Maidstone,
Kent ME14 4NJ
Tel: (01622) 736974

Wines, vineyard tours.
Open: Mon-Sun 10am-6pm, best to
telephone in advance
Cards: Access, Visa

DIRECTIONS: Caring Lane is on the
south side of A20 Maidstone to
Ashford road, 1 mile west of J8 M20.
Vineyard is on right, ½ mile from
A20.

4/521
■ BAKED GOODS

Herschell House Foods
102 Glendale Gardens, Leigh-on-Sea,
Essex SS9 2AY
Tel: (01702) 710315
Fax: (01702) 471740

Substantial pies, quiches and
confectionery.
Open: Mon-Fri 7am-3pm. Closed
bank hols
Cards: No

DIRECTIONS: Western edge of
Southend. Enter on A13. Turn right
at 2nd traffic lights (Westleigh
School). Down Westleigh Avenue to
Glendale Gardens. Turn left.

4/522
● FURNITURE

Barry M Jones
Rustic Crafts Workshop, Bixley Lane,
Beckley, Rye, East Sussex TN31 6TH
Tel: (01797) 260522

Furniture and artefacts for the home
and garden.
Open: Sun 9am-6pm, other times by
appointment
Cards: No

DIRECTIONS: 100 yards off the
main A268 Rye-Hawkhurst road,
between the villages of Peasmarsh and
Beckley, approx 4½ miles east of Rye.

4/523
■ WINE

Biddenden Vineyards Ltd
Little Whatmans, Gribble Bridge Lane,
Biddenden, Kent TN27 8DH
Tel: (01580) 291726
Fax: (01580) 291933

Wines and ciders.
Open: Mon-Fri 10am-5pm, Sat 11am-
5pm, Sun 12 noon-5pm, Nov-Feb
weekends and bank hols 12 noon-
3pm. Closed 24 Dec-2 Jan
Cards: Access, Switch, Visa

DIRECTIONS: 1½ miles from
Biddenden, south on A262 and after
approx ¾ mile, bear right at Woolpack
corner, and follow vineyard signs.

4/524
■ WINE

The Harbourne Vineyard
Wittersham, Tenterden, Kent TN30 7NP
Tel/Fax: (01797) 270420

Wines, apple wine, vines.
Open: Mon-Fri 2pm-6pm, Sat 9am-
7pm, Sun 12 noon-5pm. Closed 2
weeks in August
Cards: Access, Visa

DIRECTIONS: On B2082 1 mile
from Wittersham on Tenterden to
Rye road.

4/525
■ MEAT/POULTRY/GAME

Wadhurst Park Speciality Foods
Morghew Farm, Smallhythe Road,
Tenterden, Kent TN30 7LR
Tel: (01580) 763158
Fax: (01580) 765840

Home-produced venison, wild boar,
crayfish and game.
Open: Mon-Sat 9.30am-5pm, Sun
by appointment. Closed 25 Dec
Cards: No

DIRECTIONS: From A28 at
Tenterden take B2082 Rye road.
Entrance ½ mile on right. Signposted
Wadhurst Park Ltd. Follow signs to
Farm Shop.

4/526
■ HONEY

Homestall Honey Farm
Homestall Farm, High Halden, Ashford,
Kent TN26 3BS
Tel: (01233) 850490

Honey, honeycombs, candles,
beeswax, beeswax polish, honey
novelties.
Open: Daily 9am-6pm
Cards: No

DIRECTIONS: On A28 Ashford to
Tenterden road. 1 mile south of High
Halden. On left. Follow sign.

4/527
● CERAMICS

David Sharp Ceramics
55 The Mint, Rye, Sussex TN31 7EN
Tel: (01797) 222620

Ceramic house plaques, animals and
studio ware.
Open: Summer Mon-Sat 9.30am-
5pm, Sun 10am-4pm, winter Mon-
Sun 10am-4pm. Closed 25 Dec
Cards: Access, Visa

DIRECTIONS: About 10 miles east of
Hastings on the A259. The pottery
showroom is at the junction of the
Mint and Mermaid Street.

4/528
● CERAMICS
Rye Pottery Ltd
77 Ferry Road, Rye, East Sussex TN31 7DJ
Tel: (01797) 223038
Fax: (01797) 224834

Hand-painted figures.
Open: Mon-Fri 9am-12.30pm, 2pm-
5pm, Sat 9.30am-12.30pm, 2.30pm-
5pm. Closed bank hols
Cards: Access, Visa

DIRECTIONS: On the B2089, 200
yards beyond the Rye railway
crossing, on the road to Battle.

4/529
■ MEAT/POULTRY/GAME
Marney Meats
Layer Marney Tower, Layer Marney,
Nr Colchester, Essex CO5 9US
Tel/Fax: (01206) 330784

Venison, pork, lamb, beef, ham,
sausages and bacon.
Open: Apr-Sept 2pm-6pm. Oct-Mar
9am-1pm. Other times by
appointment
Cards: No

DIRECTIONS: Between Tiptree and
Colchester signposted with brown
tourist signs off B1022. Shop is in
Layer Marney Tower. Ring bell.

4/530
● PLANTS
Oldbury Nurseries
Brissenden Green, Bethersden, Nr Ashford,
Kent TN26 3BJ
Tel: (01233) 820416

Fuchsias and pelargoniums.
Open: Feb-June Mon-Sun 9.30am-
5pm, partial opening July, closed Aug-
Jan
Cards: Access, Visa

DIRECTIONS: Off the A28 7 miles
from Ashford towards Tenterden,
signposted to nursery on A28. 2 miles
from Bethersden village.

4/531
■ CIDER
Pawley Farm Cider
Pawley Farm, Painters Forstal, Faversham,
Kent ME13 0EN
Tel: (01795) 532043

Cider.
Open: Mon-Sun 8am-9pm
Cards: No

DIRECTIONS: On A2 from
Canterbury to Sittingbourne 1st left
past junction of A251 (Ashford) to
village of Painters Forstal. Take right
fork for Ospringe. Farm 150 yards
past Alma pub.

4/532
✸ MULTIPLE
Apple Craft Centre
Macknade, Selling Road, Faversham,
Kent ME13 8XF
Tel: (01795) 590504

Banjos, balloons, chairs, drawings,
pottery, wood-turning.
Open: Daily 9.30am-5.30pm. Closed
25-27 Dec
Cards: No

DIRECTIONS: On A2 at Faversham,
1 mile from J7 of M2.

4/533
● PLANTS
Madrona Nursery
Harden Road, Lydd, Kent TN29 9LT
Tel: (01797) 320868

Ornamental trees, shrubs, perennials,
grasses and ferns.
Open: Mid-Mar-Oct Tue-Thur 2pm-
8pm
Cards: No

DIRECTIONS: Behind Lydd railway
station, off Harden Road which is
between Lydd Station and Dungeness
roundabout. Brown signboard points
to gravel track.

4/534
■ FRUIT/VEGETABLES
Perry Court Farm Shop
Perry Court, Canterbury Road, Bilting,
Ashford, Kent TN25 4ES
Tel/Fax: (01233) 812408

Fruit and vegetables, fruit trees,
garden centre. Tearoom. Pick your
own.
Open: 9am-6pm. Closed 25 and 26
Dec
Cards: No

DIRECTIONS: On A28 Ashford to
Canterbury road, 4 miles north of
Ashford on right. Between the two
Wye crossroads.

4/535
✳ MULTIPLE
Evegate Farm
Station Road, Smeeth, Ashford,
Kent TN25 6SX
Tel: (01303) 812334

Gold and silverware, baby and
maternity clothes, furniture, sweets,
wood-turning.
Open: Usually Tue-Sun 10am-
5.30pm. Advisable to telephone in
advance
Cards: No

DIRECTIONS: Travelling on A20
from Ashford towards Hythe near
Smeeth, turn left (southwards) at
crossroads signposted to Evegate.
Farm is 400 metres on left.

4/536
■ MEAT/POULTRY/GAME
Richardson's Butchers
66 High Street, Brightlingsea,
Essex CO7 0AQ
Tel: (01206) 302259

Sausages, hams, turkeys, sweet pickled
bacon.
Open: Mon-Wed, Fri, 7.30am-5pm,
Thur, Sat 7am-1pm. Closed Sun
Cards: No

DIRECTIONS: Hurst Green end of
High Street.

4/537
● CERAMICS
Robus Pottery & Tiles
Evington Park, Hastingleigh, Ashford,
Kent TN25 5JH
Tel/Fax: (01233) 750330

Garden pots and tiles, architectural
pieces.
Open: Mon-Sat 9am-5pm
Cards: No

DIRECTIONS: From M20 follow A28
through Wye to Hastingleigh, on
crossroads ½ mile outside
Hastingleigh.

4/538
■ FISH/SHELLFISH
Seasalter Shellfish
(Whitstable) Ltd
East Quay, The Harbour, Whitstable,
Kent CT5 1AB
Tel: (01227) 272003
Fax: (01227) 264829

Oysters, clams and shellfish.
Open: Mon-Fri 9am-5pm. May to Oct
Sat and Sun 10am-4pm
Cards: No

DIRECTIONS: Along Sea Street.
Turn left at Harbour Garage.

4/539
● CERAMICS
Sellindge Pottery & Crafts
The Pottery, Barrow Hill, Sellindge,
Ashford, Kent TN25 6JP
Tel: (01303) 812204
Fax: (01303) 814004

Handmade pottery.
Open: Mon-Sat 10am-5pm
Cards: Access, Visa

DIRECTIONS: On the A20 at
Sellindge, ½ mile between Ashford
and Folkestone.

4/540
■ MEAT/POULTRY/GAME
Peartree Farm Foods
High Birch Road, Weeley Heath, Clacton-on-Sea, Essex CO16 9BU
Tel: (01255) 830921
Fax: (01255) 831473

Cooked and smoked meats.
Open: Mon-Fri 9am-1pm, 2pm-5pm.
Collection of orders at weekends by appointment
Cards: No

DIRECTIONS: At Clacton, turn right at War Memorial to Bentley Road. Left 1 mile to High Birch Road.

4/541
● PLANTS
J Bradshaw and Son
Busheyfields Nursery, Herne, Herne Bay, Kent CT6 7LJ
Tel/Fax: (01227) 375415

Climbing and wall plants such as clematis and honeysuckle.
Open: Mar-Oct Tue-Sat 10am-5pm
Cards: No

DIRECTIONS: On A291 Herne Bay to Canterbury road, 1 mile south of the village of Herne.

4/542
■ WINE
Elham Valley Vineyard
Breach, Barham, Canterbury, Kent CT4 6LN
Tel/Fax: (01227) 831266

Still and sparkling wines.
Open: Tue-Sat 10.30am-5.30pm, Sun 12 noon-5.30pm. Open bank hols, Christmas-Easter hours may vary
Cards: Access, Visa

DIRECTIONS: Midway between Canterbury and Folkestone on the B2065 between Barham and Elham.

4/543
● WOOD
Jali Ltd
Albion Works, Church Lane, Barham, Canterbury, Kent CT4 6QS
Tel: (01227) 831710
Fax: (01227) 831950

Fretwork products including decorative trims, shelves, brackets, pelmets, trellis, folding screens.
Open: Mon-Fri 9am-5.30pm.
Weekends by appointment only.
Closed bank hols and Christmas week
Cards: Access, Switch, Visa

DIRECTIONS: On A2 from Canterbury to Dover. Take A260 Folkestone exit. Follow over A2. At T-junction turn right. Next left to crossroads. Turn left, 200 yards on right through metal gate.

4/544
● TOYS
Canterbury Bears Ltd
The Old Coach House, Court Hill, Littlebourne, Canterbury, Kent CT3 1XU
Tel: (01227) 728238 and 720802
Fax: (01227) 728487

Teddy bear manufacturers. Tours by appointment only.
Open: Mon-Fri 8am-5pm. Closed bank hols and Christmas
Cards: Access, Amex, Diners, Visa

DIRECTIONS: On Canterbury to Wingham road 3 miles from Canterbury turn left at Jubilee Road then left on to Court Hill.

4/545
● FORGEWORK
Nailbourne Forge
Builders Square, Court Hill, Littlebourne, Canterbury, Kent CT3 1TX
Tel/Fax: (01227) 728336

Blacksmith, small range of interior ironwork.
Open: Daily 8.30am-6pm. Closed Christmas
Cards: No

DIRECTIONS: On A257 Canterbury to Sandwich road. Turn left in Littlebourne into Jubilee Road. At

T-junction turn left. Turn right down track. Turn right into courtyard after gates.

4/546
■ CONFECTIONERY

Wards of Adisham
Little Bossington Farmhouse, Bossington Road, Adisham, Canterbury, Kent CT3 3LN
Tel: (01227) 720596

Home-made fudge.
Open: All week 9am-5pm. Closed Jan and Feb
Cards: No

DIRECTIONS: Off B2046 between Barham crossroads and Wingham just north of Adisham village. Yellow farmhouse with beams. From village take Bossington Road.

4/547
● CERAMICS

Nonington Pottery
Farthingales, Old Court Hill, Nonington, Nr Dover, Kent CT15 4LQ
Tel: (01304) 840174

Pottery, water features, decorative roof fittings, large pots, garden ceramics.
Open: Any time by appointment
Cards: Visa

DIRECTIONS: From A2 take B2046. Follow signs into Nonington. At the Royal Oak pub turn left into Vicarage Lane, follow the lane to the bottom, pottery is opposite the church tower on a sharp double bend.

4/548
■ WINE

Staple Vineyard
Church Farm, Staple, Canterbury, Kent CT3 1LN
Tel: (01304) 812571

Wine and locally made honey, fudge, chutney, mustard and preserves.
Open: Easter-Sept daily 10am-5pm, Winter best to telephone in advance. Closed over Christmas
Cards: Access, Visa

DIRECTIONS: A2 Canterbury to Dover road, exit towards Wingham and take Staple Road as you enter Wingham, or A257 from Canterbury towards Sandwich, enter Wingham then right past Red Lion and left signed to Staple.

4/549
■ SMOKED PRODUCE

Kileravagh Smoked Foods
Unit 6/7, Hedgend Industrial Estate, St Nicholas at Wade, Birchington, Kent CT7 0NB
Tel: (01843) 847086
Fax: (01843) 848000

Smoked salmon, sea trout, smoked meats and game.
Open: Telephone first, but usually Mon-Fri 8am-4pm. Closed bank hols
Cards: Access, Visa

DIRECTIONS: On A299 Herne Bay to Margate road at St Nicholas at Wade. Turn off to St Nicholas and follow signs to estate (½ mile). Factory at rear of estate.

4/550
● CERAMICS

Summerfield Pottery & Potters' Supplies
Summerfield Farm, Summerfield, Woodnesborough, Sandwich, Kent CT13 0EW
Tel: (01304) 611937

Stoneware water features, domestic ware, house name-plates and numbers, clocks and terracotta pots.
Open: Mon-Sat 9am-5pm
Cards: Access, Visa

DIRECTIONS: From Staple leave the Black Pig pub on right and pottery is 600 yards around corner.

4/551
■ WINE

Ash Coombe Vineyard
Coombe Lane, Ash, Canterbury, Kent CT3 2BS
Tel: (01304) 813396

White and red wines.
Open: Aug Mon-Sun 11am-6pm, Sat-Sun and bank hols 11am-6pm, Thur-Fri by appointment
Cards: No

DIRECTIONS: A257 signposted off
Ash bypass between Canterbury and
Sandwich.

4/552
■ WINE

St Nicholas Vineyard
Moat Farm House, Moat Lane, Ash,
Canterbury, Kent CT3 2DG
Tel: (01304) 812670
Fax: (01304) 813911

Wine.
Open: Apr-Dec Mon-Fri 10am-6pm,
Jan-Mar Sat-Sun 10am-6pm
Cards: No

DIRECTIONS: Signposted on the
A257 Canterbury to Sandwich road
on the Ash bypass. Tourism signs in
Ash village complete the directions.

4/553
■ ICE-CREAM

Solleys Farms Limited
The Dairy, Ripple, Deal, Kent CT14 8JL
Tel/Fax: (01304) 374100

Dairy ice-cream.
Open: Mon-Fri 8am-4pm. Open Sat
pm during school summer holidays
Cards: No

DIRECTIONS: 4 miles from Dover
on A258. Turn right at Ringwould –
under railway turn right. Turn right at
Plough Inn, past church on right.
Follow signs to Dairy.

MAP 5

5/554
● CERAMICS
Studio Pottery
Caerfarchell, Solva, Haverfordwest,
Dyfed SA62 6XG
Tel: (01437) 720970

Stoneware vessels and sculptural
items.
Open: Easter to Oct daily 10am-6pm.
Otherwise Mon-Fri 10am-4pm or by
appointment. Closed Jan/Feb
Cards: No

DIRECTIONS: 2½ miles from St
David's along A487 to Fishguard.

5/555
● TEXTILES
The Woollen Mill
Middle Mill, Solva, Haverfordwest,
Dyfed SA62 6XD
Tel: (01437) 721597

Woollen mill producing carpets and
floor rugs.
Open: Mon-Fri 9.30am-5.30pm.
Easter to end Sept also Sat 9.30am-
5.30pm and Sun 2pm-5.30pm. Closed
Christmas
Cards: No

DIRECTIONS: Signposted from A487
between Solva and St David's.

5/556
■ MEAT/POULTRY/GAME
Haven Ostriches
Whitegates, Little Haven, Haverfordwest,
Dyfed SA62 3LA
Tel/Fax: (01437) 781552

Fresh and frozen ostrich meat,
smoked fillet and pâté. Fresh geese
and ducks.
Open: Daily 9am-5pm
Cards: Access, Visa

DIRECTIONS: A40 to Haverfordwest.
Follow signs to Broad Haven along
beach front up hill towards Little
Haven. First entrance on left after bus
stop.

5/557
● TEXTILES
Melin Tregwynt
Melin Tregwynt Mill, Castle Morris,
Haverfordwest, Dyfed SA62 5UX
Tel: (01348) 891225
Fax: (01348) 891694

Working woollen mill making
blankets, rugs and bedspreads.
Open: Mon-Fri 9am-5pm
Cards: Access, Amex, Visa

DIRECTIONS: Take A487 Fishguard
to St David's road for approximately
4 miles. Follow brown signs at second
cross roads. Nearest village is St
Nicholas.

5/558
■ CHEESE
Llangloffan Farmhouse Cheese Centre
Llangloffan Farm, Castle Morris, Haverford
West, Dyfed SA62 5ET
Tel/Fax: (01348) 891241

Welsh cheeses, honey, jam and ice-
cream. Demonstrations of cheese-
making.
Open: Mon-Sat 9am-5.30pm. Closed
25-26 Dec, 1 Jan
Cards: No

DIRECTIONS: 3 miles from
Fishguard on A487 Fishguard to St
David's Road, signposted.

5/559
■ BAKED GOODS
Cottage Caterers
Min-yr-Afon, Jordanston Bridge, Castle
Morris, Haverfordwest, Dyfed SA62 5UH
Tel: (01348) 891296

Pies, pastries and cooked French
dishes.
Open: Mon-Sat 8am-late. Closed Sun
(and Mon in Jan and Feb)
Cards: No

DIRECTIONS: From Fishguard on
A40 Haverfordwest road take right
turn signposted St David's. After 200
yards turn left signposted Jordanston.
Exactly 2 miles on the right.

5/560
● KNITWEAR

Helena Mathias Naturals
43 West Street, Fishguard, Dyfed SA65 9AD
Tel: (01348) 872282

Pure new wool Aran knitwear.
Open: Mon-Sat 10am-5pm. Closed
Wed pm during winter
Cards: Access, Visa

DIRECTIONS: Take road to
Fishguard harbour from the square.
On left-hand side before pedestrian
crossing.

5/561
● WOOD

Robintree
The Workshop, Parc-y-Shut, Fishguard,
Dyfed SA65 9AD
Tel: (01348) 875112

Hand-carved wooden rocking-horses
and furniture.
Open: Mon-Sat 9am-6pm. Closed 2
weeks in summer, 1 week at
Christmas
Cards: No

DIRECTIONS: A40 from
Haverfordwest to Fishguard. First
right after square into Hamilton
Street. First right again into Parc-y-
Shut car park. Workshop in top right
hand corner.

5/562
■ FISH/SHELLFISH

Carew Oyster Farm
Tything Barn, West Williamston, Cresselly,
Nr Kilgetty, Dyfed SA68 0TN
Tel: (01646) 651452
Fax: (01646) 651703

Oysters.
Open: Mon-Sat 8am-6pm, Sun 9am-
1pm. Closed 25 and 26 Dec, 1 Jan
Cards: No

DIRECTIONS: Carew is on A4075.
West Williamston signposted by
bridge in village. Oyster Farm 1 mile
past picnic site for Carew Castle and
Tidal Mill.

5/563
■ WINE

Cwm Deri Vineyard
Martletwy, Narberth, Dyfed SA67 8AP
Tel: (01834) 891274

Wine, meads and country fruit wine.
Open: Easter to end Sept 12 noon-
5pm. Closed Wed. Oct-Dec & Mar
Sat-Sun 12 noon-5pm. Closed
Jan/Feb
Cards: Visa

DIRECTIONS: Drive westwards off
A4075 at Cross Hands (signposted
Martletwy). In 2 miles fork left at
cottages (signposted Lawrenny). Turn
right into lane after ½ mile. Vineyard
400 yards.

5/564
■ FRUIT/VEGETABLES

Greenmeadow Mushroom Farm
Greenmeadow, Bush Lane, Templebar
Road, Kilgetty, Dyfed SA68 0RB
Tel: (01834) 813190

Fresh mushrooms.
Open: Mon-Fri 8am-5pm, Sat-Sun
8am-1pm. Closed 24-26 Dec and ½
days on other bank hols
Cards: No

DIRECTIONS: From village of
Pentlepoir (A478 Kilgetty-Tenby
Road) take turn into Templebar Road.
½ mile, first turn right into Bush
Lane.

5/565
● CERAMICS

Begelly Pottery
Shipping Farm, Begelly, Kilgetty,
Dyfed SA68 0XB
Tel: (01834) 811204

Stoneware pots, kitchenware to
tableware and flower pots and vases
Open: Mar-Oct daily 9.30am-5.30pm.
Sat 9am-12 noon. During winter
telephone first
Cards: Access, Visa

DIRECTIONS: Signposted on A478
between Tenby and Narberth.

5/566
● FORGEWORK
E B Owen & Son
Forgemill Works, Templeton, Narberth,
Dyfed SA67 8SG
Tel: (01834) 860452

An old established village blacksmiths
shop that specialises in ornamental
and architectural ironwork or
anything delicate and difficult.
Open: 9am-5pm Mon-Fri
Cards: No

DIRECTIONS: On the A478 road in
the village of Templeton midway
between Tenby and Narberth.

5/567
● TEXTILES
Studio in the Church
Login, Whitland, Dyfed SA34 0XA
Tel: (01437) 563676

Mohair shawls, ruanas, stoles, hats
and scarves. Ceramics, brooches, silk
and silver art.
Open: Mon-Fri 10am-5pm but
advisable to telephone first in winter
months
Cards: Access, Visa

DIRECTIONS: Studio signs on A478
Tenby to Cardigan road near
Efailwen. From Whitland, 7 miles
north of A40 via Henllan Amgoed and
Cwmmiles.

5/568
● NEEDLECRAFTS
Glenys Sida
Cysgod-y-Garn, Mynachlogddu,
Clynderwen, Dyfed SA66 7RY
Tel: (01994) 419631

Painting and drawing, pictures in
collage, appliqué and embroidery.
Open: Mon-Sun 9am-6pm
Cards: No

DIRECTIONS: Take A478 towards
Cardigan, after Efailwen turn left at
junction Cross Inn and VG Petrol and
supermarket, to Mynachlogddu.
About 3 miles to village turn right at
T-junction towards Crymych. Large
white house, first on left set back from
the road.

5/569
■ FLOUR
Y Felin (St Dogmaels)
Mill Street, St Dogmaels, Cardigan,
Dyfed SA43 3DY
Tel: (01239) 613999

Range of stoneground flours. Tours
of the mill. Tearoom.
Open: Mill: Mon-Sat 10am-5.30pm.
Sun 2pm-5.30pm. Tearoom: Mon-Fri
10.30am-5.30pm, Sun 2pm-5.30.
Closed Sat and Nov to Easter
Cards: No

DIRECTIONS: Take A487 from
Cardigan over river Teifi. 1st right
B4546 for St Dogmaels. On entering
village take 2nd left. Mill is 50 yards
on left-hand side.

5/570
● WOOD
Old Forge Crafts
Alltybont, Llanglydwen, Whitland,
Dyfed SA34 0XP
Tel: (01994) 419241

Hand-carved Welsh lovespoons.
Clocks, plates, pot stands and wood-
turning.
Open: Easter-end Sept Mon-Fri
10am-5pm. Winter by appointment
only
Cards: No

DIRECTIONS: 3 miles east of A478
Tenby to Cardigan road at Efailwen
on right approaching Llanglydwen.

5/571
● CERAMICS
Michael and Carol Francis Ceramics
Llandre, Llanfyrnach, Crymych,
Dyfed SA35 0DA
Tel/Fax: (01239) 831657

Blue and white stoneware ceramics.
Open: Easter-end Sept Mon-Fri
10am-4.30pm. Closed bank hols
Cards: Access, Visa

DIRECTIONS: 9 miles south of
Cardigan near Crymych off A478.

5/572
■ PRESERVES

Wendy Brandon Preserves
Felin Wen, Boncath, Dyfed, SA37 0JR
Tel: (01239) 841568
Fax: (01239) 841746

Chutneys, pickles, fruit mustards, marmalades, jams, fruit vinegars, flavoured oils.
Open: Mon-Fri 9am-5pm, Sat 9am-12noon. Closed 24 Dec to 2 Jan
Cards: No

DIRECTIONS: 4 miles south of Cardigan on A478. Turn left into Boncath and in village centre turn right signed to Bwlchygroes. 1 mile down the road on right by stream.

5/573
■ CHEESE

Caws Cenarth
Fferm Glyneithinog, Pontseli, Boncath, Dyfed SA37 0LH
Tel: (01239) 710432

Welsh farmhouse cheese.
Open: All reasonable hours, advisable to telephone first
Cards: No

DIRECTIONS: At Newcastle Emlyn take Penrherber road, continue to first crossroads, turn right then through next crossroads, and left at next crossroads. Continue ¼ mile to farm entrance on right. Farm is approx 3½ miles from Newcastle Emlyn.

5/574
■ CHEESE

Penbryn Cheese
Ty Hen, Sarnau, Llandysul, Dyfed SA44 6RD
Tel: (01239) 810347

Penbryn cheese.
Open: Mon-Sat 12 noon-5pm
Cards: No

DIRECTIONS: Take A487 Cardigan to Aberystwyth road. 8 miles north of Cardigan turn left for Penbryn. Just above church.

5/575
■ PRESERVES

Welsh Rarebit Products
Penbontbren Hotel, Glynarthen, Cardigan, Dyfed SA44 6PE
Tel: (01239) 810248
Fax: (01239) 811129

Preserves, honey and mustards.
Open: 9am-6pm
Cards: Access, Amex, Diners, Visa

DIRECTIONS: South from Aberystwyth on A487. Take first left after Sarnau (signposted Penbontbren). North on A487 from Cardigan take second right about 1 mile after Tanygroes.

5/576
■ SMOKED PRODUCE

Rhydlewis Trout Farm & Smokery
Rhydlewis, Llandysul, Dyfed SA44 5QS
Tel/Fax: (01239) 851224

Smoked salmon and trout; also fresh trout.
Open: No set hours, but usually in
Cards: No

DIRECTIONS: Just off B4334 from Henllan north west of Rhydlewis village. Signposted to Smokery from B4334. In lane opposite Nant y Breni farm.

5/577
■ CHEESE

Welsh Farmhouse Cheese
Felin Gernos, Maesllyn, Llandysul, Dyfed SA44 5NB
Tel: (01239) 858841

Unpasteurised cheeses, Caerphilli, plain smoked and flavoured Cheddar.
Open: Open all hours, best to telephone in advance
Cards: No

DIRECTIONS: Turn off the A486 at Croeslan signposted Maesllyn. 9 miles south from the A487 main coast road Fishguard to Bangor. Take 1st left off the minor road straight over minor crossroad.

5/578
■ CHEESE

Teifi Cheese
Glynhynod, Ffostrasol, Llandysul,
Dyfed SA44 5JY
Tel: (01239) 851528

Farmhouse cheeses made from
unpasteurised, raw cows' milk. Also
flavoured with nettles, seaweed,
cumin seed and chives. Raw Jersey
butter.
Open: Daily 9am-6pm
Cards: No

DIRECTIONS: Off A486 5 miles
north-west of Llandysul.

5/579
■ DAIRY PRODUCE

Bryn Cerdin Farm Produce
Capel Cynon, Llandysul, Dyfed SA44 4TJ
Tel: (01239) 851371

Jersey cream, butter and buttermilk.
Open: Summer daily except Mon,
winter weekends only
Cards: No

DIRECTIONS: North from
Llandysul, 1 mile past village of
Ffostrasol. Farm drive on right, well
signposted.

5/580
■ CHEESE

Pen-y-Bont Goat Cheese
Mount Pleasant, Pen-y-Bont, Carmarthen,
Dyfed SA33 6PP
Tel: (01994) 484315

Hard goats' cheese.
Open: By appointment only
Cards: No

DIRECTIONS: Leave B4299 for Pen-
y-Bont, through village, up hill and
turn left.

5/581
■ MEAT/POULTRY/GAME

Quail World
Penrhiwllan, Llandysul, Dyfed SA44 5NR
Tel: (01559) 370105

Quail, quail eggs, pies, pâté, smoked
quail and quail eggs.

Open: Daily 9am-6pm
Cards: No

DIRECTIONS: Between Newcastle
Emlyn and Llandysul. Phone for
directions.

5/582
■ MEAT/POULTRY/GAME

Albert Rees
HS 15 Market Precinct, Carmarthen,
Dyfed SA31 1QZ
Tel: (01267) 231204

Hams, bacon and sausages.
Open: Tue-Sat 9am-5pm
Cards: No

DIRECTIONS: Near clock tower.

5/583
● FURNITURE

M & J Billington Pine Furniture & Gifts
1 Wind Street, Llandysul, Dyfed SA44 4LZ
Tel: (01559) 362393

Pine furniture from wood reclaimed
from old chapels.
Open: Mon-Sat 9.30am-5.30pm.
Closed Sun and bank hols
Cards: Access, Visa

DIRECTIONS: 18 miles north of
Carmarthen. On right of main street
through Llandysul on one-way
system.

5/584
■ FISH/SHELLFISH

Fish on the Quay
Cadwgan Place, Aberaeron,
Dyfed SA46 0BU
Tel: (01545) 571294

Fresh fish and shellfish.
Open: Mon-Sat 8.30am-6pm. July-
Aug Sun 9.30am-4.30pm. Winter
Mon to Sat 9.45am-4.30pm
Cards: No

DIRECTIONS: In courtyard of Hive
on the Quay. On wharf between
inner and outer harbour in middle of
Aberaeron.

5/585
■ HONEY

Welsh Honey
Llys Aeron, Lampeter Road, Aberaeron,
Dyfed SA46 0ED
Tel: (01545) 570276

Welsh honey in glass and stoneware
jars.
Open: Any reasonable hour. Closed 14
days in Autumn and Christmas/New
Year
Cards: Visa

DIRECTIONS: On A452 200 yards
beyond the Welcome to Aberaeron
sign.

5/586
■ WINE

Gwinllan Ffynnon Las Vineyard
Lampeter Road, Aberaeron,
Dyfed SA46 0ED
Tel: (01545) 570234

Medium-dry wine.
Open: Apr-Oct Mon-Sat 2pm-5pm.
Otherwise by appointment
Cards: No

DIRECTIONS: On A482 Aberaeron to
Lampeter road ½ mile from town
centre.

5/587
■ FLOUR

Melin Maesdulais Watermill
Melin Maesdulais, Porthyrhyd, Carmarthen,
Dyfed SA32 8BT
Tel: (01267) 275472

Wholemeal, brown, bran and rye
flours.
Open: Daily 9am-5.30pm
Cards: No

DIRECTIONS: 4 miles west of Cross
Hands, just off B4310 between
Drefach and Porthyrhyd.

5/588
■ FISH/SHELLFISH

Teifi Valley Fish
Ty Mawr, Llanybydder, Dyfed SA40 9RE
Tel: (01570) 480789

Fresh trout, salmon, sea trout, smoked
salmon.

Open: Daily 8am-dusk
Cards: No

DIRECTIONS: 2 miles from
Llanybydder towards Llansawel on
B4337.

5/589
■ FLOUR

Felin Newydd
Crugybar, Llanwrda, Dyfed SA19 8UE
Tel: (01558) 650375

Stoneground wholemeal flour.
Open: By appointment only
Cards: No

DIRECTIONS: On A482 between
Lampeter and Llanwrda. At junction
with B4302 from Llandeilo.

5/590
■ MEAT/POULTRY/GAME

D I J Davies Butchers
Newington Shop, Chapel Street, Tregaron,
Dyfed SY25 6HA
Tel: (01974) 298976

Dry salt bacon.
Open: Tue-Sat 9am-5.30pm. Half day
Thur
Cards: No

DIRECTIONS: On A485 on right
hand side of road entering Tregaron.

5/591
● TOYS

Heather Wood Hand Puppets
Parc Lodge, Llansadwrn, Dyfed SA19 8LW
Tel: (01550) 777170

Hand puppets.
Open: By appointment only
Cards: No

DIRECTIONS: Take Llansadwrn turn
off A40 between Llandovery and
Llandeilo. Then approx 1 mile.

MAP 6

6/592
● CERAMICS
Alexander Ceramics Limited
Unit 20, Ynyscedwyn Industrial Estate,
Ystradgynlais, Powys SA9 1DT
Tel/Fax: (01639) 844072

Ceramic giftware.
Open: Mon-Fri 8am-5.30pm. Closed
Christmas-New Year
Cards: No

DIRECTIONS: 16 miles north of
Swansea on A4067 Swansea to Brecon
road. Located opposite Rugby Club in
Ystradgynlais.

6/593
■ FRUIT/VEGETABLES
Baron Jackson Welsh Mushrooms
Mushroom Farm, Bryn Road, Coychurch,
Bridgend, Mid Glamorgan CF35 5EY
Tel/Fax: (01656) 766436

Mushrooms.
Open: Mon-Fri 7.30am-3.30pm, Sun
7am-12.30pm. Closed Sat
Cards: No

DIRECTIONS: Off A473, 2 miles
from J35 of M4.

6/594
■ HONEY
Mr Lee's Honey Company
Cwm Crogau, Llanfihangel-Brynpabuan,
Llanafan Fawr, Builth Wells,
Powys LD2 3SG
Tel: (01597) 860473

Blossom, wildflower and wildwood
honey.
Open: Daily 9.30am-5.30pm but
telephone in advance
Cards: No

DIRECTIONS: Off A483 Builth Wells
to Llanwrtyd Wells road, 2 miles after
Beulah take right turn for 1½ miles.

6/595
■ CONFECTIONERY
Truffles
4-5 Church Street, Llantwit Major,
South Glamorgan CF61 1SB
Tel: (01446) 792954

Chocolates.
Open: Mon-Sat 9.30am-5pm, Sun
2pm-6pm. Closed 25 and 26 Dec
Cards: No

DIRECTIONS: Take A48 to
Cowbridge from J37 of M4. Before
Cowbridge take B4270 to Llantwit
Major. In old part of town, opposite
the monument.

6/596
■ WINE
Glyndwr Vineyard
Folly Farm, Llanblethian, Cowbridge,
South Glamorgan CF7 7JF
Tel: (01446) 774564

Red, white and rosé wines.
Open: Mon-Fri 8am-6pm
Cards: Visa

DIRECTIONS: Along A48 to
Cowbridge, turn south to Llantwit
Major. Right at Cross Inn pub and
third house on right.

6/597
● CERAMICS
Marston Pottery
Lower Cefn-Faes, Rhayader,
Powys LD6 5LT
Tel: (01597) 810875

Domestic stoneware and salt-glazed
pottery.
Open: Mon-Sat 9am-5.30pm, Sun by
arrangement. Closed 25 and 26 Dec
Cards: Access, Switch, Visa

DIRECTIONS: ¾ mile from the
centre of Rhayader, signposted from
the St Harmon turn off on the A470.

6/598
■ WINE
Cariad Wines
Llanerch Vineyard, Hensol, Pendoylan,
South Glamorgan CF7 8JU
Tel: (01443) 225877
Fax: (01443) 225546

Wine, elderflower spritz and cider.
Open: Daily 10am-5pm
Cards: Access, Visa

DIRECTIONS: 1 mile south of J34,
M4. Signposted from the junction.

6/599
■ ICE-CREAM
The Fruit Garden
Groes Faen Road, Peterston-super-Ely,
Cardiff, South Glamorgan CF5 6NE
Tel: (01446) 760358

Fruit farm with dairy ice-creams and
sorbets.
Open: June-Aug daily 9.30am-8pm
Cards: No

DIRECTIONS: In village 6 miles west
of Cardiff. AA signposted from main
roads.

6/600
■ BAKED GOODS
St Fagans Bakery (Dderwen)
Welsh Folk Museum, St Fagan, Cardiff,
South Glamorgan CF5 6XB
Tel: (01222) 569441
Fax: (01222) 578413

Bakery.
Open: Daily 10am-5pm. Closed
Christmas-New Year
Cards: No

DIRECTIONS: J33 of M4 and follow
signs to St Fagan (4 miles west of
Cardiff). Opposite the Plymouth Arms.
Past the mill within the grounds.

6/601
■ MEAT/POULTRY/GAME
Graig Farm
Dolau, Llandrindod Wells, Powys LD1 5TL
Tel/Fax: (01597) 851655

Additive-free meat, game and fish.
Open: Mon-Sat 9am-6pm
Cards: No

DIRECTIONS: On A488 Knighton to
Penybont Road. On Knighton side of
Dolau. (Sometimes marked as
Llanfihangel Rhydithon).

6/602
✱ MULTIPLE
The Hay Makers
The Courtyard, Hay-on-Wye, Hereford &
Worcester HR3 5AE
Tel: (01497) 820058

Bookbinding, furniture, pottery,
sculpture and silk painting.
Open: Jan-Mar Thur-Sat 10.30am-
1pm, 2pm-5pm, Apr-June and Oct-
Nov Mon, Wed-Sat 10.30am-1pm,
2pm-5pm, July-Sep Mon to Sat
10.30am-1pm, 2pm to 5pm. Closed
Sun
Cards: Access, Visa

DIRECTIONS: Down short passage
off High Town, opposite chemist.

6/603
● WOOD
From the Wood
Studio 6, The Craft Centre, Oxford Road,
Hay-on-Wye, Hereford & Worcester
HR3 1XX
Tel: (01497) 821355

Wood-turning, bowls, platters, vases.
Bark pictures and puzzles.
Open: 10am-5.30pm. Closed 25 Dec,
1 Jan
Cards: Access, Visa

DIRECTIONS: On A438 between
Hereford and Brecon. At top of main
town car park.

6/604
● FURNITURE
Chris Armstrong Country Furniture
Paddock House, Clifford, Hereford &
Worcester HR3 5HB
Tel: (01497) 831561

Native hardwood furniture,
ladderback and spindleback rush-
seated chairs, wooden rakes.
Open: Usually open, best to telephone
in advance
Cards: No

DIRECTIONS: On the B4352 Hay-on-Wye to Bredwardine road, ¾ mile east of the Castlefield Inn, workshop is right on the road with a sign on it.

6/605
■ FRUIT/VEGETABLES
Berryhill Farm
Coedkernew, Newport, Gwent NP1 9UD
Tel: (01633) 680827
Fax: (01633) 680907

Seasonal fruit, vegetables and plants.
Open: Apr-Oct and Dec 9.30am-7pm (depending on daylight hours). Closed Jan-Mar and Nov
Cards: Access, Visa

DIRECTIONS: Take J28 of M4. Farm on A48 between Castleton and Tredegar Park. On seaward side of road.

6/606
■ MEAT/POULTRY/GAME
C E Wells and Son
14 The Square, Clun, Craven Arms, Shropshire SY7 8JA
Tel: (01588) 640208

Beef, lamb, pork, pork pies, sausages and baked hams.
Open: Mon 8am-12 noon, Wed 8am-1pm, Tue, Thur-Sat 8am-5.30pm
Cards: No

DIRECTIONS: 9 miles west of Craven Arms (A49). 7 miles north of Knighton (A488).

6/607
■ HONEY
Gwent Vales Apiaries
Bryn-y-Pant Cottage, Upper Llanover, Abergavenny, Gwent NP7 9ES
Tel: (01873) 880625

Honey and beeswax candles.
Open: Daily 9am-9pm
Cards: No

DIRECTIONS: Off A4042, signposted to Upper Llanover.

6/608
■ FISH/SHELLFISH
Crucorney Trout Farm
Llanvihangel Crucorney, Abergavenny, Gwent NP7 7NB
Tel: (01873) 890545
Fax: (01873) 890812

Trout.
Open: Mon-Sun 9am-5pm. Closed 25 and 26 Dec
Cards: No

DIRECTIONS: Take A465 Abergavenny to Hereford road. 3 miles north of Abergavenny turn left to Llanvihangel. Turn left past Skirrid Inn. ½ mile further on right-hand side.

6/609
■ ICE-CREAM
September Dairy Products
Newhouse Farm, Almeley, Kington, Hereford & Worcester HR3 6LJ
Tel: (01544) 327561

Ice-cream, eggs, fruit, honey, cider and cream.
Open: Daily 9am-7pm. Closed 25 Dec
Cards: No

DIRECTIONS: Off A4111 take right-hand turning to Almeley 1½ miles north of Eardisley or 5 miles south of Kington.

6/610
● PAPER PRODUCTS
Christopher Marbling
14 Hereford Street, Presteigne, Powys LD8 2AR
Tel: (01544) 260466

Hand-marbled stationery, papers, albums, books and greetings cards.
Open: By appointment only
Cards: Access, Visa

DIRECTIONS: On B4356 and B4355 between Knighton and Kington. From Presteigne town centre towards Leominster, on left-hand side of Hereford Street, past Baptist Chapel.

6/611
■ MEAT/POULTRY/GAME

Upper Pant Farm
Llandewi Rhydderch, Abergavenny
Gwent NP7 9TL
Tel: (01873) 858091
Fax: (01873) 858717

Organic beef, lamb and pork.
Open: Mon-Sun 9am-5pm
Cards: No

DIRECTIONS: From junction of A40
and A465 outside Abergavenny, take
road towards Usk. After 200 yards
turn left. Take first turning left after
1½ miles.

6/612
■ ICE-CREAM

Shepherds Ice Cream
Cwm Farm, Peterchurch, Hereford &
Worcester HR2 0TA
Tel: (01981) 550716

Ice-cream from sheep's milk
Open: 10am-4pm, but telephone in
advance
Cards: No

DIRECTIONS: Take turning to
Urishay out of Peterchurch. 2nd
right, then 2nd right again.

6/613
■ CIDER

**Ben Crossman's Prime
Farmhouse Cider**
Mayfield Farm, Hewish, Nr Weston-super-
Mare, Avon BS24 6RQ
Tel: (01934) 833174

Traditional farmhouse ciders, free-
range eggs, potatoes and vegetables in
season.
Open: Mon-Sat 8.30am-6.30pm, Sun
12 noon-1pm
Cards: No

DIRECTIONS: M5 J21, 1 mile on the
A370 towards Bristol on the right.

6/614
■ CIDER AND PERRY

**Dunkertons Cider Co & the
Cider House Restaurant**
Luntley, Pembridge, Leominster,
Hereford & Worcester HR6 9ED
Tel: (01544) 388653

Ciders and perry, draught and bottled,
single apple ciders, restaurant.
Open: Mon-Sat 10am-6pm
Cards: Access, Visa

DIRECTIONS: A44 Leominster to
Pembridge, left in centre of village
(New Inn), 1 mile on left.

6/615
● CERAMICS

Pembridge Terracotta
East Street, Pembridge, Leominster,
Hereford & Worcester HR6 9HB
Tel: (01544) 388696

Hand-thrown flowerpots and
Victorian urns.
Open: Tue-Sat 9.30am-5.30pm,
summer usually also Sun-Mon
Cards: Access, Amex, Diners, Visa

DIRECTIONS: On A44 between
Leominster and Kington in the
middle of Pembridge almost opposite
the garage.

6/616
● WOOD/METAL

Paul Caton Bowl Carver
Wellspring Cottage, Deerfold, Lingen,
Bucknell, Shropshire SY7 0EE
Tel: (01568) 86607

Hand-carved bowls in British timbers,
also in marble and bronze. Also
bronze bells.
Open: Mon-Sun by appointment
Cards: No

DIRECTIONS: 10 miles west of
Ludlow, on lane midway between
Wigmore and Lingen.

6/617
● CERAMICS

Old School Pottery
Edgton, Craven Arms, Shropshire SY7 8HN
Tel: (01588) 680208

Glazed stoneware, functional and
decorative pottery.
Open: Tue-Sun 10am-6pm
Cards: No

DIRECTIONS: South of Church
Stretton on A49, turn right at
Marshbrook (B4370). At T-junction
turn left, then right after 200 yards.
Edgton is 1½ miles.

6/618
● CORACLES

Peter Faulkner Coracles
24 Watling Street, Leintwardine,
Shropshire SY7 0LW
Tel: (01547) 540629

Traditional hide-covered coracles.
Open: By appointment only
Cards: No

DIRECTIONS: On A4113, 9 miles
west of Ludlow.

6/619
■ CIDER

Richard's Cider
Corner Cottage, Smallway, Congresbury,
Nr Bristol, Avon BS19 5AA
Tel: (01934) 832054
Fax: (01934) 876646

Cider, cheese, pickles, eggs.
Open: Mon-Sat 8.30am-6.30pm, Sun
12-1.30pm
Cards: No

DIRECTIONS: Between Bristol and
Weston-super-Mare, on the A370. At
Congresbury turn on to the B3133
towards Clevedon, Corner Cottage is
approx ¼ mile on the left-hand side.

6/620
■ FARM PRODUCE

Brecon Court Deer Farm Shop
Llansoy, Nr Usk, Gwent NP5 1DT
Tel: (01291) 650366
Fax: (01291) 650555

Venison and wine.
Open: Daily 9.30am-5.30pm. Closed
bank hols
Cards: No

DIRECTIONS: Between Raglan and
B4293 near Llansoy and the Star Inn.

6/621
■ WINE

Offa's Vineyard
Old Rectory, Llanvihangel-Ystern-Llewern,
Monmouth, Gwent NP5 4HL
Tel: (01600) 85241

Licensed wine shop.
Open: Mon-Fri 2pm-5pm
Cards: No

DIRECTIONS: On B4233 Monmouth
to Abergavenny road, turn left at
Penrhos signpost. First left then 500
yards.

6/622
■ MEAT/POULTRY/GAME

Hereford Duck Company
Trelough House, Wormbridge, Hereford &
Worcester HR2 9DH
Tel: (01981) 570767
Fax: (01981) 570577

Trelough ducks, also breasts, legs,
eggs, sausages, pâté-de-foie.
Open: Thur and Fri 10am-6pm, Sat
9am-4pm. Otherwise by appointment
Cards: No

DIRECTIONS: On A465 Hereford to
Abergavenny Road, 8 miles south-
west of Hereford. Turn left at
Wormbridge sign, then immediately
right. 3rd drive on left.

6/623
● LEATHER GOODS

The Glanarrow Box Company
Glanarrow Mill, Eardisland, Nr Leominster, Hereford & Worcester HR6 9BY
Tel: (01544) 388403
Fax: (01544) 388581

Hand-stitched leather trunks, cases and boxes.
Open: By appointment only
Cards: No

DIRECTIONS: 5 miles west of Leominster on way to Kington.

6/624
■ FOOD HAMPERS

Tavernors
Yew Tree House, Lucton, Nr Leominster, Hereford & Worcester HR6 9PJ
Tel/Fax: (01568) 780384

Hampers packed with British foods and wines.
Open: Advisable to telephone first
Cards: Access, Amex, Diners, Visa

DIRECTIONS: ¼ mile south-east of Lucton School.

6/625
● FISHING

Graham Trout Flies Ltd
Eastcombe, Garway, Hereford & Worcester HR2 8RE
Tel: (01600) 84288
Fax: (01600) 84380

Trout and salmon flies.
Open: Mon-Sat 9am-5pm. Closed Christmas
Cards: Access, Visa

DIRECTIONS: Just off A466 Monmouth to Hereford Road. 6 miles out of Monmouth on left.

6/626
■ DAIRY PRODUCE

Alvis Bros Ltd
Lye Cross Farm Redhill, Bristol, Avon BS18 7RH
Tel: (01934) 862320

Farmhouse Cheddar cheese and home-produced pork.

Open: Mon-Fri 8am-5.30pm, Sat 8am-12.30pm. Closed bank hols
Cards: No

DIRECTIONS: On A38 Bristol to Burnham-on-Sea road. 2 miles past Bristol Airport. Past Darling Arms (on right) and as approaching bottom of hill entrance is on left.

6/627
● PLANTS

Queenswood Garden Centre
Wellington, Hereford & Worcester HR4 8BB
Tel: (01432) 830880
Fax: (01432) 830833

Local plants, produce and garden furniture.
Open: Daily 9am-5.30pm. Closed 25-26 Dec, 1 Jan and Easter Day
Cards: Access, Amex, Switch, Visa

DIRECTIONS: 5 miles north of Hereford on A49 (Leominster road).

6/628
● FORGEWORK

Sam Thompson Blacksmiths
The Forge, Downes's Yard, 10 South Street, Leominster, Hereford & Worcester HR6 8JB
Tel: (01568) 614140

Handmade ironwork, window frames, fire places, door furniture, gates, brackets, tie bars.
Open: Mon-Fri 9.30am-5.30pm, best to telephone in advance
Cards: No

DIRECTIONS: In yard up alley next door to Black Horse pub opposite Sydonia leisure centre and swimming pool.

6/629
■ MEAT/POULTRY/GAME

Newhall Ostrich Farm Ltd
Pwllmeyric, Chepstow, Gwent NP6 6LF
Tel: (01291) 629352
Fax: (01222) 888976

Ostrich meat, feathers and hides.
Open: Mon-Sat 8am-6pm. Closed bank hols. Telephone for appointment
Cards: No

DIRECTIONS: Telephone for directions. West of Chepstow opposite New Inn pub.

6/630
■ FARM PRODUCE

Green Acres Organic Growers
Green Acres, Dinmore, Hereford & Worcester HR4 8ED
Tel: (01568) 797045

Meat, poultry, wine, cider, vegetables, fruit and preserves.
Open: Tue-Sat 9am-5.30pm, Sun and Mon by arrangement. Closed 25 Dec-1 Jan
Cards: No

DIRECTIONS: On A49 6 miles north of Hereford and 6 miles south of Leominster on south side of Dinmore Hill.

6/631
● JEWELLERY

Wood Yard Gallery
Wood Yard, off Corve Street, Ludlow, Shropshire SY8 2PX
Tel: (01584) 874959

Silver and gold jewellery, silver giftware.
Open: Mon-Fri 10am-5pm, Sat by appointment only. Closed 24 Dec-3 Jan and bank hols
Cards: Visa

DIRECTIONS: From the traffic lights at top of Corve Street, Wood Yard is the first alleyway on the right past the Feathers Hotel in the centre of Ludlow.

6/632
■ DELICATESSEN FOODS

G & P Roser
Coleford Road, Tutshill, Chepstow, Gwent NP6 7DJ
Tel: (01291) 622063

Sausages, pies, bread, wine, game, fish, cheese, butter.
Open: Mon-Fri 8am-5.30pm except Wed 8am-1pm. Sat 8am-4pm. Closed Christmas
Cards: No

DIRECTIONS: Take A48 from Chepstow to Gloucester. Take left turn to Tutshill. Turn right at 2 mini-roundabouts on to Coleford Road. 2nd building on right next to Cross Keys pub.

6/633
■ WINE

Tintern Parva Vineyards
Parva Farm, Tintern, Gwent NP6 6SQ
Tel: (01291) 689636

Dry white, medium dry and rosé wines.
Open: Daily 10am-6pm
Cards: No

DIRECTIONS: From Chepstow, pass Tintern Abbey on right. Vineyard signposted from Wye Valley Hotel. Turn off as if into car park, continue up lane. Vineyard at top.

6/634
● TEXTILES

Woodstock House Craft Centre
Woodstock House Brimfield, Nr Ludlow, Shropshire SY8 4NY
Tel: (01584) 711445

Jackets and waistcoats, patchwork and quilting, craft holidays.
Open: Mon-Sat 9am-5.30pm. Closed Jan
Cards: No

DIRECTIONS: On A49 4 miles south of Ludlow and 7 miles north of Leominster.

6/635
■ WINE

Bodenham English Wines
Broadfield Court Estate, Bodenham, Hereford & Worcester HR1 3LG
Tel: (01568) 797483
Fax: (01568) 797859

Wines.
Open: May-Sept Mon-Sat 11am-4.30pm, Oct-Apr Mon-Sat 10am-4pm, variable closures
Cards: No

DIRECTIONS: On A417, 2 miles from A49 junction signposted Broadfield Vineyard.

6/636
● HERBS

Arne Herbs
Limeburn Nurseries, Chew Magna, Bristol,
Avon BS18 8QW
Tel: (01275) 333399

Herbs and rare plants (some toxic).
Open: Most days 10am-5pm, but best
to telephone in advance
Cards: No

DIRECTIONS: 300 yards north of the
B3130 on the west side of Chew
Magna, approach via crossroads on
B3130 taking unclassified road
signposted Bishopsworth.

6/637
● TOYS

Wood-U-Like Bears
30 Red House Lane, Westbury-on-Trym,
Bristol, Avon BS9 3RZ
Tel: (01179) 629465
Fax: (01179) 593514

Mechanical collectors' bears from
9cm to 19cm, dressed or in fur.
Open: Telephone for appointment.
Mon-Fri 9am-5pm. Closed Christmas
Cards: No

DIRECTIONS: Follow A4018 from
J17 of M5, to Westbury-on-Trym. At
end of dual carriageway turn right at
4th set of traffic lights, then 5th
turning on right opposite playing
fields.

6/638
● CERAMICS

McCubbins
The Pottery, East Street, St Briavels,
Lydney, Gloucestershire GL15 6TQ
Tel: (01594) 530297

Domestic stoneware pottery and
silver/gold jewellery.
Open: Easter-Christmas Thur-Mon
10am-1pm, 2pm-5pm. Christmas-
Easter Sat-Sun 10am-1pm, 2pm-5pm
Cards: No

DIRECTIONS: 6 miles south of
Monmouth. Turn left at Bigsweir
bridge to St Briavels. Opposite playing
fields.

6/639
● CIDER AND PERRY

Franklins Cider Farm
The Cliffs, Little Hereford, Nr Ludlow,
Shropshire SY8 4LW
Tel: (01584) 810488

Cider and perry.
Open: 9am-6.30pm
Cards: No

DIRECTIONS: 3 miles from Tenbury
Wells on the A456 to Ludlow on the
edge of the village of Little Hereford.
Opposite a large lay-by.

6/640
■ SAUSAGES

Felix van den Burghe
40 High Street, Westbury-on-Trym, Bristol,
Avon BS9 3DZ
Tel: (0117) 950 9484

Sausages.
Open: Daily 5am-6.30pm. Closed
bank hols
Cards: No

DIRECTIONS: 100 yards from main
post office.

6/641
■ DAIRY PRODUCE

Woonton Court Farm
Woonton Court, Leysteps, Leominster,
Hereford & Worcester HR6 0HL
Tel: (01568) 750232

Guernsey milk and cream. Free-range
eggs.
Open: Daily: 8am-9pm
Cards: No

DIRECTIONS: On A49 1 mile from
Leominster turn right on A4112 for 3
miles. Turn right to Woonton and
follow lane for ½ mile through farm
buildings.

6/642
● PLANTS
Burford House Gardens
Burford House, Tenbury Wells, Hereford &
Worcester WR15 8HQ
Tel: (01584) 810777
Fax: (01584) 810673

Treasures Plant Centre, the National
Clematis Collection, Pen-y-Wern
Craft Gallery and shop, and the
Buttery Restaurant. Art, craft and
gardening courses run throughout the
year.
Open: 10am until dusk. Closed 25
Dec and 1 Jan
Cards: Access, Visa

DIRECTIONS: Between
Kidderminster and Leominster on the
A456, 1 mile west of Tenbury Wells.

6/643
● PLANTS
Blackmore & Langdon Ltd
Stanton Nurseries, Pensford, Bristol,
Avon BS18 4JL
Tel: (01275) 332300

Begonias and delphiniums, phlox,
aquilegia, gloxinias, polyanthus.
Open: Mon-Sun 9am-5pm
Cards: No

DIRECTIONS: On B3130 south of
Bristol, between Pensford on A37 and
Bristol Airport on the A38.

6/644
● FORGEWORK
Almondsbury Forge Works Ltd
Sundays Hill, Almondsbury, Bristol,
Avon BS12 4DS
Tel: (01454) 613315
Fax: (01454) 613303

Brassware, fire grates and accessories,
gates and railings.
Open: Mon-Fri 9am-4.30pm, Sat
9.30am-4pm. Closed 24 Dec-7 Jan
Cards: Access, Visa

DIRECTIONS: Take A38 Bristol to
Gloucester, ¼ mile from M4/M5
interchange at Almondsbury, left over
lane, right into Sundays Hill, on next
left bend.

6/645
■ FARM PRODUCE
The Kitchen Garden
Old Down House, Tockington, Bristol,
Avon BS12 4PG
Tel: (01454) 413605
Fax: (01454) 413955

Home-produced dairy ice-cream,
jams, honey, chutney, cakes, meats.
Open: Summer Tue-Sun 10am-6pm,
Winter Tue-Sun 10am-4pm. Closed
bank hols
Cards: Access, Visa

DIRECTIONS: Follow signs to
Oldown with county park logo from
roundabout at M4 J21 or from A38 at
Alveston.

6/646
● CERAMICS
Bridget Drakeford Porcelain
Upper Buckenhill Farmhouse, Fownhope,
Hereford & Worcester HR1 4PU
Tel: (01432) 860411

Hand-thrown decorative porcelain:
bowls, vases, teapots, lamps.
Open: Mon-Fri 10am-5pm.
Otherwise telephone for
appointment. Closed 25 Dec-2 Jan
Cards: No
DIRECTIONS: On B4224 2 miles out
of Fownhope village towards Ross-
on-Wye.

6/647
● SADDLERY GOODS
A T Veater and Son
6 Station Road, Clutton, Nr Bristol,
Avon BS18 4RD
Tel: (01761) 452460

Master saddler.
Open: Mon-Sun 9am-5.30pm. Closed
Wed
Cards: No

DIRECTIONS: 2nd turning on left
opposite bus shelter in centre of
village.

6/648
■ HONEY

Teme Valley Honey Farm
Sutton House Farm, Sutton, Tenbury Wells,
Hereford & Worcester WR15 8RJ
Tel: (01584) 810424

Honey, honeycomb and beeswax products.
Open: Reasonable hours, but telephone first
Cards: No

DIRECTIONS: On side of B4214 Tenbury/Bromyard road. 2 miles from Tenbury on right.

6/649
✴ MULTIPLE

Wobage Farm Pottery Workshops
Wobage Farm, Upton Bishop, Nr Ross-on-Wye, Hereford & Worcester HR9 7QP
Tel: (01989) 780233

Crafts, furniture, jewellery, pottery, woodcarving.
Open: Sat-Sun 10am-5pm, otherwise by appointment
Cards: No

DIRECTIONS: 4 miles north-east of Ross-on-Wye. On B4224 ¼ mile from Moody Cow pub going towards Hereford.

6/650
■ MEAT/POULTRY/GAME

Hicks Gate Farm Shop
Hicks Gate Farm, Keynsham, Bristol, Avon BS18 2AB
Tel: (0117) 9867753

Sausages, home-cooked hams, turkeys.
Open: Daily 8am-8pm
Cards: No

DIRECTIONS: On A4 Bristol to Bath road. Take road to Keynsham; signposted from roundabout.

6/651
● GARDEN ORNAMENTS

Forest Stonecraft
Yew Tree Cottage, Bradley Hill, Soudley, Nr Cinderford, Gloucestershire GL14 2UQ
Tel: (01594) 824823
Fax: (01594) 824317

Garden stoneware and indoor ornaments from small animals to water features.
Open: Mon-Sun 9am-5pm. Closed Christmas week
Cards: No

DIRECTIONS: Follow sign to Soudley and Dean Heritage Museum from A48 at Blakeney. Through village to end of houses, turn left, ¼ mile left again to clearing in woods, take left fork to very end house (4th).

6/652
● CERAMICS

Jack and Joan Doherty Ceramics
Hooks Cottage, Lea Bailey, Ross-on-Wye, Hereford & Worcester HR9 5TY
Tel: (01989) 750644

Hand-thrown porcelain pots, raku-fired sculptural animal forms.
Open: Telephone in advance
Cards: No

DIRECTIONS: Off A40 Gloucester to Ross road, at Lea Village. Take road signposted to Micheldean, then road on right signposted to Drybrook. After ½ mile pottery on right.

6/653
■ CIDER AND PERRY

Lyne Down Cider
Lyne Down Farm, Much Marcle, Ledbury, Hereford & Worcester HR8 2NT
Tel/Fax: (01531) 660691

Traditional farmhouse cider and perry.
Open: Mon-Sun 9am-5pm, but best to telephone in advance. Closed Christmas to Easter
Cards: No

DIRECTIONS: Between Ross-on-Wye and Ledbury on the A449. Signposted on the main road.

6/654
■ CIDER

H Westons and Sons Ltd
The Bounds, Much Marcle, Ledbury,
Hereford & Worcester HR8 2NQ
Tel: (01531) 660233
Fax: (01531) 660619

Cider.
Open: Mon-Fri 9am-4.30pm, Sat
10am-1pm
Cards: Access, Visa

DIRECTIONS: From J2 take the
Ledbury A417, then take the Ross-on-
Wye road A449 into Much Marcle.
Turn right ¼ mile on right.

6/655
● TOYS

Jim Edmiston Toys
Unit 15C, Church Farm, Corston, Bath,
Avon BA2 9EX
Tel: (01225) 874772
Fax: (01225) 460186

Painted wooden toys, from badges,
boxes, jigsaws and mobiles to larger
pieces.
Open: Mon-Fri 10am-5pm by
appointment
Cards: No

DIRECTIONS: On A4 Bath to Bristol
road, 2 miles west of Bath, at Globe
pub roundabout. Follow signs to
Corston. Take second right to Church
Farm.

6/656
■ CIDER

Tony Cullimore's Services
Berkeley Heath Farm, Berkeley,
Gloucestershire GL13 9EW
Tel: (01453) 810220
Fax: (01453) 811987

Farmhouse cider and honey, country
wines and potatoes.
Open: winter Mon-Fri 8am-5pm, Sat
8.30am-1pm, summer Sat-Sun
10.30am-5pm also. Closed holidays in
winter
Cards: No

DIRECTIONS: On the B4066
between Berkeley and the A38.

6/657
■ CIDER AND PERRY

Summers' Cider & Perry
Slimbridge Lane, Halmore, Berkeley,
Gloucestershire GL13 9HH
Tel: (01453) 811218

Ciders and perrys.
Open: Mon-Sat 9am-1pm, 2pm-6pm
Cards: No

DIRECTIONS: On edge of village of
Halmore which is approx 2 miles west
of Prince of Wales hotel on A38.

6/658
■ WINE

English and Country Fruit Wines
St Anne's Vineyard, Oxenhall, Nr Newent,
Gloucestershire GL18 1RW
Tel: (01989) 720313

Wine from grapes, elderflower,
tayberry.
Open: Mar-Dec Wed-Fri 2pm-7pm,
Sat 10am-7pm, Sun 12 noon-3pm,
bank hols 10am-7pm, Jan-Feb by
appointment
Cards: No

DIRECTIONS: 2 miles along
Horsefair Lane off A4221 Ross road
just north of Newent. Take B4215
from Gloucester which links with
B4221 at Newent, or J3, M50 take
B4221.

6/659
● PLANTS

Rushfields of Ledbury
Ross Road, Ledbury, Hereford &
Worcester HR8 2LP
Tel: (01531) 632004

Herbaceous plants and shrubs,
geraniums.
Open: Wed-Sat 11am-5pm
Cards: Access, Amex, Visa

DIRECTIONS: 400 yards from bypass
roundabout on A449 Ross road.

6/660
● CERAMICS

Homend Pottery
205 The Homend, Ledbury, Hereford &
Worcester HR8 1BS
Tel: (01531) 634571

Hand-thrown decorated creamware
pots. Bread crocks, bowls, lampbases,
clocks, jugs and vases.
Open: Tue-Sat 10.30am-5pm. Closed
Wed pm
Cards: Access, Visa

DIRECTIONS: Workshop on main
street towards Hereford, 500 yards
from centre of town, just past cottage
hospital.

6/661
● PLANTS

Wintergreen Nurseries
Bringsty, Worcester, Hereford &
Worcester WR6 5UJ
Tel: (01886) 821858

Hardy plants, unusual herbaceous and
alpine plants and conifers.
Open: Mar-Oct Wed-Sun 10am-
5.30pm, other times by appointment
Cards: No

DIRECTIONS: On A44 12 miles west
of Worcester, 3 miles east of
Bromyard.

6/662
● CERAMICS

English Country Pottery
Station Road, Wickwar, Wotton-under-
Edge, Gloucestershire GL12 8NB
Tel: (01454) 299100
Fax: (01454) 294053

Hand-painted pottery, mugs, jugs,
vases, lampbases.
Open: Mon-Fri 8.30am-4.30pm,
closed end July-early Aug and over
Christmas
Cards: No

DIRECTIONS: On Kingswood to
Wotton-under-Edge road, just out of
Wickwar High Street, past traffic
lights on the left.

6/663
■ FARM PRODUCE

Taynton Farm Shop
Taynton, Gloucestershire GL19 3AW
Tel: (01452) 790220

Cakes, pies, quiches, pastries, ducks
and chickens.
Open: Daily 9am-6pm. Closed 25 and
26 Dec, 1 Jan
Cards: No

DIRECTIONS: 2 miles on B4216
Taynton to Newent Lane at Huntley.

6/664
● JEWELLERY

Newent Silver & Gold
15 Broad Street, Newent,
Gloucestershire GL18 1AQ
Tel: (01531) 822055

Jewellery in gold, silver and platinum.
Open: Mon-Sat 9.15am-1pm, 2pm-
5pm. Closed Wed at 1pm, also 25
Dec-1 Jan
Cards: Access,Visa

DIRECTIONS: Newent town centre,
4 miles off M50 J3, or follow signs
from Gloucester via A40 and B4215 –
about 9 miles.

6/665
● GLASS

The Glassbarn
31 Culver Street, Newent,
Gloucestershire GL18 1DB
Tel/Fax: (01531) 821173

Glassmaker and gallery.
Open: Tue-Fri 10am-12.30pm,
1.30pm-5pm, Sat 10am-12.30pm
Cards: Access, Visa

DIRECTIONS: In centre of Newent
(which is 9 miles north-west of
Gloucester) take B4261 towards
Huntley, 100 yards on the right.

6/666
■ WINE

Three Choirs Vineyards
Newent, Gloucestershire GL18 1LS
Tel: (01531) 890223
Fax: (01531) 890877

Wines, restaurant, tastings. Tours by
appointment.
Open: Mon-Sun 10am-5.30pm.
Closed 25 Dec-1 Jan
Cards: Access, Switch, Visa

DIRECTIONS: Follow tourist signs
from Newent.

6/667
■ WINE
Coddington Vineyard
Coddington, Nr Ledbury, Hereford &
Worcester HR8 1JJ
Tel: (01531) 640668

Dry and medium-dry white wines.
Vineyard and gardens open by
appointment.
Open: Daylight hours, closed last 2
weeks in November
Cards: No

DIRECTIONS: From Ledbury take
B4214. After railway bridge turn right.
1½ miles to T-junction, turn right
and first left. 1½ miles to T-junction
turn left then first left ('Woofields').
Vineyard on right.

6/668
■ BAKED GOODS
Hobbs House Bakery
39 High Street, Chipping Sodbury, Bristol,
Avon BS17 6BA
Tel: (01454) 321629
Fax: (01454) 329757

Bread, confectionery, sandwiches,
pasties, sausage rolls, marmalades and
jams.
Open: Mon-Sat 8am-6pm
Cards: No

DIRECTIONS: Opposite the Old
Grammar School.

6/669
■ CHEESE
Smarts' Traditional Gloucester Cheeses
Old Ley Court, Chapel Lane, Birdwood,
Churcham, Gloucestershire GL2 8AR
Tel: (01452) 750225

Single or Double Gloucester cheese.
Open: Mon 2pm-5pm, Tue-Thur
9am-5pm, Fri 9am-1pm

Cards: No
DIRECTIONS: From Gloucester take
A40 to Birdwood. Chapel Lane is on
left immediately before Mobil garage.
Follow lane approx ½ mile. Farm is
on left.

6/670
● TEXTILES
Roger Oates Country Weavers
The Long Barn, Eastnor, Ledbury, Hereford
& Worcester HR8 1EL
Tel: (01531) 632718
Fax: (01531) 631361

Textiles, fashion and home
accessories.
Open: Mon-Sat 11am-5pm. Closed 25
Dec-1 Jan
Cards: Access, Visa

DIRECTIONS: 2 miles from centre of
Ledbury on A438 Ledbury to
Tewkesbury road.

6/671
■ FISH/SHELLFISH
Severn & Wye Smokery
Walmore Hill, Minsterworth,
Gloucestershire GL2 8LA
Tel: (01452) 750777
Fax: (01452) 750776

Fresh and smoked wild salmon.
Open: Mon-Sat 8.30am-5.30pm
Cards: No

DIRECTIONS: On A48 Gloucester to
Chepstow road between
Minsterworth and Westbury on
Severn. Opposite Walmore Hill
primary school.

6/672
● PLANTS
The Picton Garden
Old Court Nurseries, Colwall, Malvern,
Hereford & Worcester WR13 6QE
Tel: (01684) 540416

Michaelmas daisies and herbaceous
perennials.
Open: Apr-Oct Wed-Sun 10am-1pm,
2.15pm-5.30pm, Sept-Oct; by
appointment
Cards: No

DIRECTIONS: In Colwall village on B4218 (Walwyn Road), between Malvern and Ledbury.

6/673
■ CIDER AND PERRY
Norbury's Cider Company
The Farm Buildings, Holywell, Storridge, Nr Malvern, Hereford & Worcester WR13 5HD
Tel: (01886) 832206

Cider, perry and fruit wines, walnuts for pickling (July), fruits in season.
Open: Any reasonable hours. Closed 25 Dec
Cards: No

DIRECTIONS: 7 miles from Worcester, 20 miles from Hereford on A4103 Worcester to Hereford road, signposted to The Norrest and Crowcroft.

6/674
■ MEAT/POULTRY/GAME
Goodman's Geese
Walsgrove Farm, Great Witley, Hereford & Worcester WR6 6JJ
Tel: (01299) 896272
Fax: (01299) 896889

Free-range geese and turkeys.
Open: May-mid June Mon-Fri 10am-6.30pm. Mid-June/July Mon-Fri 9am-6.30pm
Cards: No

DIRECTIONS: In village on B4203 Bromyard Road. Follow signs.

6/675
● WOOD
Lark Designs
206 High Street, Batheaston, Avon BA1 7QZ
Tel: (01225) 852143

Stationery and cards, clocks, decorated mirrors, bookends, flying mobiles, cat and duck shapes.
Open: By appointment
Cards: No

DIRECTIONS: On A4 east of Bath, towards Chippenham.

6/676
● TEXTILES
Colin Squire and Janice Williams
Sheldon Cottage, Epney, Saul, Gloucestershire GL2 7LN
Tel: (01452) 740639

Commemorative and ecclesiastical embroidered furnishings, hand-woven furnishings, decorative hangings.
Open: Mon-Sun 9.30am-5.30pm by appointment
Cards: No

DIRECTIONS: 2 miles from A38 at Moreton Valence. The left-hand drive by Dangerfield farm.

6/677
● PLANTS
Chris Pattison
Brookend, Pendock, Gloucestershire GL19 3PL
Tel: (01531) 650480

Shrubs and alpines, Japanese maples, gentians and dwarf shrubs.
Open: Mon-Fri 9am-5pm, including bank hols. Closed Christmas week
Cards: No

DIRECTIONS: Take A417 from J2 on M50, towards Gloucester, 2nd left, nursery 1 mile on the left.

6/678
● MUSICAL INSTRUMENTS
Lionel K Hepplewhite Violin, Viola and Cello Maker
Soundpost Workshop, 8 North End Lane, Malvern, Hereford & Worcester WR14 2ES
Tel: (0684) 562203

Hand-crafted violins, violas and cellos.
Open: By appointment
Cards: No

DIRECTIONS: From Worcester to Malvern on A449 turn on to B4208, after 2 miles, on left. From South, 1 mile from Barnards Green turn right at traffic lights on to B4208; 200 yards on left.

6/679
● MUSICAL INSTRUMENTS
Hibernian Violins
24 Players Avenue, Malvern, Hereford &
Worcester WR14 1DU
Tel: (01684) 562947

Stringed musical instruments,
especially violin and viol family.
Open: Mon-Fri 9am-5pm
Cards: No

DIRECTIONS: Take A449 from
Worcester. Enter Malvern and turn
right at first pedestrian crossing (Lr
Howsell Road), take 4th left.

6/680
● PLANTS
**Eastgrove Cottage Garden
Nursery**
Sankyns Green, Little Witley, Hereford &
Worcester WR6 6LQ
Tel: (01299) 896389

Nursery, hardy plants, flower garden.
Open: Apr-July Thur-Mon 2pm-5pm;
Sept-14 Oct Thur-Sat 2pm-5pm
Cards: No

DIRECTIONS: On road between
Shrawley (B4196) and Great Witley
on A443. 8 miles north of Worcester.

6/681
■ WINE
Tiltridge Vineyard
Upper Hook Road, Upton-on-Severn,
Hereford & Worcester WR8 0SA
Tel: (01684) 592906
Fax: (01684) 594142

White wines.
Open: Mon-Sat 11am-6pm, Sun &
bank hols 12 noon-5.30pm. Closed
25-26 Dec
Cards: No

DIRECTIONS: Turn down New
Street in centre of Upton-on-Severn
and take the left fork after ½ mile.
Vineyard on left soon after crossing
old railway bridge.

6/682
● TEXTILES
Margaretha Bruce-Morgan
Guarlford Court, Guarlford, Malvern,
Hereford & Worcester WR13 6NX
Tel: (01684) 564211

Handwoven, rugs, coverlets, drapes,
table runners, cushions.
Open: By appointment
Cards: No

DIRECTIONS: On B4211 2 miles out
of Malvern, opposite Church.

6/683
■ WINE
Astley Vineyard
Astley, Stourport-on-Severn, Hereford
& Worcester DY13 0RU
Tel/Fax: (01299) 822907

White wines.
Open: Mon-Sat 10am-5pm, Sun
12 noon-5pm
Cards: No

DIRECTIONS: Just off B4196 Holt
Heath to Stourport-on-Severn road,
at the southern end of Astley. Take
Crundles Lane opposite brown
heritage sign, vineyard 300 yards on
right.

6/684
■ PRESERVES
Farthing Fayre
Farthings, The Street, Horsley, Nailsworth,
Gloucestershire GL6 0PU
Tel: (01453) 834937

Olives, chutneys, fruit vinegars,
flavoured olive oils.
Open: 10am-4pm, but telephone first
Cards: No

DIRECTIONS: Opposite village stores
car park.

6/685
■ CIDER AND PERRY
Hartland's Farmhouse Cider
Tirley Villa, Tirley,
Gloucestershire GL19 4HA
Tel: (01452) 780480

Farmhouse cider (dry, medium and
sweet), perry.

Open: Mon-Sat 9am-6pm, Sun 9am-1pm
Cards: No

DIRECTIONS: On A417 turn right on to B4211. After 2 miles turn right on to the B4213. 1 mile on turn right towards Tirley Court: Tirley Villa is first house on right.

6/686
● PLANTS

R F Beeston
294 Ombersley Road, Worcester,
Hereford & Worcester WR3 7HD
Tel: (01905) 453245

New and unusual alpine plants.
Open: March-Oct Wed-Fri 10am-1pm, 2pm-5pm else by appointment. Closed Nov-Feb
Cards: No

DIRECTIONS: Turn off A449 400 yards north of Worcester. Follow signs to Bevere Green, continuing beyond No Through Road sign (right fork), nursery 400 yards on right.

6/687
● PLANTS

The Botanic Nursery
Atworth, Melksham, Wiltshire SN12 3NU
Tel: (01225) 706597
Fax: (01225) 700953

Lime-tolerant plants and perennials.
Open: Wed-Mon 10am-1pm, 2pm-5pm, telephone first in Jan
Cards: Access, Visa

DIRECTIONS: Centre of Atworth village on main A365 (by clock tower); 9 miles east of Bath.

6/688
● HERBS

Selsley Herb Shop
4 George Street, Nailsworth,
Gloucestershire GL6 0AG
Tel: (01453) 833118
Fax: (01453) 753674

Culinary and fragrance gift products.
Open: Mon-Sat 9.30am-5pm
Cards: Access, Visa

DIRECTIONS: Overlooking clock tower in centre of Nailsworth on A46 3 miles south of Stroud.

6/689
● CERAMICS

The Pottery
Rooksmoor Mills, Bath Road, Stroud,
Gloucestershire GL5 5ND
Tel/Fax: (01453) 873322

Handmade and painted pottery.
Open: Mon-Sun 10am-4pm
Cards: Access, Visa

DIRECTIONS: On A46, 1 mile south of Stroud.

6/690
■ MEAT/POULTRY/GAME

Checketts of Ombersley
Ombersley, Nr Droitwich, Hereford & Worcester WR9 0EW
Tel: (01905) 620284

Sausages, meat, poultry and game.
Open: Tue-Fri 8am-1pm, 2pm-5.30pm, Sat 8am-5pm. Closed bank hols
Cards: No

DIRECTIONS: Off the A449 between Worcester and Kidderminster; opposite church in village.

6/691
■ CHEESE

Ansteys of Worcester
Broomhall Farm, Kempsey,
Worcester WR5 2NT
Tel/Fax: (01905) 820232

Cheese-makers.
Open: Mon-Sat 9am-5.30pm
Cards: No

DIRECTIONS: Situated off A38 2 miles south of Worcester just before village of Kempsey.

6/692
● PLANTS

Stone House Cottage Nurseries
Stone, Nr Kidderminster, Hereford & Worcester DY10 4BG
Tel/Fax: (01562) 69902

Climbers, wall shrubs and unusual plants. Garden open.
Open: Mar-Oct Wed-Sat 10am-6pm and some Sundays
Cards: No

DIRECTIONS: 2 miles south-east of Kidderminster on A448, turn next to Stone church.

6/693
● CERAMICS

Hookshouse Pottery
Westonbirt, Tetbury, Gloucestershire GL8 8TZ
Tel: (01666) 880297

Hand-thrown stoneware, individual pieces, domestic ware and frost-proof garden pots.
Open: Daily 10am-6pm. Closed 25 Dec
Cards: Visa

DIRECTIONS: 2 miles south-west of Tetbury from Bath along A433. Turn left at Hare and Hounds hotel. After 150 yards sign at small crossroads.

6/694
● WOOD

Painswick Woodcraft
3 New Street, Painswick, Gloucestershire GL6 6XH
Tel: (01452) 814195

Domestic hand-turned woodware, lamps, bowls, mirrors and vases.
Open: Mar-Dec Tue-Sat 9.30am-5pm, mid-Jan-Feb Tue-Sat 9.30am-4pm, bank hols and Mon in Aug 10am-5pm
Cards: Access, Visa

DIRECTIONS: Close to the traffic lights on the A46 Bath to Stroud road in Painswick. Opposite Painswick Pharmacy and next door to Painswick Newsagents.

6/695
● LEATHER GOODS

MacGregor and Michael
37 Silver Street, Tetbury, Gloucestershire GL8 8DL
Tel: (01666) 502179

Hand-stitched leather goods, attaché cases, briefcases, bags, belts, boxes, luggage.
Open: Mon-Fri 9am-6pm. Closed 1pm-2pm. Sat by appointment
Cards: No

DIRECTIONS: On B4014 Tetbury to Malmesbury road, at the bottom of hill on right, just past the Green, just before a bridge on the edge of Tetbury.

6/696
■ MEAT/POULTRY/GAME

Tetbury Traditional Meats
31 Church Street, Tetbury, Gloucestershire GL8 8JG
Tel: (01666) 502892

Angus beef, pies, dry-cured bacon, sausages, smoked chicken, Gloucester ham and salami.
Open: Tue-Thur 8am-5.30pm. Fri 8am-6pm, Sat 8am-3pm. Closed bank hols and first week of Jan
Cards: No

DIRECTIONS: Take J16 of M4. Take A46 to Tetbury. Opposite church.

6/697
● PLANTS

Cowcombe Farm Herbs
Gipsy Lane, Chalford, Stroud, Gloucestershire GL6 8HP
Tel: (01285) 760544

Herb and wildflower nursery. Native trees and cottage garden plants.
Open: Easter-end Sept Wed-Fri 2pm-5pm, Sat-Sun 10am-5pm. Closed Oct to Easter except Dec
Cards: No

DIRECTIONS: Just off A419 6 miles from Stroud, by Aston Down Airfield. Signposted from main road.

6/698
● PLANTS

Hoo House Nursery

Hoo House, Gloucester Road, Tewkesbury,
Gloucestershire GL20 7DA
Tel: (01684) 293389

Alpine and herbaceous perennials.
Open: Mon-Sat 2pm-5pm
Cards: No

DIRECTIONS: On A38 2 miles south
of Tewkesbury, on southbound side
of dual carriageway between Odessa
pub and Hoo garage.

6/699
● PLANTS

Old Manor Nursery

Twyning, Gloucestershire GL20 6DB
Tel: (01684) 293516

Alpines, herbaceous perennials.
Open: Mar-Oct Mon only 2pm-5pm
(or dusk if earlier) including bank hols
Cards: No

DIRECTIONS: Leave M50 at J1. Turn
left at Twyning sign, ½ mile on Old
Manor gate is on left-hand side.

6/700
● TOYS

Toys for Children

Prospect Hill, Stourbridge,
West Midlands, DY8 1PN
Tel/Fax: (01384) 378725

English hardwood toys: farm animals,
buildings, vehicles, wildlife animals,
nativity.
Open: Mon-Fri 9am-1pm Sat 10am-
1pm. Advisable to telephone first,
particularly in July-Aug
Cards: No

DIRECTIONS: Left off Hagley Road
(A491) into Union Street. Next left
into Prospect Hill. Halfway up hill on
left at end of driveway.

6/701
■ WINE

Crickley Windward Vineyard

Peak View Farm, Green Lane, Little
Witcombe, Gloucestershire GL3 4TX
Te/Fax: (01452) 863555

White and rosé wines.
Open: Tue-Sat 12 noon-5.30pm.
Closed 25 Dec-Easter
Cards: No

DIRECTIONS: Off A417 through
Birdlip village and down Birdlip Hill.

6/702
● LIME WASH

The Traditional Lime Company

Church Farm, Leckhampton, Cheltenham,
Gloucestershire GL51 5XX
Tel: (01242) 525444
Fax: (01242) 237727

Lime putties, mortars, plasters,
renders and lime wash.
Open: Mon-Fri 8am-6pm. Closed
bank hols and Christmas to New Year
Cards: No

DIRECTIONS: On A4070 from
Cheltenham towards Birdlip and
Cirencester. Turn right at Malvern
Inn on Leckhampton Hill. Past Sue
Ryder Home and church on left.
Right into yard past dairy.

6/703
● FORGEWORK

Nigel B King, Blacksmith and Engineer

285 Old Bath Road, Cheltenham,
Gloucestershire GL53 9AJ
Tel: (01242) 524274

Wrought ironwork: gates, balustrades.
Open: Mon-Fri 8am-1pm, 2pm-
5.30pm, but telephone first
Cards: No

DIRECTIONS: Take the
Leckhampton road out of
Cheltenham towards Birdlip on to the
Old Bath Road, The Forge is next
door to the Wheatsheaf pub.

6/704
■ CIDER
Tilley's Farmhouse Cider
Moat Farm, Malleson Road, Gotherington,
Nr Cheltenham, Gloucestershire GL52 4ET
Tel: (01242) 676807

Cider.
Open: Mon-Fri 8am-8pm
Cards: No

DIRECTIONS: Between Cheltenham
and Evesham off the A435, 3 miles
from Cheltenham and 10 miles from
Evesham.

6/705
● CERAMICS
Conderton Pottery
The Old Forge, Conderton, Nr Tewkesbury,
Gloucestershire GL20 7PP
Tel: (01386) 725387

Salt-glazed stoneware, oven-to-table,
kitchen and garden pots.
Open: Mon-Fri 9am-5.30pm. Closed
25, 26 Dec
Cards: Access, Visa

DIRECTIONS: In village of
Conderton, 10 miles north of
Cheltenham off A435 Cheltenham to
Evesham road. Brown signpost at
Teddington-Hands roundabout
A435/A438.

6/706
● CERAMICS
Daub & Wattle (Ceramics) Ltd
5 Windsor Street, Bromsgrove, Hereford &
Worcester B61 8HG
Tel: (01527) 574004

Pottery mugs, bowls, vases, house
numbers, oil burners and larger
pottery pieces.
Open: Tue-Sat 9.30am-5.30pm, mid-
Nov-24 Dec Mon-Sat 9.30am-
5.30pm
Cards: Access, Visa

DIRECTIONS: On A38 Birmingham-
Droitwich road, in centre of
Bromsgrove at rear of the High Street
opposite the car park.

6/707
● CERAMICS
Craft Pottery
Westernville, Kemble, Cirencester,
Gloucestershire GL7 6AW
Tel: (01285) 770651

Handmade domestic stoneware,
terracotta pots. Goats' milk and herb
plants.
Open: Mon-Sun 9am-7pm
Cards: No

DIRECTIONS: Between A433
Cirencester to Tetbury and A429
Cirencester to Malmesbury roads.
Opposite Kemble railway station
(booking office side).

6/708
✱ MULTIPLE
Brewery Arts
Brewery Court, Cirencester,
Gloucestershire GL7 1JH
Tel: (01285) 657181

Candles, ceramics, furniture, baskets,
textiles, jewellery, leather, knitwear,
forgework, embroidery, silkscreen
printing.
Open: Mon-Sat 10am-5pm. Advisable
to telephone for appointment. Closed
bank hols
Cards: No

DIRECTIONS: 50 yards from Market
Place.

6/709
✱ MULTIPLE
Winchcombe Pottery
Broadway Road, Winchcombe,
Cheltenham, Gloucestershire GL54 5NU
Tel: (01242) 602462

Wood-fired stoneware pottery,
frames, plants, sculpted pieces,
furniture.
Open: Mon-Fri 8am-5pm, Sat 10am-
4pm and May-Sept also Sun 12 noon-
4pm. Closed Good Friday and
Christmas
Cards: Access, Visa

DIRECTIONS: 1 mile north of
Winchcombe on Broadway road
(B4632 was A46).

MAP 7

7/710
● TOYS

Rocking Horse Stable
Cotwall End Countryside and Craft Centre,
Catholic Lane, Sedgley, Dudley,
West Midlands DY3 3YE
Tel: (01902) 887657

Hand-carved wooden rocking-horses
and carousel animals, refreshments.
Open: Apr-Sept daily 9am-6.30pm,
Oct-Mar daily 9am-4.30pm. Closed
25 Dec
Cards: No

DIRECTIONS: At Sedgley, turn off
the A459 into Gospel End Street, left
into Snady Fields Road (brown tourist
sign). Turn left into Cotwall End
Road, and left into Catholic Lane.

7/711
■ FISH/SHELLFISH

Preston Mill Trout Farm
Preston Mill, Cirencester,
Gloucestershire GL7 6ET
Tel: (01285) 653924

Fresh and smoked trout, smoked
trout pâté.
Open: Mon-Sat 9am-5.30pm. Closed
25-26 Dec, 1 Jan, Easter
Cards: No

DIRECTIONS: 1 mile south-east of
Cirencester. Off A419 Siddington/
South Cerney Road.

7/712
● FURNITURE

Paul Spriggs, Woodcraftsman and Rushworker
The Croft, Silver Street, South Cerney,
Cirencester, Gloucestershire GL7 5TR
Tel: (01285) 860296

Rush-seated chairs in English
hardwoods.
Open: By appointment
Cards: No

DIRECTIONS: Leave Cirencester by
A419, after ½ mile turn right off dual
carriageway to South Cerney.The
Croft is 3rd bungalow on the left as
you enter the village.

7/713
● FORGEWORK

Harry Green, Blacksmith
The Smithy, Dunnington, Nr Alcester,
Warwickshire B49 5NN
Tel: (01789) 490125

Ornamental ironwork, restoration and
forgework.
Open: Mon-Sat 9am-5pm
Cards: No

DIRECTIONS: Between Alcester and
Evesham, turn off A435 towards
Broom and Bidford. The forge is
opposite the telephone box.

7/714
● GARDEN FURNITURE

Barnsley House GDF
Barnsley House, Barnsley, Nr Cirencester,
Gloucestershire GL7 5EE
Tel: (01285) 740561
Fax: (01285) 740628

Teak garden furniture and bespoke
work.
Open: Mon-Fri 9.30am-5.30pm, Sat
10.30am-5.30pm
Cards: Access, Visa

DIRECTIONS: In Barnsley village on
B4425, 4 miles north-east of
Cirencester.

7/715
● PLANTS

Cotswold Garden Flowers
Sands Lane, Badsey, Evesham, Hereford &
Worcester WR11 6BS
Tel/Fax: (01386) 47337

Unusual perennials.
Open: Mar-Sept Mon-Fri 8am-5pm,
Sat-Sun 10am-6pm. Oct-Feb Mon-
Fri 8am-4.30pm
Cards: No

DIRECTIONS: Take Wickhamford
road out of Badsey village. Sands Lane
is last road on left (signposted).
Nursery ½ mile after tarmac stops.

7/716
● BASKETS

The Basket Maker

Main Street, South Littleton, Evesham,
Hereford & Worcester WR11 5TJ
Tel: (01386) 830504

Baskets in willow and cane.
Open: Mon-Fri 9am-5.30pm, Sat
9am-2pm, other times by
arrangement
Cards: No

DIRECTIONS: On B4085 Badsey to
Bidford on Avon road, 3 miles north-
east of Evesham, in main street.

7/717
■ MEAT/POULTRY/GAME

Kite's Nest Farm

Broadway, Hereford & Worcester WR12 7JT
Tel: (01386) 853320
Fax: (01386) 853621

Organic free-range beef.
Open: Please telephone first. Closed
25 Dec
Cards: No

DIRECTIONS: From Broadway
(where A44 and B4632 meet) follow
road to Snowshill for 1 mile. Farm
sign on left.

7/718
● POULTRY

Domestic Fowl Trust

Honeybourne, Nr Evesham, Hereford &
Worcester WR11 5QJ
Tel: (01386) 833083
Fax: (01386) 833364

Birds, chicks and hatching eggs,
housing and feedstuffs.
Open: Daily 10.30am-5pm. Closed Fri
Cards: Access, Visa

DIRECTIONS: From Broadway turn
right at Willersey follow brown tourist
signs. From Evesham follow brown
tourist signs from bypass.

7/719
● CERAMICS

Hilary LaForce Ceramics

25 Mill Lane, Broom, Alcester,
Warwickshire B50 4HF
Tel: (01789) 778515

Decorative terracotta pots.
Open: Telephone for appointment
Cards: No

DIRECTIONS: 7 miles from
Stratford-upon-Avon on road to
Evesham.

7/720
✱ MULTIPLE

Manor Farm Craft Centre

Wood Lane, Earlswood, Solihull, West
Midlands B94 5JH
Tel/Fax: (01564) 702729

Farm shop, ice-cream, upholstery,
cushions, ceramics, stained glass,
dried flowers, curtains, bedspreads,
print-making.
Open: Tue-Sun 10am-5pm. Advisable
to telephone
Cards: No

DIRECTIONS: Off B4102 Solihull to
Redditch road. Follow tourist board
signs in Earlswood. Near Red Lion
pub.

7/721
● PLANTS

Fibrex Nurseries Ltd

Honeybourne Road, Pebworth, Stratford-
upon-Avon, Warwickshire CV37 8XT
Tel: (01789) 720788
Fax: (01789) 721162

Hedera (ivies), hardy ferns and
pelargoniums.
Open: Sept-Nov, Jan-Mar Mon-Fri
12 noon-5pm, Apr-Aug Tue-Sun
12 noon-5pm. Closed Dec
Cards: No

DIRECTIONS: B4035 from Evesham
to Honeybourne, straight on at
crossroads, nurseries on left on
approach to Pebworth.

7/722
● CERAMICS

Louise Darby
Clay Barn, Redhill, Alcester,
Warwickshire B49 6NQ
Tel: (01789) 765214

Hand-thrown stoneware and
porcelain, individual ceramics.
Open: By appointment
Cards: No

DIRECTIONS: 4 miles west of
Stratford-upon-Avon on A46. Look
for Stag Inn on left, workshop in
Redhill farmyard next to pub. 20
minutes from J15 of M40.

7/723
● FURNITURE

Oxleys Furniture
Lapstone Barn, Chipping Campden,
Gloucestershire GL55 6UR
Tel: (01386) 840466
Fax: (01386) 840455

Hand-welded aluminium furniture to
nineteenth-century designs.
Open: Mon-Sat 9am-5pm. Sun by
appointment. Closed Christmas
Cards: Access, Diners, Switch, Visa

DIRECTIONS: Take Stow road out of
Chipping Campden. 1 mile up hill
turn left to Lapstone Barn. 150 yards
down drive. Barn on left.

7/724
● SILVERWARE

The Guild of Handicraft
The Guild, Sheep Street, Chipping
Campden, Gloucestershire GL55 6DS
Tel: (01386) 841100

Gold and silversmiths.
Open: Mon-Fri 9am-5pm, Sat 9am-
12 noon
Cards: No

DIRECTIONS: In Sheep Street off the
High Street, about 50 yards from the
corner on the right.

7/725
● SILVERWARE

Robert Welch Studio Shop
Lower High Street, Chipping Campden,
Gloucestershire GL55 6DY
Tel: (01386) 840522
Fax: (01386) 841111

Cutlery, lighting, kitchenware,
candlesticks and tableware.
Open: Mon-Sat 9.30am-5.30pm, Sun
11am-5pm. Closed 25-26 Dec
Cards: Access, Visa

DIRECTIONS: A44 Oxford to
Worcester road, through Moreton-in-
Marsh. After about 5 miles turn right
to Chipping Campden. On corner of
High Street and Sheep Street.

7/726
● JEWELLERY

Ann Smith Goldsmith
Peacock House, 16 Lower High Street,
Chipping Campden,
Gloucestershire GL55 6DY
Tel: (01386) 840879

18ct gold jewellery.
Open: Telephone first, but usually
Mon-Fri 9am-5pm
Cards: No

DIRECTIONS: Opposite St
Catherine's Church at Broadway end
of High Street.

7/727
● PLANTS

John Beach (Nursery) Ltd
Tamworth Lane, Henley-in-Arden,
Warwickshire B96 5QY
Tel: (01789) 840529
Fax: (01789) 841520

Producers of clematis and climbers,
fruit trees, plants and ornamental
trees.
Open: Mon to Sat 10am-5pm, but
telephone first
Cards: Access, Amex, Diners, Switch,
Visa

DIRECTIONS: Off A3400, north of
Henley-in-Arden.

7/728
● CERAMICS

Torquil Pottery
81 High Street, Henley-in-Arden,
Warwickshire B95 5AT
Tel: (01564) 792174

Hand-thrown pots in stoneware and
porcelain.
Open: Mon-Sat 10am-6pm. Closed
bank hols
Cards: Access, Visa

DIRECTIONS: Henley-in-Arden
High Street is on the A3400, 8 miles
north of Stratford-upon-Avon.

7/729
● PLANTS

H Woolman Ltd
Grange Road, Dorridge, Solihull,
West Midlands B93 8QB
Tel: (01564) 776283
Fax: (01564) 770830

Chrysanthemums, rooted cuttings.
Open: Mon-Fri 7.30am-4.30pm
Cards: Access, Visa

DIRECTIONS: J4 of M42, A3400 to
Stratford, 1st left (Gate Lane) to end
then left into Four Ashes Road to end
then, right 100 yards entrance on
right. Opposite Railway Inn.

7/730
● CLOTHES

**Jenny Edwards-Moss (Jem
Designs)**
4 Brewery Yard, Sheep Street, Stow-on-the-
Wold, Gloucestershire GL54 1AA
Tel: (01451) 870194

Brocade and silk jackets, matching
skirts, shoes and hats.
Open: Mon-Sat 9.30am-5pm. Closed
bank hols
Cards: Access, Visa

DIRECTIONS: Brewery Yard is off
Sheep Street (A436).

7/731
● WOOD

**Julian Stanley Woodcarving
and Furniture**
Unit 5, The Sitch, Longborough, Moreton-
in-Marsh, Gloucestershire GL56 0QJ
Tel/Fax: (01451) 831122

Carved period furniture and
sculptures.
Open: By appointment, variable
holidays
Cards: No

DIRECTIONS: Turn off the A429
between Stow-on-the-Wold and
Moreton-in-Marsh to Longborough
village. Third set of industrial
buildings on the left.

7/732
● TAXIDERMY

Natural Craft Taxidermy
21 Main Street, Ebrington, Nr Chipping
Campden, Gloucestershire GL55 6NL
Tel: (01386) 593231

Victorian, modern, decorative
taxidermy. Also collectors' curios and
unusual items.
Open: By appointment only
Cards: Access, Visa

DIRECTIONS: From Chipping
Campden take B4035 to Shipston.
Turn left to Ebrington. In middle of
village opposite Home Farm.
Signposted at gate.

7/733
● PAPER PRODUCTS

Comfort Farm Crafts
Comfort Farm, Clifford Chambers,
Stratford-upon-Avon,
Warwickshire CV37 8LW
Tel/Fax: (01789) 292163

Quilling (rolled paper filigree)
workshop.
Open: By appointment
Cards: No

DIRECTIONS: 2 miles south of
Stratford-upon-Avon, turn off
Stratford-Oxford A4300 on to B4632,
signposted Broadway/Clifford
Chambers. Past village on left, past

Wayside nurseries on right. Farm drive next left.

7/734
✳ MULTIPLE
Middleton Hall Craft Centre
Middleton, Nr Tamworth,
Warwickshire B78 2AE
Tel: (01827) 283095

Water-colours, sculptures, upholstery, toys, woodcraft, garden furniture, silversmith, pine furniture, dried flowers, textiles, picture frames.
Open: Wed-Sun 11am-5pm
Cards: No

DIRECTIONS: Between The Belfry and Drayton Manor Park on A4091. Follow brown tourist signs.

7/735
● CERAMICS
Old Bell Pottery
High Street, Lechlade,
Gloucestershire GL7 3AD
Tel: (01367) 252608

Garden pottery.
Open: Mon-Sun 9.30am-dusk
Cards: Access, Visa

DIRECTIONS: In centre of Lechlade village.

7/736
■ BAKED GOODS
The Flour Bag
Burford Street, Lechlade,
Gloucestershire GL7 3AP
Tel: (01367) 252322

Traditional breads and patisserie.
Open: Mon-Sat 8am-6pm. Closed 25, 26 Dec and Easter
Cards: No

DIRECTIONS: On main street in centre of Lechlade village.

7/737
■ DELICATESSEN FOODS
The Marsh Goose Fine Foods
High Street, Moreton-in-Marsh,
Gloucestershire GL56 0AX
Tel: (01608) 652111

Home-produced range of delicatessen products.
Open: Mon-Sat 9.30am-5.30pm. Closed bank hols
Cards: Access, Amex, Switch, Visa

DIRECTIONS: Opposite War Memorial in High Street.

7/738
■ SMOKED PRODUCE
Minola Smoked Products
Kencot Hill Farmhouse, Filkins, Lechlade,
Gloucestershire GL7 3QY
Tel: (01367) 860391
Fax: (01367) 860544

'Oak log'-smoked fish, poultry and meat.
Open: Mon-Fri 8am-6pm. Sat 9am-5pm. Sometimes Sun. Closed 25 Dec
Cards: Access, Visa

DIRECTIONS: Take A361 from Burford to Lechlade. Approx 8 miles from Burford look for blue bin-liners tied to posts at end of Farm Lane on left. At top of lane.

7/739
● WOOD
Burford Woodcraft
144 High Street, Burford,
Oxfordshire OX18 4QU
Tel: (01993) 823479

Hand-crafted items made in solid wood, from light pulls and yo-yos to lamps and furniture.
Open: Mon-Sat 9.15am-5.15pm, Sun 1.45pm-4.45pm. Closed Sun, Christmas to Easter
Cards: Access, Switch, Visa

DIRECTIONS: Near the war memorial, just off the A40.

7/740
● FORGEWORK

F C Harriss & Sons
The Forge, Sturt Farm Industrial Estate,
Sturt Farm, Burford, Oxfordshire OX8 4ET
Tel/Fax: (0993) 822122

Manufacture and repair of traditional
wrought ironwork.
Open: 8am-5pm Mon-Fri. 8am-
12 noon Sat. Closed all usual bank
hols and one week at Christmas
Cards: No

DIRECTIONS: Off Witney bypass to
Windmill Restaurant roundabout.
Follow A40 towards Burford 2nd
turning on left, just past layby
(industrial estate signposted).

7/741
● KNITWEAR

The Maggie White Knitwear Company Ltd
45 High Street, Burford,
Oxfordshire OX18 4QA
Tel: (01993) 822600
Fax: (01993) 822533

Knitwear.
Open: Mon-Fri 9.30am-5.30pm
Cards: Access, Amex, Diners, Switch,
Visa

DIRECTIONS: Towards the bottom
of Burford High Street on the right.

7/742
● WOOD

Carol & Peter Moss Woodcarvers
The Knapp, Armscote, Stratford-upon-
Avon, Warwickshire CV37 8DH
Tel: (01608) 682247

Woodcarvings, gift items, furniture.
Open: 10am-6pm but telephone for
appointment
Cards: No

DIRECTIONS: Off A3400 Stratford to
Oxford road at Newbold on Stour.
Near the Waggon Wheel pub.

7/743
● PLANTS

Jackson's Nurseries
Clifton Campville, Nr Tamworth,
Staffordshire B79 0AP
Tel: (01827) 373307

Fuchsias, summer bedding plants,
vegetable plants, Christmas pot plants.
Open: Mon, Wed-Sat 9am-1pm, 2pm-
6pm. Sun 10am-1pm, 2pm-5pm.
Closed Tue, 25-26 Dec, 1 Jan, bank
hols 10am-1pm
Cards: No

DIRECTIONS: M42 J11 take B5493
(A453) Tamworth, 1½ miles, No
Mans Heath turn right, 2 miles
Clifton Campville, nursery on the
hill.

7/744
■ WINE

Edby Wines
Castle Vineyard, Blackbourton Road,
Bampton, Oxfordshire OX18 2PE
Tel: (01993) 842028

Wines and vines.
Open: Sat 10am-dusk, Sun 12 noon-
dusk, also summer evenings until
dusk. Closed Christmas
Cards: No

DIRECTIONS: Take the Clanfield
Road out of Bampton. Follow sign to
Blackbourton. Vineyard is 1 mile on
left.

7/745
● FURNITURE

David E. Bennett
The Villa, Swinbrook Road, Carterton,
Oxfordshire OX18 1DT
Tel: (01993) 841158

Wood-turning, chairs and cabinets.
Windsor and rush-seated chairs and
stools in native timbers.
Open: By appointment only
Cards: No

DIRECTIONS: North of Carterton,
towards end of Swinbrook Road on
right.

7/746
● MUSICAL INSTRUMENTS

Paul Fischer Luthier
West End Studio, West End, Chipping
Norton, Oxfordshire OX7 5EY
Tel: (01608) 642792

Handmade concert guitars from
baroque to present day.
Open: Mon-Fri 9am-5.30pm
Cards: No

DIRECTIONS: 500 yards from town
centre on B4450.

7/747
✳ MULTIPLE

**Oxfordshire Craft Guild
Marketing Co-Operative**
7 Goddards Lane, Chipping Norton,
Oxfordshire OX7 5NP
Tel: (01608) 641525

Ceramics, jewellery, pewterwork,
stained glass and textiles.
Open: Tue-Sat 10am-5pm. Closed
most bank hols; phone for
confirmation
Cards: Access, Amex, Diners, Visa

DIRECTIONS: In town centre next to
the theatre.

7/748
● CERAMICS

Whichford Pottery
Whichford, Nr Shipston on Stour,
Warwickshire CV36 5PG
Tel: (01608) 684416
Fax: (01608) 684833

Terracotta flowerpots from seed pans
to baroque urns.
Open: Mon-Fri 9am-5pm, Sat 10am-
4pm. Closed 25 Dec-4 Jan
Cards: No

DIRECTIONS: In village, off main
road between Shipston on Stour and
Chipping Norton.

7/749
● CERAMICS

Jan Bunyan Ceramics
4 Bridge Road, Butlers Marston,
Warwickshire CV35 0NE
Tel: (01926) 641560

Oven-proof tableware.
Open: Mon-Fri 10am-5.30pm, other
times by appointment
Cards: No

DIRECTIONS: 1 mile south-west of
Kineton on Kineton-Halford road, 4
miles from J12 of M40.

7/750
● CERAMICS

Furnace Lane Pottery
Unit 7, Furnace Lane, Moira, Swadlincote,
Derbyshire DE12 6AT
Tel: (01283) 552218

Hand-thrown, wood-fired pots,
teapots, jugs, bowls, mugs and
casseroles.
Open: Mon-Thur 9.30am-5pm, Fri
9.30am-3pm. Closed 24 Dec-2 Jan
Cards: No

DIRECTIONS: Moira is 3 miles west
of Ashby de la Zouch. Access to the
workshop is via Furnace Lane from
the B5003.

7/751
● BAROMETERS

Peter Wiggins Restoration
Raffles Farm, Southcombe, Chipping
Norton, Oxfordshire OX7 5QH
Tel: (01608) 642652

Mercurial barometers.
Open: Mon-Sat 9am-6pm
Cards: No

DIRECTIONS: From Chipping
Norton, take the London road (east).
Opposite garage on A34.

7/752
■ BAKED GOODS
Meg Rivers Cakes
Middle Tysoe, Warwickshire CV35 0SE
Tel: (01295) 688101
Fax: (01295) 680799

Rich fruit, seed and madeira cakes.
Also wedding and Christmas cakes
and puddings.
Open: 10am-4pm. Closed 24 Dec-
5 Jan
Cards: Access, Amex, Switch, Visa

DIRECTIONS: Halfway between
Banbury and Stratford-upon-Avon.
Take A422, turn off to Tysoe. In
centre of village opposite Peacock
pub, under two large beech trees.

7/753
■ PRESERVES
Shaken Oak Products
Shaken Oak Farm, Hailey, Witney,
Oxfordshire OX8 5UX
Tel: (01993) 868398

Mustard and preserves.
Open: Sat-Sun and bank hols (except
Christmas) 10am-6pm, and by
appointment
Cards: No

DIRECTIONS: On B4022 north of
Witney. Turn right after Hailey
towards New Yatt. At next crossroads,
straight across. Farm is up lane at next
fork.

7/754
● FURNITURE
Martin Dodds Country Furniture
Spelsbury Road, Charlbury,
Oxfordshire OX7 3LP
Tel: (01608) 810944

Furniture made from English
hardwoods, elm especially.
Open: Mon-Sat 10am-6pm. Closed
bank hols, 25-26 Dec
Cards: No

DIRECTIONS: On the B4026
between Chipping Norton and
Charlbury – 1 mile from Charlbury.

7/755
● WOOD
Swanalong
Middle Farm, Taston, Charlbury,
Oxfordshire OX7 3JL
Tel: (01608) 811072

Painted wood items for the home.
Open: By appointment Mon-Sat
9.30am-5.30pm. Closed Christmas to
New Year
Cards: Access, Visa

DIRECTIONS: Take A3400 Oxford to
Stratford-upon-Avon road. Turn left
at Enstone on B4022 to Charlbury.
Second right for Taston. Opposite
village stone cross.

7/756
■ BAKED GOODS
Take Two Cooks
Rosello, Harbury, Leamington Spa,
Warwickshire CV33 9JD
Tel: (01926) 612417

Continental-style patisserie.
Open: Phone orders daily 9am-5pm
Cards: No

DIRECTIONS: Near village hall in
Harbury.

7/757
✳ MULTIPLE
Ferrers Centre for Arts & Crafts
Staunton Harold, Ashby de la Zouch,
Leicestershire LE65 1RU
Tel: (01332) 863337

Musical instruments, ceramics,
clothes, textiles, furniture, models.
Open: Tue-Sun 11am-5pm (4.30pm
in winter). Advisable to telephone
Cards: Access, Visa

DIRECTIONS: Off B587 3 miles
south of Melbourne. Follow signs
into Staunton Harold (private estate).

7/758
✳ MULTIPLE
The Mill Workshop
The Mill, Hardwick, Witney,
Oxfordshire OX8 7QE
Tel/Fax: (01865) 300407

Silverware and jewellery.
Open: By appointment but Mon-Fri
9am-5pm
Cards: Access, Visa

DIRECTIONS: 3 miles south of
Witney off A415. Left to Stanton
Harcourt, then left again immediately
into Hardwick. On the only corner in
village.

7/759
● FORGEWORK
P Giannasi
The Close, High Street, South Newington,
Nr Banbury, Oxfordshire OX15 4JN
Tel: (01295) 720703

Wrought iron and decorative
metalwork. Wood-turning using
native woods; bowls a speciality.
Open: All reasonable hours, but best
to telephone in advance
Cards: No

DIRECTIONS: On the A361 6 miles
south-west of Banbury heading
towards Chipping Norton. Turn left
into village opposite Wykham Arms
pub and turn right at church into
High Street.

7/760
● NEEDLECRAFTS
Traditional Cottage Crafts
Sinclair, Avon Dassett, Leamington Spa,
Warwickshire CV33 0AL
Tel: (01295) 690362

Smocking, patchwork, embroidery.
Open: By appointment only
Cards: No

DIRECTIONS: Off A4100 Banbury to
Warwick road, 7 miles north of
Banbury. Turn right into Avon
Dassett. In centre of the village next to
the reading room.

7/761
■ HEALTH FOODS
Ryton Organic Gardens Shop
Ryton-on-Dunsmore, Coventry,
Warwickshire CV8 3LG
Tel: (01203) 303517
Fax: (01203) 639229

Organic foods and breads.
Open: 9am-5.30pm. Closed 25-27 Dec
Cards: Access, Visa

DIRECTIONS: Signposted on A45,
8 miles south of Coventry near
Wolston.

7/762
● LEATHER GOODS
Bosworth Crafts
23 Main Street, Market Bosworth,
Nuneaton, Warwickshire CV13 0JN
Tel: (01455) 292061

Hand-carved leather goods and gifts.
Open: Mon-Sat 9am-5pm. Closed
bank hols
Cards: Access, Amex, Diners, Visa

DIRECTIONS: Midway between
Coalville and Hinckley off A447. Take
B585 signposted Market Bosworth.
Opposite Red Lion Hotel and next to
post office.

7/763
● CLOTHES
Country Tradition
10 Hall Street, Ibstock,
Leicestershire LE67 6JD
Tel/Fax: (01530) 263683

Country clothing from tweed and
moleskin.
Open: Mon-Thur 9am-4.30pm. Fri
9am-1pm. Closed 1 week at
Christmas, 2 weeks early July
Cards: Access, Visa

DIRECTIONS: North-west of
Leicester, 6 miles from J22 of M1.

7/764
● CERAMICS

Piggott Sculpture
2 Manor Road, Bladon, Nr Woodstock,
Oxfordshire OX20 1RT
Tel: (01993) 811489

Models (dragons, mermaids, Gothic
grotesques).
Open: Mon-Sun 10am-6pm. Closed
25-26 Dec
Cards: No

DIRECTIONS: 7 miles north of
Oxford. Take A44, turn left at
Woodstock roundabout to Bladon on
A4095. 1 mile into village, left at
Lamb pub, 200 yards up hill on
crossroads.

7/765
● SILVERWARE

Gunilla Treen Designs
Buttermilk Cottage, Barford St Michael,
Oxfordshire OX15 0PL
Tel: (01295) 720521
Fax: (01295) 721756

Jewellery, mirrors, napkin rings in
aluminium and silver.
Open: By appointment only
Cards: No

DIRECTIONS: Take Chipping
Norton road out of Deddington.
Through Hempton, right turn to
South Newington. About ½ mile on
left.

7/766
● FURNITURE

Neville and Lawrence Neal
22 High Street, Stockton, Nr Rugby,
Warwickshire CV23 8JZ
Tel: (01926) 813702

Spindle and ladderback chairs with
rush seats made from local ash and
oak, and rushes from local rivers.
Open: Mon-Fri 8.30am-12.30pm,
1.30pm-5.30pm, or at weekends by
appointment. Closed bank hols
Cards: No

DIRECTIONS: Just off A426 Rugby to
Southam road, 9 miles south of
Rugby. In village next to newsagents.

7/767
● CERAMICS

Brinklow Pottery
11 The Crescent, Brinklow, Nr Rugby,
Warwickshire CV23 0LG
Tel: (01788) 832210

Functional and decorative stoneware,
tableware, commemorative pieces,
name plaques, sculptures.
Open: Tue-Sat 10am-6pm, Sun 10am-
4pm. Closed Mon and 25 Dec-1 Jan
Cards: Access, Visa

DIRECTIONS: On B4455, midway
between Coventry and Rugby in the
centre of Brinklow, opposite the
church.

7/768
● TEXTILES

Sharon J Webb
Gladstone Villas, 56 North Street, Whitwick,
Coalville, Leicestershire LE6 4EA
Tel: (01530) 811708

Textiles, clothing, soft furnishings,
glassware and ceramics.
Open: By appointment
Cards: No

DIRECTIONS: Take A50 signposted
Coalville and Ashby. At 7th
roundabout, turn right past
McDonalds on left. Follow signs for
Whitwick (1 mile). At crossroads turn
right on to North Street.

7/769
■ BEER

Bodicote Brewery
Plough Inn, Bodicote, Banbury,
Oxfordshire OX15 4BZ
Tel: (01295) 262327

Beer.
Open: Mon-Sat 11am-2.30pm, Sun
12 noon-3pm, 7pm-10.30pm
Cards: No

DIRECTIONS: On Banbury-Oxford
road, 1½ miles south of Banbury.
From Banbury take flyover from
Oxford, 3 left turns after Adderbury.

7/770
● SILVERWARE

J & L Poole
38 Wootton Road, Abingdon,
Oxfordshire OX14 1JD
Tel: (01235) 520338

Silversmith and jeweller using
precious metals.
Open: By appointment
Cards: No

DIRECTIONS: Showroom is in
private house on B4107 about ½ mile
north of Abingdon town centre, 100
yards past the John Mason School.

7/771
● PAINTS

Biofa Natural Paints
5 School Road, Kidlington,
Oxfordshire OX5 2HB
Tel: (01865) 374964

Natural paints, varnishes, waxes, oils
and wood treatments.
Open: By appointment
Cards: No

DIRECTIONS: Turn off A4165
Oxford to Banbury road at Green
Road. Follow into School Road.
Building on left next to corner where
School Road meets High Street.

7/772
● MUSICAL INSTRUMENTS

Michael Fleming
13 Upland Park Road, Oxford,
Oxfordshire OX2 7RU
Tel/Fax: (01865) 512807

Early bowed instruments, mainly
viola da gamba family, also violins,
bows.
Open: By appointment only
Cards: No

DIRECTIONS: From Oxford city
centre, 3 miles north up Banbury
Road. Upland Park Road is 200 yards
on left before roundabout at junction
with Sutherland Avenue.

7/773
■ FARM PRODUCE

Peach Croft Farm Country Shop
Peach Croft Farm, Radley, Abingdon,
Oxfordshire OX14 2HP
Tel: (01235) 520094
Fax: (01235) 522688

Fruit, vegetables, turkeys and geese.
Open: 9am-5pm. Closed 25 Dec-3 Jan
Cards: Access, Visa

DIRECTIONS: A34 exit to Abingdon
(north). Left at roundabout into 12
Acre Drive. Farm signposted.

7/774
● JEWELLERY

Wendy Greene Handmade Fashion Jewellery
94 Maplewell Road, Woodhouse Eaves,
Loughborough, Leicestershire LE12 8RA
Tel: (01509) 890403

Bead, metal, flower and leaf fashion
jewellery.
Open: By appointment. Closed
weekends
Cards: No

DIRECTIONS: Third house down
from Broombriggs Country Farm
Park entrance.

7/775
● LACE

Hand Knitted Lace
37 Atherstone Road, Loughborough,
Leicestershire LE11 2SH
Tel: (01509) 266302

Hand-knitted decorative lace in
cotton and silk.
Open: By appointment only
Cards: No

DIRECTIONS: Take ring road
through Loughbrough. After first
roundabout, 50 yards up the hill turn
left after row of shops into Atherstone
Road.

7/776
● MUSICAL INSTRUMENTS

Robert Goble and Son Ltd.
Greatstones, Kiln Lane, Headington,
Oxfordshire OX3 8HQ
Tel/Fax: (01865) 61685

Handmade reproductions of
seventeenth- and eighteenth-century
harpsichords and spinets.
Open: Mon-Fri 8am-5pm, weekends
by appointment
Cards: No

DIRECTIONS: Close to A40 junction
on Oxford ring road.

7/777
● STONE

Nigel Owen
42 High Street, Yelvertoft,
Northamptonshire NN6 6LQ
Tel: (01788) 822281

Lamps, clocks, barometers made from
stone and marble.
Open: Mon-Sat 9am-5.30pm
Cards: No

DIRECTIONS: 2 miles from Crick
village.

7/778
● PLANTS

Goscote Nurseries Ltd
Syston Road, Cossington, Leicester,
Leicestershire LE7 4UZ
Tel: (01509) 812121

Trees, conifers, heathers,
rhododendrons, Japanese maples,
magnolias, clematis, climbing plants
and alpines.
Open: Mon-Fri 8am-5pm, Sat 9am-
5pm, Sun 10am-5pm. Closed 4.30pm
in winter, and over Christmas
Cards: Access, Visa

DIRECTIONS: A6 Leicester to
Loughborough Road or A46 Newark
to Leicester road. Take B5328 which
joins A6 and A46, Goscote nurseries is
on the B5328 1 mile from the A6.

7/779
● PAPER PRODUCTS

Tic Tok Design
162 Barrow Road, Sileby, Loughborough,
Leicestershire LE12 7LR
Tel: (01509) 814803

Greetings cards and interior
accessories. Model and prop maker.
Open: By appointment only
Cards: No

DIRECTIONS: Take A6 towards
Leicester. Leave at Barrow-on-Soar
exit. Turn right at 1st roundabout,
right at second roundabout. Road
becomes Barrow Road.

7/780
✱ MULTIPLE

Old Dairy Farm Centre
Upper Stowe, Nr Weedon,
Northamptonshire NN7 4SH
Tel: (01327) 340525

Wood-turning, lace, knitwear,
furniture, wrought iron.
Open: 9 Jan-28 Feb 10am-4.30pm. 1
Mar-24 Dec 10am-5.30pm. Closed
Christmas to New Year
Cards: Access, Visa

DIRECTIONS: 2 miles south of
Weedon on A5. 2 miles from J16 of
M1. Opposite the little church.

7/781
● PLANTS

Philip Tivey & Son
28 Wanlip Road, Syston,
Leicestershire LE7 1PA
Tel: (0116) 2692968

Nursery, chrysanthemums, dahlias,
geraniums, fuchsias.
Open: Mon-Sun 9am-4pm. Closed
Dec-Feb
Cards: Switch

DIRECTIONS: From J23 of M1, take
A512 to Loughborough, A6 to
Leicester. Turn left on to Wanlip
Road before Thurmaston.

7/782
● FURNITURE
Ash Design
The Coach House, School Lane, Houghton
on the Hill, Leicestershire LE7 9GD
Tel/Fax: (0116) 2433233

Contemporary furniture from hi-fi
stands to outdoor bridges and gazebos.
Open: By appointment
Cards: Access, Visa

DIRECTIONS: On A47 (Leicester to
Peterborough road) 30 minutes from
either M1 or A1 junctions.

7/783
● NURSERY
Kayes Garden Nursery
1700 Melton Road, Rearsby,
Leicestershire LE7 4YR
Tel: (01664) 424578

Hardy herbaceous plants and climber.
Open: Mar-Oct Wed-Sat 10am-
5.30pm, Sun 10am-12 noon, Nov-
Dec, Feb Fri-Sat 10am-4pm. Closed
Jan
Cards: No

DIRECTIONS: On A607 Leicester to
Melton Mowbray road, 9 miles north-
west of Leicester.

7/784
● FURNITURE
Bates & Lambourne
The Camp, Rycote Lane, Milton Common,
Nr Thame, Oxfordshire OX9 2NP
Tel: (01844) 278978

Contemporary and country-style
furniture.
Open: Mon-Fri 8am-6pm, Sat 8am-
1pm. Closed bank hols
Cards: No

DIRECTIONS: On the A 329 Thame
to Wallingford road, ½ mile from J7
of M40.

7/785
● PLANTS
Bernwode Plants
Wotton Road, Ludgershall, Aylesbury,
Buckinghamshire HP18 9NZ
Tel: (01844) 237415

Plants.
Open: Mar-Oct Wed-Sun 10am to
6pm; other times by appointment
Cards: No

DIRECTIONS: From the A41
between Bicester and Aylesbury, turn
south at Kingswood, follow signposts
to Brill and Wotton. Situated on the
next public road junction, 2 miles
from Kingswood.

7/786
● PLANTS
Buckingham Nurseries and Garden Centre
Tingewick Road, Buckingham,
Buckinghamshire MK18 4AE
Tel: (01280) 813556
Fax: (01280) 815491

Bare-rooted hedging and young trees.
Open: Summer Mon-Fri 8.30am-
6pm, Sun 9.30am-6pm. Winter Mon-
Fri 8.30am-5.30pm, Sun 9.30am-
5.30pm
Cards: Access, Switch, Visa

DIRECTIONS: Approx 1 mile west of
Buckingham on A421, nearly opposite
Buckingham Golf Club.

7/787
● PLANTS
Coton Manor Garden
Guilsborough, Coton Manor, Northampton,
Northamptonshire NN6 8RQ
Tel: (01604) 740219
Fax: (01604) 740838

Hardy geraniums, hostas, hebes,
ground cover and herbaceous plants.
Open: Apr-Sept Wed-Sun 12 noon-
6pm. Oct-Mar Mon-Fri 9am-5pm
Cards: No

DIRECTIONS: 1 mile south of
Guilsborough between A50 and A428,
8 miles north-west of Northampton.

7/788
● PLANTS

Unusual Alpines and Hardy Plants
Bungalow No 5, Main Street,
Theddingworth, Lutterworth,
Leicestershire LE17 6QZ
Tel: (01858) 880496

Alpine and hardy plants.
Open: Mon–Sun 10am–6pm
Cards: No

DIRECTIONS: On the A427 between
Market Harborough and Lutterworth.
Bungalow on main road opposite
Crown pub.

7/789
■ DAIRY PRODUCE

Ark Farm Sheep Dairy Centre
Ark Farm, Tiffield, Towcester,
Northamptonshire NN12 8AB
Tel: (0327) 350202

Ewes' milk, yoghurt, ice-cream,
home-reared lamb and pork.
Open: 2.30pm–5pm. Closed
Christmas
Cards: No

DIRECTIONS: On edge of Tiffield
village one mile from A43 north of
Towcester.

7/790
● CERAMICS

Design Ceramics
Unit 1, Dovecote Pottery, Upper
Harlestone, Northamptonshire NN7 4EL
Tel: (01604) 402697

Hand-thrown kitchenware, teasets,
casseroles, candle-holders, vases and
handbuilt sculptural forms.
Open: Mon–Fri 7.30am–4pm, but
telephone first at weekends. Closed
bank hols
Cards: No

DIRECTIONS: Off the A428
Northampton to Rugby road ½ mile
from the Althorp Estate.

7/791
● SPINNING WHEELS

Timbertops Spinning Wheels
Wheel Lodge, 159 Main Street, Asfordby,
Melton Mowbray, Leicestershire LE14 3TS
Tel: (01664) 812320

Wheels for hand-spinners in oak and
English yew.
Open: Mon–Sun 10am–4pm by
appointment only
Cards: No

DIRECTIONS: 8 miles north of
Leicester on the A6006, on the corner
of Main Street and Mill Lane, almost
opposite the Blue Bell pub.

7/792
■ FARM PRODUCE

Seldom Seen Farm
Billesdon, Leicestershire LE7 9FA
Tel: (0116) 2596742

Farm shop and pick-your-own fruit.
Geese and bronze turkeys.
Open: June–mid-Sept 10am–8pm. Dec
9.30am–5pm. Closed Jan–May, Sept-
end Nov
Cards: Access, Amex, Diners, Switch,
Visa

DIRECTIONS: 8 miles east of
Leicester on A47. Off B6047 between
A47 and Tilton on the Hill.

7/793
▧ WINE

Waddesdon Manor Gift and Wineshop
Waddesdon Manor, Waddesdon, Nr
Aylesbury, Buckinghamshire HP18 0JH
Tel: (01296) 651282
Fax: (01296) 651293

Wine.
Open: Mar–Apr and Oct–Dec Wed–
Sun 11am–5pm. Apr–Oct Wed–Sun
11am–6pm. Closed Jan and Feb
Cards: Access, Visa, Switch

DIRECTIONS: On A41 between
Bicester and Aylesbury.

7/794
● PLANTS

E L F Plants
Cramden Nursery, Harborough Road
North, Northampton,
Northamptonshire NN2 8LV
Tel: (01604) 846246

Dwarf and slow-growing shrubs and
conifers.
Open: Thur-Sat 10am-5pm, other
times by arrangement. Closed Dec-
Jan
Cards: No

DIRECTIONS: On A508 on northern
edge of Northampton. Look out for
yellow sign on cemetery wall.

7/795
● CERAMICS

Brixworth Pottery
Beech Hill, Church Street, Brixworth,
Northamptonshire NN6 9BZ
Tel: (01604) 880758

As the Guide went
to press this business
closed down

7/796
● CERAMICS

Frank Haynes Gallery
50 Station Road, Great Bowden, Market
Harborough, Leicestershire LE16 7HN
Tel: (01858) 464862

Ceramics, paintings, cards and
framing.
Open: Thur-Sun 10am-5pm. Closed
Christmas
Cards: No

DIRECTIONS: Station Road leads
from Great Bowden centre to Market
Harborough station. Nearest main
road is A6.

7/797
● SADDLERY GOODS

S Milner & Son
Unit 4, Rural Industries, John O'Gaunt,
Twyford, Nr Melton Mowbray,
Leicestershire LE14 2RE
Tel: (01664) 454839
Fax: (01664) 454744

Saddlery and suppliers of equestrian
equipment.
Open: Mon, Tue, Thur 9am-6pm,
Wed, Fri, Sat, 9am-5pm. Sun 10am-
1pm. Closed bank hols
Cards: Access, Amex, Diners, Visa

DIRECTIONS: Turn off B6047 in
Twyford to John O'Gaunt. 1 mile on
right down long drive. Sign on left.

7/798
■ BAKED GOODS

Ye Olde Pork Pie Shoppe
10 Nottingham Street, Melton Mowbray,
Leicestershire LE13 1NW
Tel/Fax: (01664) 62341

Pork pies.
Open: Mon-Sat 8am-5pm. Closed 25
and 26 Dec
Cards: No

DIRECTIONS: Between Nottingham
and Stamford on A606. Nottingham
Street is pedestrianised and runs
northwards off Market Place.

7/799
● FURNITURE

Hollies Farm Handcrafts
Hollies Farm, Little Dalby, Melton Mowbray,
Leicestershire LE14 2UQ
Tel/Fax: (01664) 454553

Hardwood furniture-makers.
Open: Mon-Fri 9am-5pm, Sat-Sun
and bank hols 11am-4.30pm. Closed
25 Dec, 1 Jan
Cards: Access, Visa

DIRECTIONS: 1 mile off A606
Melton Mowbray to Oakham Road in
centre of Little Dalby.

7/800
✽ MULTIPLE
East Carlton Countryside Park
East Carlton, Nr Market Harborough,
Leicestershire LE16 8YD
Tel: (01536) 770977

Glass, flowers, cakes, knitwear.
Open: Summer Mon-Fri 9.30am-
4.45pm. Sat 10.30am-5.15pm. Sun
10.30am-5.45pm. Winter Mon-Sun
9.30am-3.45pm
Cards: No

DIRECTIONS: 3 miles west of Corby.
Large sign on left .

7/801
● CERAMICS
Speen Pottery
Valley Cottage, Highwood Bottom,
Speen, Princes Risborough,
Buckinghamshire HP27 0PY
Tel: (01494) 488206

Hand-thrown and decorated
tableware, commemorative plates and
bowls.
Open: Mon-Sun 9am-6pm
Cards: No

DIRECTIONS: Leave High Wycombe
on A4128, follow road to Speen (5
miles). Drive through village and
down hill across hairpin bend into
Highwood Bottom. Pottery sign in
hedge.

7/802
● FORGEWORK
**George James & Sons
Blacksmiths**
22 Cransley Hill, Broughton, Kettering,
Northamptonshire NN14 1NB
Tel/Fax: (01536) 790295

Forged ironwork, restoration of
wrought and cast iron.
Open: Mon-Fri 8.30am-5.30pm, Sat
by appointment. Closed bank hols
Cards: No

DIRECTIONS: Follow road to village
centre and take turning signposted
Great Cransley. Workshop is situated
100 yards up the hill on the right.

7/803
▥ BEER
The Chiltern Brewery
Nash Lee Road, Terrick, Aylesbury,
Buckinghamshire HP17 0TQ
Tel: (01296) 613647
Fax: (01296) 612419

English beers, ales and barley wine,
mustards and chutneys.
Open: Mon-Sat 9am-5pm. Closed 25-
26 Dec, 1 Jan
Cards: No

DIRECTIONS: Situated on B4009, 3
miles south of Aylesbury off the A413.

7/804
● FORGEWORK
J F Spence & Son
The New Forge, Station Road, Uppingham,
Leicestershire LE15 9TX
Tel: (01572) 822758
Fax: (01572) 821348

Wrought ironwork, gates, fencing,
rose arbours and fire baskets.
Open: Mon-Fri 8am-12.30am,
1.30pm-5pm, Sat 9am-12.30pm.
Closed bank hols
Cards: No

DIRECTIONS: At Uppingham
roundabout take A6003 Corby/
Kettering road. 1st turn left after
market place, between church yard
and old cemetery, after 300 yards bear
left, signposted to industrial estate.

7/805
● FORGEWORK
Mentmore Smithy
Stag Hill, Mentmore, Leighton Buzzard,
Bedfordshire LU7 0QE
Tel: (01296) 661760
Fax: (01296) 662502

Forgework and decorative ironwork.
Open: Mon-Fri 8am-5.30pm
Cards: No

DIRECTIONS: Opposite and below
the Stag Inn on the Cheddington road
in Mentmore, which is approximately
4 miles south of Leighton Buzzard
towards Tring.

7/806
● PLANTS

The Herb Nursery
Grange Farm Thistleton, Oakham,
Leicestershire LE15 7RE
Tel: (01572) 767658

Herbs, wild flowers, cottage garden
plants and geraniums.
Open: Daily 9am-6pm (or dusk in
winter). Closed Christmas to New
Year
Cards: No

DIRECTIONS: Halfway between
Stamford and Grantham, in middle of
Thistleton village 3 miles west of A1.

7/807
● PLANTS

**John Chambers' Wildflower
Seeds**
15 College Street, Irthlingborough,
Wellingborough, Northamptonshire
NN9 5TU
Tel: (01933) 652562
Fax: (01933) 652576

Seeds including wildflower species,
herbs, grasses and everlasting flowers.
Open: Mon-Fri 9am-5pm. Sat by
appointment. Closed Christmas
Cards: Access, Visa

DIRECTIONS: Overlooking central
roundabout and green in
Irthlingborough.

7/808
● PLANTS

Hill Farm Herbs
Park Walk, Brigstock, Kettering,
Northamptonshire NN14 3HH
Tel: (01536) 373694
Fax: (01536) 373246

Herbs and cottage garden plants.
Open: Mar-end Oct 10.30am-5.30pm.
Nov-Feb 10.30am-4.30pm
Cards: Access, Switch, Visa

DIRECTIONS: Signposted in
Brigstock village, off A6116.

7/809
● LIME WASH

Cy-Pres (Brigstock) Ltd
14 Bells Close, Brigstock, Kettering,
Northamptonshire NN14 3JG
Tel: (01536) 373431

Lime mortars, plasters and renders,
limewash distemper and historic
paints.
Open: Mon-Sat 9am-5pm, but
telephone first
Cards: No

DIRECTIONS: On A6116.

7/810
■ MEAT/POULTRY/GAME

R Waller
Long Grove Wood Farm,
234 Chartridge Lane, Chesham,
Buckinghamshire HP5 2SG
Tel/Fax: (01494) 772744

Aylesbury duck breeders.
Open: Mon-Sun 9am-6pm. Closed
25 Dec
Cards: No

DIRECTIONS: About 1 mile from
Chesham town centre, road
signposted Chartridge.

7/811
■ CONFECTIONERY

Sophie's Chocolates
3-4 The Gatehouse, Elgiva Lane, Chesham,
Buckinghamshire HP5 2JD
Tel: (01494) 782999

Chocolates made from dairy cream,
alcohol, fruit and nuts.
Open: Mon-Fri 10am-5pm, Sat
9.30am-5pm. Closed 1 week after
Christmas
Cards: No

DIRECTIONS: Off High Street in a
flagstoned courtyard.

7/812
● BOOKBINDING

Harmatan Leather Ltd
Westfield Avenue, Higham Ferrers,
Northamptonshire NN10 8AX
Tel: (01933) 412151
Fax: (01933) 412242

Goatskin for bookbinding.
Open: Mon-Sun 8.30am-5pm
Cards: No

DIRECTIONS: Off Thrift Street in
Higham Ferrers.

7/813
● TEXTILES

Pheasant House
Littleheath Lane, Berkhamsted,
Hertfordshire HP4 2RT
Tel: (01442) 871485

Fabrics and made-to-measure
garments.
Open: By appointment only
Cards: Access, Visa

DIRECTIONS: On A4251 at Bourne
End Church turn into Little Heath
Lane. Pheasant House is about 1 mile
on the left.

7/814
■ WINE

Frithsden Vineyard
Frithsden, Hemel Hempstead,
Hertfordshire HP1 1PA
Tel: (01442) 864732

Wines.
Open: Mon-Sat 10am-5pm, Sun
12 noon-3pm. Closed 25-26 Dec
Cards: No

DIRECTIONS: Tourist board
signposted from Berkhampsted High
Street. A4146 to Leighton Buzzard
road for 3 miles to Water End, take
2nd left for Frithsden, 1 mile to
junction, turn left. After ¼ mile go
right into Frithsden, right after Alford
Arms – 120 yards.

7/815
■ COFFEE

Boaters Flavoured Coffee Co
5 Ampthill Business Park, Station Road,
Ampthill, Bedfordshire MK45 2QP
Tel: (01525) 404781
Fax: (01525) 404981

Flavoured arabica coffee beans.
Open: Nov, Dec Mon-Sat 9am-6pm.
Jan-Oct Mon-Fri 9am-6pm. Closed
Christmas and New Year
Cards: Access, Amex, Switch, Visa

DIRECTIONS: On A507 between
Clophill and Millbrook, adjacent to
Royal Mail sorting office.

7/816
■ PRESERVES

Les Fines Herbes
8 St Mary's Hill, Stamford,
Lincolnshire PE9 2DP
Tel/Fax: (01780) 57381

Vinegars, oils, mustards and jellies.
Open: Mon-Sat 9am-5pm except
Thur 9am-12.30pm. Closed bank hols
Cards: Access, Amex, Visa

DIRECTIONS: 10 miles north of
Peterborough off A1 at roundabout
on to B1176. Over town bridge,
opposite Town Hall.

7/817
✸ MULTIPLE

The Craft Studios
43 Main Street, Woodnewton, Oundle,
Northamptonshire PE8 5EB
Tel/Fax: (01780) 470866

Pottery, wood-carving, marionettes.
Open: 9am-5pm but telephone first
Cards: Access, Visa

DIRECTIONS: At Warmington, on
A605, follow signs to Fotheringhay,
then continue for 2 miles to
Woodnewton.

7/818
● FORGEWORK

Fotheringhay Forge and Woodburners

The Forge, Fotheringhay, Peterborough, Cambridgeshire PE8 5HZ
Tel: (01832) 226323
Fax: (01832) 226212

Hot forged ironwork, curtain rails, interior furniture, beds, firebaskets, canopies, gates.
Open: Tue-Fri 10am-12 noon, 2pm-4pm, also Sept-Mar Sat 10am-4pm, April-Aug Sat 9am-1pm
Cards: Access, Switch, Visa

DIRECTIONS: A1, A47 or A605 to Fotheringhay, the Forge is behind the Falcon pub.

7/819
■ SAUSAGES

Fieldsahead

3 Greenways, Sawtry, Cambridgeshire PE17 5UR
Tel: (01487) 830595

Sausages, hams, pickles.
Open: Mon-Sat 8.30am-5.30pm. Closed Christmas and bank hols
Cards: No

DIRECTIONS: Off A1 to Sawtry opposite Greystone's pub.

7/820
● CERAMICS

Louise Shotter Pottery

108 London Road, St Ippollitts, Hitchin, Hertfordshire SG4 7RD
Tel: (01462) 455789

Painted white earthenware, decorative and functional.
Open: By appointment
Cards: No

DIRECTIONS: Between Hitchin and Langley on B656. On the left just past the crossroads in the village.

7/821
● FORGEWORK

Henry Isaac

The Foundry, St Ippollitts, Hitchin, Hertfordshire SG4 7NX
Tel: (01462) 453155
Fax: (01462) 421618

Iron foundry: fireplaces and related products including gas fires, surrounds, fire baskets. Railings and finials.
Open: Mon-Fri 8am-1pm, 2pm-5pm. Sat 8am-12 noon
Cards: No

DIRECTIONS: B656 Hitchin to Welwyn road, 1½ miles south of Hitchin. From Hitchin turn left at St Ippollitts crossroads. At bottom of hill.

7/822
■ MEAT/POULTRY/GAME

Ashwell Delicatessen

Farrowby Farm, New Inn Road, Hinxworth, Hertfordshire SG7 5EY
Tel: (01462) 733700
Fax: (01462) 733302

Free-range pig farm. Home-smoked ham, bacon and sausages.
Open: Mon-Sat 9am-6pm. Closed Christmas and New Year
Cards: Access, Switch, Visa

DIRECTIONS: From Baldock (J10, A1(M)) take A1 to Biggleswade. After 2 miles turn right to Hinxworth. Farm is signposted immediately on right.

7/823
■ SAUSAGES

Parkinsons of Crowland

6 West Street, Crowland, Peterborough, Lincolnshire PE6 0ED
Tel: (01733) 210233

Pork sausages and brawn.
Open: Mon 8am-12 noon, Tue-Fri 8am-5.30pm. Sat 8am-4pm
Cards: No

DIRECTIONS: Midway between Peterborough and Spalding on A1073. Leave A47 at Eye for Spalding.

MAP 8

8/824
● CERAMICS
Lannock Pottery
Weston Barns, Hitchin Road, Weston,
Hertfordshire SG4 7AX
Tel: (01462) 790356
Fax: (01462) 790704

Stoneware pottery, oven-to-tableware,
vases, garden pots, fountains, lamps.
Open: Mon-Sat 10am-5pm, Sun
11am-5pm. Closed 25 Dec to first Sat
after 1 Jan
Cards: Access, Visa

DIRECTIONS: J9 of A1(M)
Letchworth, towards Baldock, 200
yards left along B197, 300 yards left to
Weston. Middle of village opposite the
Red Lion pub.

8/825
● GLASS
Foxhall Studio
Kelshall, Nr Royston, Hertfordshire SG8 9SE
Tel: (01763) 287209

Stained glass, from lampshades to
window panels.
Open: Daily 9am-5pm
Cards: No

DIRECTIONS: From Royston take
the A505 to Baldock. Turn left
towards Therfield and Kelshall.

8/826
● FURNITURE
ASP Cabinet Maker
The Brick Barn, Dears Farm, Fardells Lane,
Elsworth, Cambridgeshire CB3 8JE
Tel: (01954) 267312

Furniture in oak, ash, cherry and
walnut.
Open: Mon-Sat 8am-1pm, 2pm-6pm
Cards: No

DIRECTIONS: Behind the sports field
in the centre of Elsworth about 10
miles west of Cambridge.

8/827
● CERAMICS
Clover Pottery
5 Oldhurst Road, Pidley, Huntingdon,
Cambridgeshire PE17 3BY
Tel: (01487) 841026

Stoneware, hand-thrown pots, jugs,
mugs. Also porcelain.
Open: By arrangement
Cards: Access, Amex, Visa

DIRECTIONS: 8 miles north-east of
Huntingdon, on B1040. 120 yards
past the Mad Cat pub on the left, on
right across from red Georgian house.

8/828
■ BEER
Fox and Hounds
Barley, Nr Royston, Hertfordshire SG8 8HU
Tel: (01763) 848459

Barley brewery, 3 own brews
Open: Mon-Fri 12 noon-2.30pm,
6pm-11pm, Sun 12 noon-3pm, 7pm-
10.30pm. All day bank hols and
around Christmas
Cards: Access, Visa

DIRECTIONS: Nr Royston off A10 or
just off A505, on the B1368.

8/829
■ WINE
Coton Orchards
Cambridge Road, Coton,
Cambridgeshire CB3 7PJ
Tel: (01954) 210234

Vineyard and fruit farm: wine, cider,
apple juice, nursery plants, soft fruit
and vegetables.
Open: Mon-Sun 9am-6pm. Closed 25
Dec, 1 Jan
Cards: No

DIRECTIONS: 1½ miles west of
Cambridge, near American Cemetery.
400 yards from J13 of M11.

8/830
■ HERBS

N & R J Dyer
Millfield, Willingham,
Cambridgeshire CB4 5HG
Tel: (01954) 202085/231257

Potted fresh herbs.
Open: Mar-Jun Sat and bank hols,
other times by appointment
Cards: No

DIRECTIONS: Off A14 from
Cambridge junction for Longstanton.
Take B1050 to Willingham. Turn
second right 1 mile from level crossing.

8/831
● ROCKING-HORSES

**Michael Pearson Fine Rocking
Horses**
Whitegates, Button End, Harston,
Cambridgeshire CB2 5NX
Tel: (01223) 871072

Rocking-horses and rocking water
fowl.
Open: By appointment only
Cards: No

DIRECTIONS: From J11 of M11 take
A10 south to Harston. Through
village and right to Haslingfield at
Queens Head pub. Button End is first
right. Last house but one on right.

8/832
● GLASS

Roger Phillippo
The Bakehouse, Church Street, Harston,
Cambridgeshire CB2 5NP
Tel: (01223) 870277

Hand-engraved glassware.
Open: Mon, Wed, Thur, Fri 9am-
6pm, Tue, Sat 9am-1pm. Closed
August
Cards: No

DIRECTIONS: On the A10 1 mile
west of J11 on the M11 at the Royston
end of the village. The Haslingfield
road branches off the A10, the shop is
100 yards on the left hand side.

8/833
● PLANTS

Honeysome Aquatic Nursery
The Row, Sutton, Nr Ely,
Cambridgeshire CB6 2PF
Tel: (01353) 778889

Pond, bog and moisture-loving plants.
Open: Mon-Fri 9.30am-5pm, Sat
9.30am-12 noon. By appointment
only. Closed mid-Oct to mid Apr
Cards: No

DIRECTIONS: 6 miles west of Ely, in
Sutton village, at west end of the road
named The Row.

8/834
● JEWELLERY

**Clare Murray and Mathew
Warwick**
Shephards Bakery, Station Road, Tydd
Gote, Wisbech, Cambridgeshire PE13 5QA
Tel: (01945) 420242

Jewellery, turned and carved wooden
boxes, pencils and penknives.
Open: By appointment
Cards: No

DIRECTIONS: Tydd Gote is 5 miles
north of Wisbech on the A1101. Turn
off towards Sutton Bridge 300 yards
on the right.

8/835
■ MEAT/POULTRY/GAME

Naturally Yours
The Horse and Gate, Witcham Toll, Ely,
Cambridgeshire CB6 2AB
Tel/Fax: (01353) 778723

Additive-free meat, bacon and oven-
ready dishes.
Open: Mon-Fri 9am-9pm, Sat-Sun
10am-4pm, by appointment at
weekends
Cards: No

DIRECTIONS: On the A142 at the
junction with A1421, the red house
on the corner.

8/836
■ SMOKED PRODUCE
Simply Salmon & Fine Foods
Severals Farm, Arkesden, Saffron Walden,
Essex CB11 4EY
Tel: (01799) 550143
Fax: (01799) 550039

Smoked salmon, smoked chicken and
meats, pâté, gift hampers.
Open: Mon-Fri 9am-1pm. Closed
bank hols
Cards: Access, Visa

DIRECTIONS: Take B1383 north-
east from Bishop's Stortford to
Newport. Turn left on B1038 to
Clavering. Turn right in Wicken
Bonhunt to Arkesden.

8/837
● CERAMICS
Anna McArthur Ceramic Artist
Skachbow, 95 Green End, Landbeach,
Cambridgeshire CB4 4ED
Tel: (01223) 860629

Inlaid porcelain bowls, clocks and
earrings.
Open: Mon-Sat by appointment only
Cards: No

DIRECTIONS: Turn off A10 north of
Cambridge to Landbeach, through
village. Third from last house on left.

8/838
● CERAMICS
Twentypence Pottery
Twentypence Road, Wilburton, Ely,
Cambridgeshire CB6 3RN
Tel: (01353) 741353

Domestic stoneware pottery and
terracotta gardenware.
Open: Mon-Fri 9am-6pm. Closed
Wed
Cards: No

DIRECTIONS: On junction of
Wilburton High Street and
Twentypence Road.

8/839
● SCULPTURE
Louis Lejeune Ltd
The Berristead, 1 Station Road, Wilburton,
Ely, Cambridgeshire CB6 3RP
Tel: (01353) 740444
Fax: (01353) 741599

Sculptors and bronze founders, car
mascots and trophy sculpture.
Open: Mon-Thur 9am-4.30pm by
appointment only
Cards: No

DIRECTIONS: At 30mph sign at east
end of Wilburton (A1123) turn north
into Station Road.

8/840
● FURNITURE
David Prue, Cabinet Maker
26 Radwinter Road, Saffron Walden,
Essex CB11 3JB
Tel: (01799) 522558

Queen Anne and William and Mary-
style walnut pieces.
Open: Mon-Fri 8.30am-5.30pm, Sat
8.30am-4pm, other times by
appointment. Closed bank hols
Cards: No

DIRECTIONS: On right going out of
Saffron Walden towards Radwinter.
Approx 200 yards after traffic lights,
signposted.

8/841
■ SMOKED PRODUCE
River Farm Smokery Shop
Junction Wilbraham Road, Bottisham,
Cambridgeshire CB5 9BU
Tel: (01223) 812577
Fax: (01223) 812319

Traditional oak-smoked fish and
meats.
Open: Mon-Sat 10am-5pm. Closed
Sun, 25-28 Dec
Cards: No

DIRECTIONS: On A1303 from
Cambridge to Newmarket on
junction to Wilbrahams and
Fulbourn.

8/842
● SCALE MODELS
Guild Master Models
Willow Cottage, High Street, Nordelph,
Norfolk PE38 0BL
Tel: (01366) 324351

Scale models of cars, boats etc.
Open: By appointment
Cards: Access, Visa

DIRECTIONS: 4 miles out of
Downham Market on A1122 to
Wisbech. Over bridge, back towards
Downham, opposite Chequers pub.
Mooring staithe outside on Well Creek.

8/843
■ WINE
Chilford Hundred Wine Company
Balsham Road, Linton,
Cambridgeshire CB1 6LE
Tel: (01223) 892641
Fax: (01223) 894056

Wine.
Open: May-Sept, daily 11am-5pm
Cards: Access, Amex, Visa

DIRECTIONS: Between Linton and
Balsham – follow signs from A11 and
A604.

8/844
● PLANTS
Langthorns Plantery
Little Canfield, Dunmow, Essex CM6 1TD
Tel/Fax: (01371) 872611

Trees, shrubs, herbaceous and alpines.
Conservatory plants.
Open: Daily 10am-5pm. Closed from
Christmas to New Year
Cards: Access, Switch, Visa

DIRECTIONS: 5 miles east of J8 of
M11. Signposted off A120 to
Langthorns.

8/845
● FORGEWORK
Glendale Forge
Monk Street, Thaxted, Essex CM6 2NR
Tel: (01371) 830466
Fax: (01371) 831419

Ornamental ironwork.

Open: Mon-Fri 9am-5pm, Sun 10am-
12 noon. Closed Sat
Cards: No

DIRECTIONS: On B184 1½ miles
south of Thaxted.

8/846
■ MEAT/POULTRY/GAME
C E Brown – Licensed Game Dealer
Southlawns, Shudy Camps,
Cambridgeshire CB1 6RA
Tel: (01799) 584461

Game, wild venison, poultry and
sausages.
Open: Mon-Sat 8am-5pm, Sun 9am-
12 noon
Cards: No

DIRECTIONS: Turn off A604 at
Linton, go through Bartlow, take the
first left into Shudy Camps. Third
house on left.

8/847
● PLANTS
Padlock Croft
Padlock Road, West Wratting,
Cambridgeshire CB1 5LS
Tel: (01223) 290383

Campanula, symphyandra,
adenophora and platycodon, alpines
and perennial plants.
Open: Apr-Oct Wed-Sat 10am-6pm,
evenings and winter by appointment
only
Cards: No

DIRECTIONS: On A604 between
Linton and Horseheath turn north on
unnumbered road signposted to
Balsham, West Wratting. Padlock
Road on left at entry of village.

8/848
■ PRESERVES
English Country Chandlers Ltd
4 The Flitch Estate, Great Dunmow,
Essex CM6 1XJ
Tel: (01371) 875744
Fax: (01371) 875135

Preserves, chutneys, mustards, teas
and biscuits.

Open: Mon-Fri 9am-5pm. Closed one week at Christmas
Cards: No

DIRECTIONS: A120 from M11 towards Dunmow. Through town centre to Flitch Estate on right.

8/849
■ SMOKED PRODUCE

Smokeries Ltd
Unit 10, Flitch Industrial Estate, Great Dunmow, Essex CM6 1EL
Tel: (01371) 873321
Fax: (01371) 876351

Smoked salmon.
Open: Mon-Fri 8.30am-4.30pm. Sat 9am-12 noon. Closed bank hols
Cards: No

DIRECTIONS: On A120 between Bishops Stortford and Braintree near town centre.

8/850
■ SAUSAGES

Musks Ltd
1 The Rookery, Newmarket, Suffolk CB8 8EQ
Tel: (01638) 661824
Fax: (01638) 561874

Sausages.
Open: Mon-Sat 9am-5pm
Cards: No

DIRECTIONS: In Newmarket shopping centre.

8/851
● HERALDRY

Dudley Bateman, Heraldic Artist
Revonah, 10 Bourne Close, South Wootton, Kings Lynn, Norfolk PE30 3LZ
Tel/Fax: (01553) 672381

Wall shields depicting coats of arms, paintings, keyrings, paperweights, table mats.
Open: By appointment
Cards: Access, Visa

DIRECTIONS: 3 miles east of King's Lynn, off Avon Road, off Nursery Lane.

8/852
■ FRUIT/VEGETABLES

Eros Asparagus
Kenny Hill, Bury St Edmunds, Suffolk IP28 8DS
Tel: (01353) 675394

Asparagus (May, June). Asparagus crowns (roots) (September to April).
Open: 9am-6pm. Closed Christmas
Cards: No

DIRECTIONS: On the A101, 4 miles north of Mildenhall.

8/853
■ WINE

Felsted Vineyards
The Vineyards, Crix Green, Felsted, Essex CM6 3JT
Tel: (01245) 361504

Wines. Fruit liqueurs, preserves. Tours by arrangement.
Open: Tue-Sat 10am-7pm, Sun 12 noon-3pm. Closed 25 Dec-1 April
Cards: Access, Visa

DIRECTIONS: 2 miles from Essex county showground on A131, along unclassified road marked Felsted. In the triangle of roads formed from A131, A120 and A130.

8/854
● PLANTS

Norfolk Lavender Ltd
Caley Mill, Heacham, Norfolk PE31 7JE
Tel: (01485) 570384
Fax: (01485) 571176

Lavender, gifts, plants, herbs, heathers.
Open: Oct-Mar 10.30am-4.30pm, Apr-Sept 9.30am-5pm. Closed over Christmas
Cards: Access, Visa

DIRECTIONS: On A149 at junction with B1454, 10 miles north of King's Lynn.

8/855
■ MEAT/POULTRY/GAME
R F & J Scoles
1 Chapel Road, Dersingham, King's Lynn, Norfolk PE31 6PW
Tel: (01485) 540309

Sausages, home-cured ham.
Open: Mon-Thur 8am-5pm, Fri 8.30am-5.30pm, Sat 8am-1pm
Cards: No

DIRECTIONS: Off A149 on B1440.

8/856
✹ MULTIPLE
The Granary Craft Centre
Park Farm, Snettisham, Norfolk PE31 7NQ
Tel: (01485) 542425

Toys, clocks, ceramics, needlecrafts, dried flowers, wood turning.
Open: Daily 10.30am-5pm. Closed Christmas to 1st April
Cards: No

DIRECTIONS: Turn east off the Dersingham-Snettisham bypass into Snettisham village square. Proceed eastwards past St Mary's church (tall spire). Take Bircham road to top of hill. Turn right into farm.

8/857
■ WINE
Boyton Vineyard
Stoke by Clare, Sudbury, Suffolk CO10 8TB
Tel: (01440) 61893

Wine.
Open: Most days 10.30am-6pm, all weekends. Closed February
Cards: No

DIRECTIONS: Signposted off the A1092, 3 miles from Clare.

8/858
■ MEAT/POULTRY/GAME
Longwood Farm
Tuddenham St Mary, Bury St Edmunds, Suffolk IP28 6TD
Tel/Fax: (01638) 717120

Free-range organic beef, lamb, pork, poultry. Cheeses, groceries.
Open: Wed and Fri 9.30am-4pm. Sat 9.30am-4.30pm

Cards: No

DIRECTIONS: Situated between A14 and A45 10 miles from Bury St Edmunds-Newmarket-Thetford. 200 yards up village green. Entrance to barn on right. Signposted.

8/859
● CERAMICS
John and Kate Turner
The Pottery, Narborough, Norfolk PE32 1TE
Tel: (01760) 337208

Household pottery, sculpture and garden pots.
Open: 7 days
Cards: No

DIRECTIONS: On the A47 between Swaffham and King's Lynn, next door to the Ship Inn.

8/860
■ MEAT/POULTRY/GAME
Lay and Robson
150 Swan Street, Sible Hedingham, Halstead, Essex CO9 3PP
Tel: (01787) 462617
Fax: (01787) 462611

Game, smoked food, pies, bacon, sausages, pâtés.
Open: Tue-Sat 9am-5.30pm. Closed bank hols
Cards: No

DIRECTIONS: A604 on left heading towards Colchester. Set back from road opposite newsagent.

8/861
■ DAIRY PRODUCE
Fullers
Brickwall Farm, Sible Hedingham, Halstead, Essex CO9 3RH
Tel/Fax: (01787) 460329

Dairy farm selling cream, ice-cream, cheesecake, butter and cheese.
Open: Mon-Sat 9am-5.30pm. Sun 9.30am-4.30pm, Easter to end Oct 9.30am-12.30pm
Cards: No

DIRECTIONS: On A604, on junction with B1017.

8/862
● CERAMICS

Castle Hedingham Pottery

The Pottery, St James Street, Castle
Hedingham, Nr Halstead, Essex CO9 3EW
Tel: (01787) 460036

Domestic stoneware and garden pots.
Open: Tue-Sun 9.30am-5.30pm.
Closed Jan
Cards: No

DIRECTIONS: Follow A604 from
Colchester to Sible Hedingham, 1st
right into Castle Hedingham,
following brown tourist signs to
pottery.

8/863
■ FISH/SHELLFISH

The Fish Shed

Main Road, Brancaster Staithe, King's
Lynn, Norfolk PE31 8YB
Tel: (01485) 210532

Fresh fish and shellfish. Game and
wildfowl in season. Smoked products,
herbs.
Open: Daily 10am-5pm. Closed Mon
and Dec
Cards: No

DIRECTIONS: In centre of village on
main coast road (A149). Look for
fluorescent crab sign.

8/864
● FORGEWORK

The Forge

Church Street, Gestingthorpe, Halstead,
Essex CO9 3AZ
Tel: (01787) 460126

Ornamental ironwork, restoration
work, items for the home.
Open: Mon-Fri 9am-5pm, variable
holidays
Cards: No

DIRECTIONS: Take the B1058 off
the A604 and turn left towards
Gestingthorpe. The forge is ¼ mile
from the church on the same side of
the road.

8/865
● PLANTS

B & H M Baker

Bourne Brooke Nurseries, Greenstead
Green, Halstead, Essex CO9 1RJ
Tel: (01787) 476369

Fuchsias, pot, bedding and
conservatory plants, geraniums and
chrysanthemums.
Open: Mon-Fri 9am-4.30pm, Sat-Sun
9am-12 noon, 2pm-4pm. Closed
August bank hol and Christmas
Cards: No

DIRECTIONS: A604 from
Colchester. Turn first left after
leaving Earls Colne to Greenstead
Green.

8/866
● BUILDING MATERIALS

Bulmer Brick & Tile Co Ltd

The Brickfields, Bulmer, Sudbury,
Suffolk CO10 7EF
Tel: (01787) 269232
Fax: (01787) 269040

Rubbed and gauged arches, pinnacles,
chimneys, coping bricks. Garden
edging and decorative plaques.
Open: Mon-Fri 9.30am-4pm. Sat
9.30am-11.30am
Cards: No

DIRECTIONS: 5 miles west of
Sudbury. Take A131 towards
Chelmsford. At Bulmer Tye take
B1058 and turn for Hedingham.
Exactly 1 mile from junction on right.

8/867
■ WINE

Gifford's Hall Vineyard

Hartest, Nr Bury St Edmunds,
Suffolk IP29 4EX
Tel: (01284) 830464

White and rosé wines. Also herbs in
oil and vinegar.
Open: Easter to end Oct daily
12 noon-6pm. Closed in winter
Cards: Access, Visa

DIRECTIONS: On A134 from Bury
St Edmunds or Sudbury pick up
brown tourist signs at Shimpling. Also
signs on A1092 and B1066.

8/868
■ HERBS

Rafi's Spice Box
48 Gaol Lane, Sudbury, Suffolk CO10 6JL
Tel: (01787) 881992
Fax: (01787) 881757

Spices.
Open: Mon-Tue, Thur-Fri 9am-5pm.
Sat 9am-4pm. Closed Wed and all
bank hols
Cards: No

DIRECTIONS: 19 miles from
Colchester on A134 to Sudbury.
Close to Town Hall.

8/869
● TEXTILES

Vanners Mill Shop
Gregory Street, Sudbury, Suffolk CO10 6BB
Tel: (01787) 313933
Fax: (01787) 310674

Woven silk ties, scarves and other items.
Open: Mon-Fri 9am-5pm, Sat 9am-
12 noon. Closed Sun, bank hols,
Christmas and New Year
Cards: Access

DIRECTIONS: On A131. At junction
where A131 turns left to Chelmsford,
keep clockwise. Shop 100 yards on
right (opposite fire station).

8/870
● PLANTS

Paradise Centre
Twinstead Road, Lamarsh, Nr Bures,
Suffolk CO8 5EX
Tel/Fax: (01787) 269449

Bulbs, tuberous and shade plants.
Open: Easter-Oct Sat-Sun 10am-5pm
Cards: Access, Visa

DIRECTIONS: Outside Lamarsh,
4 miles south of Sudbury, between
A131 and B1508.

8/871
● PLANTS

Copford Bulbs
Dorsetts, Birch Road, Copford, Colchester,
Essex CO6 1DR
Tel: (01206) 330008

Daffodil bulbs and hardy cyclamen.
Open: By appointment
Cards: No

DIRECTIONS: Copford is 4 miles
south-west of Colchester on A12.
Opposite Bocking Hall Farm on Birch
Road.

8/872
● PLANTS

Netherfield Herbs
Netherfield Cottage, 37 Nether Street,
Rougham, Suffolk IP30 9LW
Tel: (01359) 270452

Herb plants (culinary, aromatic,
medicinal and cosmetic).
Open: Mon-Sun 10am-6pm, or dusk
Cards: No

DIRECTIONS: Rougham is 5 miles
south-east of Bury St Edmunds on the
A14 (A45). Through the village to
Nether Street, to the south-east road
to Hessett. Netherfield Herbs is the
last cottage in Rougham on this road.

8/873
● PLANTS

Rougham Hall Nurseries
Rougham, Bury St Edmunds,
Suffolk IP30 9LZ
Tel: (01359) 270577
Fax: (01359) 271149

Hardy perennials.
Open: Thur-Mon 10am-4pm
Cards: No

DIRECTIONS: 3 miles east of Bury St
Edmunds on westbound carriageway,
exit at Beyton, 1 mile east of nursery
and head back towards Bury St
Edmunds.

8/874
■ ICE-CREAM

The Manor Farm Creamery
Thurston, Bury St Edmunds,
Suffolk IP31 3QJ
Tel: (01359) 230208
Fax: (01359) 232838

Dairy ice-cream from double cream
and pure fruits.
Open: Daily 8am-8pm
Cards: No

DIRECTIONS: 1 mile north of A14 (A45) Cambridge/Felixstowe road and 4 miles east of Bury St Edmunds. On Church Lane midway between St Peter's Thurston and St Mary's Pakenham.

8/875
● CERAMICS
Burnham Pottery
The Old Station, 2/4 Maryland, Wells-next-the-Sea, Norfolk NR23 1LX
Tel: (01328) 710847
Fax: (01328) 711566

Pottery, ceramic animals especially cats. Ceramic creatures for people to decorate.
Open: Mon-Fri 9am-5pm, Sat 10am-5pm, most Sun 10am-1pm, 3pm-5pm
Cards: No

DIRECTIONS: From Cromer direction take the 1st turn right (to town centre). Pottery is 700 yards on right. From Hunstanton, take 1st left after church, Burnham pottery is 700 yards on the right.

8/876
■ FRUIT/VEGETABLES
Crapes Fruit Farm
Rectory Road, Aldham, Colchester, Essex CO6 3RR
Tel: (01206) 212375

Unusual apples, and fresh juice.
Open: Mon-Sat 8am-5pm. Closed 25, 26 Dec
Cards: No

DIRECTIONS: 5 miles west of Colchester. First left 1 mile north of A12/A120 Marks Tey past station.

8/877
● CANDLES
The Candle Shop Arts and Crafts
3 Guild Street, Little Walsingham, Norfolk NR22 6BU
Tel: (01328) 820748

Ornamental and aromatherapy candles.
Open: Mon-Sun 10am-5.30pm, best to telephone first in winter. Closed over Christmas

Cards: No

DIRECTIONS: 5 miles along B1105 from Fakenham or Wells-next-the-Sea, 2 doors from Robin Hood pub.

8/878
● BASKETS
Rob King – English Willow Basketworks
Loke Cottage, 4 Scarning Fen, Dereham, Norfolk NR19 1LN
Tel: (01362) 695947

Willow baskets.
Open: By arrangement
Cards: No

DIRECTIONS: ½ mile west of Dereham on A47 Dereham bypass, turn south into Fen Road. Follow signs to Toftwood. Turn right into unmade road, fourth cottage on left.

8/879
● TEXTILES
Sheila Rowse Designs
The Textile Centre, Great Walsingham, Norfolk NR22 6DR
Tel: (01328) 820009
Fax: (01328) 820999

Aprons, tea-towels, textiles, clothes.
Open: Mid Mar-mid Nov Mon-Fri 9.30am-5.30pm, Sat, Sun and bank hols 10am-5pm
Cards: Access, Switch, Visa

DIRECTIONS: Take B1388 from Little Walsingham to Binham. Well signposted by tourist boards.

8/880
● TEXTILES
Peter and Jason Collingwood
Old School, Church Lane, Nayland, Colchester, Essex CO6 4JH
Tel: (01206) 262401
Fax: (01206) 262207

Handmade, reversible flat-weave rugs, wall hangings.
Open: By arrangement
Cards: No

DIRECTIONS: 6 miles north of Colchester on A134. Church Lane is opposite White Hart pub in main street.

8/881
● STRAWCRAFT
Corn-Craft
Bridge Farm, Monks Eleigh, Nr Ipswich,
Suffolk IP7 7AY
Tel: (01449) 740456
Fax: (01449) 741665

Craft shop and dried-flower farm,
refreshments.
Open: Mon-Sat 10am-5pm, Sun
11am-5pm. Closed 25-26 Dec, 1 Jan
Cards: Access, Visa

DIRECTIONS: On A1141 between
Hadleigh and Lavenham.

8/882
■ WINE
The Leaping Hare Café and Country Store
Wyken Vineyards, Stanton, Bury St
Edmunds, Suffolk IP31 2DW
Tel: (01359) 250287
Fax: (01359) 250240

Wine, quilts, rugs, garden equipment.
Refreshments.
Open: Thur, Fri, Sun 10am-6pm.
Closed 25 Dec-9 Feb
Cards: Access, Connect, Switch, Visa

DIRECTIONS: 8 miles north of Bury
St Edmunds on A143. Follow brown
tourist signs to Ixworth.

8/883
● CERAMICS
Ryburgh Pottery
1 May Green, Little Ryburgh, Fakenham,
Norfolk NR21 0LP
Tel: (01328) 829543

Wood-fired stoneware and porcelain
for kitchen and table.
Open: Telephone first
Cards: No

DIRECTIONS: 3 miles south-east of
Fakenham, off the A1067 Norwich
road, look for sign to 'Little Ryburgh
only'.

8/884
● GARDEN ORNAMENTS
Old Barn Studios
Kettlestone, Nr Fakenham,
Norfolk NR21 0JB
Tel: (01328) 878762

Garden sculpture and paintings.
Open: Every day 9am-5.30pm. Closed
Tue 2pm-5.30pm
Cards: No

DIRECTIONS: Off A148, 1½ miles
from Fakenham.

8/885
■ WINE
Elmham Wines Ltd
Elmham House, North Elmham, Dereham,
Norfolk NR20 5JY
Tel: (01362) 668167
Fax: (01362) 668573

Wine from grape and apple.
Open: By appointment
Cards: Visa

DIRECTIONS: Entrance opposite
North Elmham church, drive across
park and under archway.

8/886
■ JUICES
Copella Fruit Juices Ltd
Hill Farm, Boxford, Sudbury,
Suffolk CO10 5NY
Tel: (01787) 210496
Fax: (01787) 211396

Fruit juices and apples.
Open: Mon-Fri 9am-4.30pm
Cards: No

DIRECTIONS: From Colchester
A134 to Sudbury at Leavenheath.
Take first right just past Hare &
Hounds, B1068. Then turn left to
Boxford. Farm is ½ mile on right.

8/887
■ WINE
Harling Vineyards
Eastfield House, Church Road, East
Harling, Norwich, Norfolk NR16 2NA
Tel: (01953) 717341

White wines, tours and refreshments.

Open: Mon-Sun 10.30am-6pm.
Closed 24 Dec-1 Jan
Cards: No

DIRECTIONS: On B111 next to
church in East Harling, just 3 miles
from Garboldisham turn off on A11.

8/888
■ WINE

Carters Vineyards
Green Lane, Boxted, Colchester,
Essex CO4 5TS
Tel/Fax: (01206) 271136

Wine and vineyard.
Open: From August 1995: 11am-5pm.
Closed Oct to Easter. Best to
telephone first
Cards: No

DIRECTIONS: 4 miles north of
Colchester off A134. After Great
Horkesley turn right and follow signs.

8/889
● CERAMICS

Kersey Pottery
The Street, Kersey, Nr Ipswich,
Suffolk IP7 6DY
Tel: (01473) 822092

High-fired stoneware pottery.
Open: Tue-Sat 9.30am-5.30pm, Sun
11am-5pm. Closed Mon, 24 Dec-10
Jan, weekends only until Easter
Cards: Access, Visa

DIRECTIONS: Off the A1071
Hadleigh bypass, west of the A1141
Lavenham road.

8/890
■ FRUIT/VEGETABLES

Clay Barn Orchard
Clay Barn, Fingringhoe, Colchester,
Essex CO5 7AR
Tel: (01206) 735405

Apples, pears, quinces, medlars,
honey.
Open: Every day during daylight hours
after 7am
Cards: No

DIRECTIONS: Leave Colchester on
B1025 to West Mersea. Turn left at
bridge over river. Turn left again at

T-Junction to Fingringhoe. Orchard
400 yards on right (signposted).

8/891
● CERAMICS

The Particular Pottery
Church Street, Kenninghall, Norwich,
Norfolk NR16 2EN
Tel/Fax: (01953) 888476

Hand-thrown decorated porcelain.
Open: Tue-Sat 9am-5pm and bank
hols
Cards: Access, Amex, Visa

DIRECTIONS: Follow the B1113 and
signs to Banham Zoo. On arrival in
Kenninghall, follow signs up Church
Street.

8/892
● PLANTS

Beth Chatto Gardens Ltd
Elmstead Market, Colchester,
Essex CO7 7DB
Tel: (01206) 822007

Hardy plants.
Open: Mar-Oct Mon-Sat 9am-5pm,
Nov-Feb, Mon-Fri 9am-4pm. Closed
Sun, bank hols and over Christmas
Cards: Access, Visa

DIRECTIONS: East of Elmstead
Market on A133 Colchester to
Clacton road.

8/893
● PLANTS

Hull Farm Conifers
Spring Valley Lane, Ardleigh, Colchester,
Essex CO7 7SA
Tel: (01206) 230045
Fax: (01206) 230820

Conifers, apples, pears, plums in
season.
Open: Daily 10am-4.30pm. Closed
Christmas to mid-Jan
Cards: Visa

DIRECTIONS: About 3 miles north
east of Colchester. Spring Valley Lane
is a turning off A137 Colchester to
Ardleigh road on right.

8/894
■ METALWORK

Hoggies
Manor Farm, Battisford, Stowmarket,
Suffolk IP14 2HE
Tel: (01449) 722500
Fax: (01449) 721500

Spit-roasting equipment for hire. Spit
roasting on site.
Open: Daily 7am-7pm
Cards: No

DIRECTIONS: Follow signs to
Combs, south of Stowmarket from
A14. Past Tannery, after 2 miles turn
left and left again. Farm on left up
drive.

8/895
● METALWORK

Marshall Brass
Foulsham, Dereham, Norfolk NR20 5PR
Tel: (01362) 684105
Fax: (01362) 684280

Brass furniture fittings, antique finish,
ironwork.
Open: Daily 9am-5pm. Closed
Whitsun week, first week in August
and Christmas week
Cards: Access, Visa

DIRECTIONS: From Foulsham, 1
mile along the Reepham Road is
Keeling Hall Road, last drive on the
left.

8/896
■ FLOUR

Letheringsett Water Mill
Riverside Road, Letheringsett, Holt,
Norfolk NR25 7YD
Tel: (01263) 713153

Stoneground flour and 100% organic
flour.
Open: Tue-Fri 9am-1pm, 2pm-5pm.
Sat 9am-1pm, Sun (Whitsun to Sept)
2pm-5pm. Closed Christmas and
New Year
Cards: No

DIRECTIONS: 1 mile west of Holt on
A148 follow brown tourist signs in
village.

8/897
● CERAMICS

Made in Cley
High Street, Cley next the Sea, Nr Holt,
Norfolk NR25 7RF
Tel: (01263) 740134

Wide range of stoneware pottery,
jewellery and stone sculpture.
Open: Oct-June 10am-5pm. Closed
Wed. Sun 11am-5pm. July-Sept
10am-6pm, Sun 11am-5pm
Cards: Access, Amex, Diners, Visa

DIRECTIONS: On the A149 in the
middle of the village.

8/898
■ SMOKED PRODUCE

Cley Smoke House
High Street, Cley next the Sea, Holt,
Norfolk NR25 7RF
Tel: (01263) 740282

Smoked fish and pickled herrings, fish
pâté.
Open: Mon-Sat 9am-5pm, Sun
9.30am-5pm
Cards: No

DIRECTIONS: On A149 coast road,
1 mile east of Blakeney in middle of
village.

8/899
● PLANTS

Bressingham Plant Centre
Bressingham Gardens, Bressingham,
Diss, Norfolk IP22 2AB
Tel: (01379) 688133
Fax: (01379) 688034

Hardy perennials.
Open: Daily 10am-5.30pm. Closed 25,
26 Dec
Cards: Access, Switch, Visa

DIRECTIONS: 3 miles west of Diss
on A1066.

8/900
● CURTAIN POLES

The Bradley Collection
The Granary, Flowton Brook, Flowton,
Suffolk IP8 4LJ
Tel: (01473) 652651
Fax: (01473) 652657

Steel, wood and hand-decorated
curtain poles and acccessories, also
lighting and furniture.
Open: Weekdays by appointment only.
Closed Christmas to New Year
Cards: Access, Visa

DIRECTIONS: Details will be given
on arrangement of appointment.

8/901
● PLANTS

Denbeigh Heather Nurseries
All Saints Road, Creeting St Mary, Ipswich,
Suffolk IP8 8PJ
Tel/Fax: (01449) 711220

Heathers.
Open: By appointment
Cards: No

DIRECTIONS: Turn left off A140, 2
miles north of A14/A140 junction.

8/902
✷ MULTIPLE

Alder Carr Farm Shop
Creeting St Mary, Ipswich, Suffolk IP6 8LX
Tel: (01449) 720820

Fruit, vegetables, preserves, pottery,
wood-turning.
Open: May-Oct Tue-Sun 9.30am-
5.30pm. Nov-Dec Tue-Sun 9.30am-
4pm. Closed Mar-Apr
Cards: No

DIRECTIONS: Off A14 between
Ipswich and Stowmarket. Follow
signs to Needham Market. Turn
down Hawk's Mill Street. Just over
river turn right down drive to farm
shop.

8/903
● GLASS

Jennifer Conway
31 Oxford Road, Mistley, Manningtree,
Essex CO11 1BW
Tel/Fax: (01206) 396274

Engraved glass, landscapes, figurative
work, mirrors and goblets.
Open: Strictly by appointment only
Cards: No

DIRECTIONS: Approximately 9 miles
north-east of Colchester on A137.

8/904
✷ MULTIPLE

Mistley Quay Workshops
Swan Basin, High Street, Mistley,
Essex CO11 1HB
Tel: (01206) 393884

Musical instruments, wood, ceramics,
needlecraft, bookbinding.
Open: Daily 10am-6pm. Closed
Christmas and New Year
Cards: Amex, Visa

DIRECTIONS: 9 miles north of
Colchester. Approach via A12 or
A120, then B1352 Manningtree to
junction of Mistley Towers. Turn
right. On left 100 yards to left of Swan
Fountain.

8/905
● PLANTS

Park Green Nurseries
Wetheringsett, Stowmarket,
Suffolk IP14 5QH
Tel/Fax: (01728) 860139

Hostas, astilbes, ornamental grasses.
Open: Thur-Mon 10am-5.30pm.
Closed Nov-Feb
Cards: Access, Visa

DIRECTIONS: Take turning off A140
signposted to Park Green by tall radio
mast adjacent to Mendlesham
industrial estate.

8/906
● GARDEN PONDS

Waveney Fish Farm
Park Road, Diss, Norfolk IP22 3AS
Tel: (01379) 642697
Fax: (01379) 651315

Pond accessories, tropical fish,
moisture-loving plants.
Open: Daily 9.30am-5pm
Cards: Access, Switch, Visa

DIRECTIONS: On A1066 in Diss,
opposite the Park Hotel.

8/907
● FURNITURE

David Gregson Furniture
Bridge Green Farm, Gissing Road, Burston,
Nr Diss, Norfolk IP22 3ND
Tel: (01379) 740528

Furniture for domestic and corporate
locations.
Open: By appointment
Cards: Visa

DIRECTIONS: From A140, through
Shimpling, first right after railway
crossing, 200 yards on right.

8/908
■ BAKED GOODS

Silver Nutmeg
28 Church Street, Eye, Suffolk IP23 7BD
Tel: (01379) 870229

Wholefood cakes and savouries, both
meat and vegetarian.
Open: Sat 9am-5pm
Cards: No

DIRECTIONS: Off A140 to Eye. Left
opposite town hall, into Church
Street. Halfway down Church Street
on right.

8/909
■ FRUIT/VEGETABLES

Old Hall Farm
Attlebridge, Norwich, Norfolk NR9 5TQ
Tel: (01603) 867317

Asparagus.
Open: 9.30am-5.30pm, but advisable
to telephone
Cards: No

DIRECTIONS: On A1067 Norwich to
Fakenham Road, 1 mile north of
Taverham

8/910
■ FARM PRODUCE

Hemingstone Fruitique
Main Road, Hemingstone, Ipswich,
Suffolk IP6 9RJ
Tel/Fax: (01449) 760330

Apples, preserves, chutneys.
Open: Mon-Sat 10am-4.30pm. Closed
Sun
Cards: No

DIRECTIONS: On A14 from Ipswich
take A140 turning to Coddenham on
to B1078. Follow through
Coddenham turn 2nd right. Follow
up hill, Fruitique is on right.

8/911
● CERAMICS

Carters Ceramic Designs
Low Road, Debenham, Suffolk IP14 6QU
Tel: (01728) 860475
Fax: (01728) 861110

Collectable teapots.
Open: Mon-Fri 9am-5pm, Sat
10.30am-4.30pm, Easter-Sept Sun
Cards: Access, Visa

DIRECTIONS: From Debenham
follow signs for pottery just off the
High Street.

8/912
● PLANTS

Goldbrook Plants
Hoxne, Eye, Suffolk IP21 5AN
Tel: (01379) 668770

Nursery specialising in perennials,
hostas, hemerocallis, shade-loving
plants.
Open: Thur-Sun 10.30am-6pm or
dusk
Cards: No

DIRECTIONS: From A140 Norwich-
Ipswich road take B1118 to
Stradbroke. 4 miles to village, go past
Swan pub on right, take 1st turn on
left.

8/913
● WOOD

John Anderson
20 Silvergate, Blickling, Norwich,
Norfolk NR11 6NN
Tel: (01263) 735270

Picture frames, mirrors and boxes.
Open: Telephone for appointment
Cards: No

DIRECTIONS: North of Norwich on
A140. At Aylsham turn on to B1354.
Follow signs to Blickling Hall. Turn
left at T-junction, follow signs for
Silvergate. Turn right after first set of
terrace houses. On corner.

8/914
● CERAMICS

Paul David Jackson
Calthorpe Workshop, Aldborough Road,
Calthorpe, Norfolk NR11 7QP
Tel/Fax: (01263) 768346

Fantasy sculptures in porcelain,
illustrated wonder tales.
Open: June-Sept Wed, Fri, Sat 10am-
5.30pm, other times telephone in
advance. Closed 25 Dec
Cards: No

DIRECTIONS: On A140 north of
Norwich, through Aylsham and left
into Erpingham. Go past Spread Eagle
and open fields on right, to the
Corner House Workshop, 800 yards
on right.

8/915
● CERAMICS

A & J Young Pottery
Common Farm, Sustead Road, Lower
Gresham, Norwich NR11 8RE
Tel: (01263) 577548

Stoneware domestic pottery.
Open: Mon-Fri 9am-5pm, Sat 9am-
3pm. Closed Sun
Cards: No

DIRECTIONS: 26 miles north of
Norwich, 4 miles west of Cromer
south of Aylmerton on A148.

8/916
■ FARM PRODUCE

The Priory Farm Shop
Priory Farm, Wrabness, Manningtree,
Essex CO11 2UG
Tel: (01255) 880338

Vegetables, fruit, cakes, jams, apple
juice, pickles, eggs.
Open: Mon-Sat 9am-5.30pm. Sun
10am-1pm. Closed bank hols and 10
days after Christmas
Cards: No

DIRECTIONS: On B1352 from
Manningtree to Harwich (5 miles
from Manningtree). 150 yards from
Wheatsheaf pub.

8/917
■ FISH/SHELLFISH

The Company Shed
129 Coast Road, West Mersea,
Colchester CO5 8PA
Tel: (01206) 382700
Fax: (01206) 383284

Oysters, local fish and shellfish.
Open: Tue-Sun 9am-5pm. Closed 25-
30 Dec
Cards: No

DIRECTIONS: Cross the Strood to
Mersea island (check the tide time),
pass through West Mersea village to
the waterside.

8/918
■ WINE

Pulham Vineyards Ltd
Mill Lane, Pulham Market, Diss,
Norfolk IP21 4XL
Tel: (01379) 676672

White wines.
Open: Mon-Sat 9am-5pm
Cards: No

DIRECTIONS: Off A140, on to
B1134, first left to Mill Lane, left
again and then on left.

8/919
■ DAIRY PRODUCE

Otley College Dairy

Otley College of Agriculture, Otley, Ipswich,
Suffolk IP6 9EY
Tel: (01473) 785543
Fax: (01473) 785353

Goats' milk and goats' cheese.
Open: Mon-Fri 8am-3.30pm
Cards: No

DIRECTIONS: 7 miles north of
Ipswich on B1078.

8/920
■ WINE

Stradbroke Vineyard

Farrows Mill, Battlesea Green, Stradbroke,
Suffolk IP21 5NE
Tel: (01379) 384492

White wine.
Open: Mon-Sat 11am-11pm, Sun
1pm-6.30pm
Cards: No

DIRECTIONS: 1 mile north-west of
Stradbroke village, signposted off the
B1118.

8/921
■ FISH/SHELLFISH

Richard & Julie Davies

7 Garden Street, Cromer, Norfolk NR27 9HN
Tel: (01263) 512727

Crabs, lobsters and fish.
Open: Daily Mar-Oct. Tue, Thur, Fri,
Sat Nov-Feb. Closed Sun, Mon and
Wed pm
Cards: No

DIRECTIONS: In centre of Cromer.

8/922
■ FARM PRODUCE

Cranes Watering Farm Shop

Rushall Road, Starston, Harleston,
Norfolk IP20 9NE
Tel/Fax: (01379) 852387

Ice-cream, cream, pork.
Open: Tue-Sat 9am-5pm. Sun
9.30am-12.30pm. Closed Mon all
year, Thur in Jan, Christmas
Cards: No

DIRECTIONS: Between Dickleburgh
(A140) and Harleston (A143) about
½ mile west of Harleston police
station.

8/923
● CERAMICS

Church Cottage Pottery

Wilby, Nr Eye, Suffolk IP21 5LE
Tel: (01379) 384253

Domestic, garden, decorative pots,
enamelled metalware, pyrographed
wood. Teashop.
Open: Mon-Sat 10am-6pm, Sun 2pm-
6pm. Closed Wed and Jan
Cards: No

DIRECTIONS: 1 mile south of
Stradbroke on B1118. Opposite the
church in Wilby.

8/924
● CERAMICS

Millhouse Pottery

1 Station Road, Harleston,
Norfolk IP20 9ES
Tel: (01379) 852556

Slipware and tin-glazed pottery.
Garden pots and plants.
Open: Daily 10am-5.30pm
Cards: No

DIRECTIONS: In Harleston between
Bungay and Diss, opposite the Duke
William pub.

8/925
● CERAMICS

Deborah Baynes Pottery Studio

Nether Hall, Shotley, Ipswich,
Suffolk IP9 1PW
Tel: (01473) 788300

Wheel-thrown pottery, from mugs
and teapots to candlesticks and
planters.
Open: Reasonable hours, telephone
first
Cards: No

DIRECTIONS: On B1456 between
Shotley village and Shotley Gate on
right, immediately past Over Hall
Farm.

8/926
■ EGGS

Akenfield Eggs
Shrubbery Farm, Charsfield, Woodbridge,
Suffolk IP13 7PS
Tel: (01473) 737252

Free-range hen, duck and quail eggs.
Open: Daily 8am-6pm
Cards: No

DIRECTIONS: Take B1078 from
Wickham Market off A12. In 3 miles
Q8 petrol station. On left 200 yards
past Q8.

8/927
■ DELICATESSEN FOODS

Suffolk Larder
17 Thoroughfare, Woodbridge,
Suffolk IP12 1AA
Tel: (01394) 386676
Fax: (01394) 380483

Cured hams, chicken, lamb, mustards,
cider cake.
Open: Mon-Sat 9am-5pm. Closed
Wed pm and bank hols
Cards: No

DIRECTIONS: In centre of town off
main thoroughfare.

8/928
● PLANTS

**Norwich Heather and Conifer
Centre**
54a Yarmouth Road, Thorpe St. Andrew,
Norwich, Norfolk NR7 0HE
Tel: (01603) 39434

Heather and conifers.
Open: Mon, Tue, Wed, Fri, Sat, 9am-
5pm, Sun 2pm-5pm. Closed Thur
Cards: No

DIRECTIONS: On A1121, 3 miles
east of Norwich city centre past
Thorpe River Green and Rushcutters
pub adjacent to new bypass. Take the
turning signposted Norwich north
and east.

8/929
● CERAMICS

Cat Pottery
1 Grammar School Road, North Walsham,
Norfolk NR28 9JH
Tel: (01692) 402962

Life-size pottery cats with handmade
glass eyes.
Open: Mon-Fri 9.30am-5pm, Sat
11am-1pm, bank hols 11am-3pm
Cards: No

DIRECTIONS: In North Walsham
opposite Black Cat garage.

8/930
● HERBS

Daphne ffiske Herbs
Rosemary Cottage, The Street, Bramerton,
Norwich, Norfolk NR14 7DW
Tel: (01508) 538187

Herb plants, fragrant and medicinal.
Open: Mar-Sept Thur-Sun 10am-4pm
Cards: No

DIRECTIONS: From A47 exit to
Lowestoft along A146. Turn left
towards Kirby Bedon nursery is
opposite telephone kiosk.

8/931
■ WINE

Staverton Vineyard
The Rookery, Eyke, Woodbridge,
Suffolk IP12 2RR
Tel: (01394) 460271
Fax: (01394) 460818

Still and sparkling wines.
Open: Sat 10am-4pm, Sun 2pm-5pm in
summer. Closed Christmas to Easter
Cards: No

DIRECTIONS: Signposted 4 miles
from A12 on B1084 to Orford.

8/932
● FORGEWORK

Brian Reynolds Blacksmith
The Forge, Mundesley Road, Paston,
North Walsham, Norfolk NR28 9TE
Tel: (01263) 721871

Door and window furniture,
staircases, balustrades, gates and
railings, weathervanes, fire baskets.

Open: Mon-Fri 8am-6pm, Sat-Sun
8am-1pm, but telephone first
Cards: No

DIRECTIONS: Follow B1145 north
Walsham to Mundesley road, until T-
junction. Turn right on B1159, up hill
past Stow windmill, ½ mile on left
under beech tree.

8/933
■ WINE

**Bruisyard Vineyard and Herb
Centre**
Church Road, Bruisyard, Saxmundham,
Suffolk IP17 2EF
Tel: (01728) 638281
Fax: (01728) 638442

Wine, vineyard, herb centre, water
garden, restaurant.
Open: Mon-Sun 10.30am-5pm.
Closed 25 Dec-1 Jan
Cards: Access, Switch, Visa

DIRECTIONS: Follow brown tourist
signs from A12 Saxmundham bypass.

8/934
● SHEEPSKIN

Nursey & Son Ltd
Upper Olland Street, Bungay,
Suffolk NR35 1BQ
Tel: (01986) 892821
Fax: (01986) 892823

Leather, sheepskin and flying jackets,
slippers, hats, gloves.
Open: Mon-Fri 10am-1pm, 2pm-
5pm. Nov-Dec Mon-Sat 10am-1pm,
2pm-5pm. Closed 25, 26 Dec, 1 Jan,
Sun.
Cards: Access, Visa

DIRECTIONS: 14 miles south-east of
Norwich. On A143, A144 and A1116.
In centre of town.

8/935
■ WINE

Wissett Wines
Valley Farm Vineyards, Wissett,
Halesworth, Suffolk IP19 0JJ
Tel: (01986) 785216
Fax: (01986) 785443

English sparkling and table wines.

Open: Mon-Sat 10am-6pm, Sun
12 noon-2.45pm. Closed 25 Dec-7 Jan
Cards: No

DIRECTIONS: 2½ miles north-west
of Halesworth. Take Wissett turn off
A144 Halesworth to Bungay road.

8/936
■ JUICES/CORDIALS

Ranworth Farms Ltd
The Old House, Ranworth, Norwich,
Norfolk NR13 6HS
Tel: (01603) 270722
Fax: (01603) 270611

Apple juice.
Open: By appointment only
Cards: No

DIRECTIONS: From Acle take road
to South Walsham. Turn right at Ship
Inn.

8/937
● CERAMICS

Butley Pottery
Mill Lane Butley, Woodbridge,
Suffolk IP12 3PA
Tel: (01394) 450785
Fax: (01394) 450843

Hand-painted majolica and
lustreware. Gallery and tea barn.
Open: Apr-Sept Mon-Sun 10.30am-
5pm
Cards: Access, Visa

DIRECTIONS: A12 to Woodbridge,
B1084 to Orford. After Oyster Inn in
Butley, turn right down Mill Lane.

8/938
■ PRESERVES

Garden of Suffolk Preserves
The Granary, Woodhill Farm, Willowmarsh
Lane, Yoxford, Saxmundham,
Suffolk IP17 3JR
Tel/Fax: (01728) 668329

Jams, marmalades, jellies and lemon
curd.
Open: Any time
Cards: No

DIRECTIONS: 30 miles north of
Ipswich on A12. Go through Yoxford,
over Darsham railway crossing, and

take first left to Hevingham. Second
farm on left.

8/939
● CERAMICS
Sutton Windmill Pottery
Church Road, Sutton, Norwich,
Norfolk NR12 9SG
Tel: (01692) 580595

Stoneware pottery, tableware, lamps
and decorative pieces.
Open: Mon-Fri 9am-1pm, 2pm-6pm,
weekends by appointment. Closed 25
Dec
Cards: No

DIRECTIONS: 17 miles north-east of
Norwich via A1151 and A149. Turn
left at Sutton Staithe, 1½ miles south
of Stalham, left at garden centre, right
into Church Road.

8/940
■ SMOKED PRODUCE
Richardson's Smokehouse
The Old Smokehouse, Bakers Lane,
Orford, Suffolk IP12 2LH
Tel: (01394) 450103

Smoked fish, meat and cheese.
Open: Daily Apr-Sept 9am-5.30pm.
Rest of year 10am-4pm. Closed at
Christmas
Cards: No

DIRECTIONS: Take A12 from
Ipswich past Woodbridge, turn right
on to B1084 to Orford. Off market
square, turn up lane between Town
Hall and Oysterage (Bakers Lane) and
it is at the end on left.

8/941
● CERAMICS
Jonathan Keep Pottery
31 Leiston Road, Knodishall,
Saxmundham, Suffolk IP17 1UQ
Tel: (01728) 832901

Domestic pottery, table and
kitchenware.
Open: Mon-Sat 9.30am-5.30pm.
Closed bank hols
Cards: No

DIRECTIONS: Off B1119
Framlingham to Saxmundham road.
Opposite filling station.

8/942
● PLANTS
Fisk's Clematis Nursery
Westleton, Saxmundham, Suffolk IP17 3AJ
Tel: (01728) 648263

Clematis.
Open: Mon-Fri 9am-5pm, Apr-Oct
also Sat-Sun 10am-1pm and 2pm-
5pm. Closed 22 Dec to 2 Jan
Cards: No

DIRECTIONS: Leave the A12 at
Yoxford (coming from Ipswich). Turn
right at signpost for Westleton and
Dunwich. Nursery signpost at garage
in Westleton 2 miles from the A12.

8/943
● CERAMICS
Dorothy Midson Ceramics
Blythburgh Pottery, Chappel Lane,
Blythburgh, Suffolk IP19 9LW
Tel: (01502) 478234

Coil-built pots.
Open: Mon-Sat 11am-5pm, Sun
sometimes
Cards: No

DIRECTIONS: Heading north from
Ipswich on A12 to Lowestoft. On
entering Blythburgh, first right.
Village shop on corner, pottery at far
end of same building.

8/944
■ FISH/SHELLFISH
Harvey's Wet Fish Shop
115 High Street, Aldeburgh,
Suffolk IP15 5AR
Tel/Fax: (01728) 452145

Wet fish, smoked fish, shellfish.
Open: Mon-Sat 8.30am-1pm, 2pm-
4pm. Wed 8.30am-12.30pm. Closed 2
weeks mid-Oct
Cards: No

DIRECTIONS: Middle of Aldeburgh
High Street.

8/945
■ SAUSAGES

Salters Family Butchers
107-109 High Street, Aldeburgh,
Suffolk IP15 5AR
Tel: (01728) 452758

Local farmed meat, homemade
sausages and cooked ham.
Open: Mon, Wed 7am-1pm, Tue,
Thur, Fri 7am-5pm, Sat 7am-4pm
Cards: No

DIRECTIONS: 20 miles from Ipswich
on A12 towards Saxmundham. Then
head for coast via Snape.

MAP 9

9/946
■ BAKED GOODS
Gwynle Bakery
Pen y Bonc Road, Amlwch, Anglesey,
Gwynedd LL68 9DU
Tel: (01407) 830293

Bread, confectionery and pies.
Open: Mon-Sat 9am-5pm
Cards: No

DIRECTIONS: At Menai Bridge take
A5025 signposted Amlwch. Situated
opposite the library.

9/947
● TEXTILES
Cefyn Burgess
Glanrafon Mill, Parc Glynllifon, Llandwrog,
Caernarfon, Gwynedd LL54 5DY
Tel: (01286) 831123

Woven furnishings fabrics, rugs,
quilts, cushions.
Open: Daily 10am-5pm
Cards: No

DIRECTIONS: On A499 from
Caernarfon or Pwllheli. Opposite
village of Llandwrog. Through arch
into Park Glynllifon.

9/948
■ FISH/SHELLFISH
Anglesey Sea Zoo
Brynsiencyn, Anglesey,
Gwynedd LL61 6TQ
Tel: (01248) 430411
Fax: (01248) 430213

Sealife in 80 tanks. Oysters.
Restaurant. Gift shop.
Open: 10am-5pm. Nov-Feb 11am-
3pm
Cards: Access, Amex, Switch, Visa

DIRECTIONS: Follow brown Sea
Zoo signs from A5 or A55 on to the
A4080. (Over Britannia Bridge to
Anglesey.)

9/949
■ ICE-CREAM
Cadwalader Ice Cream
Castle Street, Criccieth,
Gwynedd LL52 0DP
Tel: (01766) 522478
Fax: (01766) 523391

Ice-cream.
Open: Summer 9.30am to dusk,
winter: Sat-Sun only
Cards: No

DIRECTIONS: Below the castle.

9/950
■ HONEY
Ffermfelyr Wyddfa – Snowdon Honey Farm
Llanberis, Gwynedd LL55 4HB
Tel: (01286) 870218

Honey and honey products including
beeswax candles, mead, cosmetics and
confectionery.
Open: Daily 7am-6pm
Cards: Access, Visa

DIRECTIONS: Beside Heights Hotel.

9/951
■ BAKED GOODS
Becws Eryri
84 High Street, Llanberis,
Gwynedd LL55 4SU
Tel: (01286) 870491

Bread, confectionery and savoury
goods including bara brith and Welsh
cakes.
Open: Mon-Sat 7am-5.30pm. Sun
7am-12 noon. Closed 25 and 26 Dec,
1 Jan
Cards: No

DIRECTIONS: 7 miles south of
Caernarfon on A4086. In centre of
village next to Padarn Lake Hotel.

9/952
■ DAIRY PRODUCE
Brynllys Farm Shop
Brynllys Farm, Dolybont, Borth,
Dyfed SY24 5LZ
Tel: (01970) 625805
Fax: (01970) 871157

Welsh cheeses, yoghurt, cream.

Open: Apr-end Sept Tue-Sat 9am-3pm. Closed 1 Oct-31 Mar
Cards: No

DIRECTIONS: 6 miles north of Aberystwyth. Off B4353 from Borth to Rhydypennalls. Take turning to Dolybont under railway bridge. Through village and first turning on left by farm sign.

9/953
■ BEER

Snowdonia Brewing Co Ltd
The Bryn Arms, Gellilydan,
Gwynedd LL41 4EH
Tel/Fax: (01766) 590379

At the time of going to press Snowdonia Brewing Co Ltd has moved premises to Shrewsbury

9/954
■ CONFECTIONERY

Chocolate House of Dolwyddelan
Old School, Church Street, Dolwyddelan,
Gwynedd LL25 0SJ
Tel: (01690) 6579

Chocolate.
Open: Sun-Fri 10am-3pm except Mon. Closed end Oct to Easter
Cards: Access, Visa

DIRECTIONS: On A470 5 miles south from Betws-y-Coed to Blaenau Ffestiniog. Turn left in Dolwyddelan and follow signs.

9/955
■ FISH/SHELLFISH

Conwy Valley Fisheries
Glyn Isa, Rowen, Conwy,
Gwynedd LL32 8TP
Tel/Fax: (01492) 650063

Smoked salmon, trout, chicken, mussels. Preserves, honeys, pâtés.
Open: Daily 9am-dusk
Cards: Access, Switch, Visa

DIRECTIONS: From Conwy Castle take left on B5106 to Trefriw. 3 miles, turn left to Rowen (near Groess Inn). 1 mile on right-hand side.

9/956
■ FLOUR

Felin Crewi Watermill
Penegoes, Machynlleth, Powys SY20 8NH
Tel/Fax: (01654) 703113

Stoneground flours and old mill muesli; working watermill.
Open: Easter to end Sept Sun-Fri 10.30am-5pm. Sat in school holidays. Winter Wed 9.30am-3.30pm
Cards: No

DIRECTIONS: 1½ miles east of Machynlleth, 50 yards off Newtown road.

9/957
■ BAKED GOODS

Cacennau Briwsion Cakes
Yr Hen Ysgol, Fford Nebo Pentrefoelas,
Betws-y-Coed, Gwynedd LL24 0HY
Tel: (01690) 770330

Welsh cakes.
Open: Mon-Fri 7am-5pm. Closed week after New Year
Cards: No

DIRECTIONS: On A5 at Pentrefoelas in old school building.

9/958
■ DELICATESSEN FOODS

Blas ar Fwyd
25 Heol yr Orsaf, Llanrwst,
Gwynedd LL26 0BT
Tel/Fax: (01492) 640215

Cheese, pâté, cured and smoked meats, cakes, soda, bread, preserves, chutney.
Open: Mon-Sat 8.30am-6pm. Closed Sun, 25 Dec and bank hols
Cards: No

DIRECTIONS: On main shopping street.

9/959
● PLANTS

Aberconwy Nursery
Graig, Glan Conwy, Colwyn Bay,
Clwyd LL28 5TL
Tel: (01492) 580875

Alpines, shrubs and herbaceous
plants.
Open: Mar-Oct Tue-Sun 9am-5pm,
Nov-Feb Tue-Sun 10am-4pm.
Closed Christmas week-1 Jan
Cards: Access, Visa

DIRECTIONS: Travelling south on
A470 from Glanconwy-Llanrwst, take
the first right after Nev's Garage,
signposted Aberconwy Nursery,
follow minor road, turning first right
at top of hill.

9/960
● KNITWEAR

Sasha Kagan Knitwear
The Studio, Y-Fron, Llawr-y-Glyn, Caersws,
Powys SY17 5RJ
Tel: (01686) 430436

Hand-knitted coats, jackets and
sweaters.
Open: 10am-3.30pm but telephone in
advance
Cards: Access, Visa

DIRECTIONS: Take A489 from
Newtown, turn right into Caersws.
Left at crossroads and continue to
Trefeglwys. Turn right at shop and
continue to Llawr-y-Glyn. Through
village take right-hand fork and Y-
Fron is on right.

9/961
● ROCKING-HORSES

A.P.E.S. Rocking Horses
Ty Gwyn, Llannefydd, Denbigh,
Clwyd LL16 5HB
Tel: (01745) 79365

Rocking-horses, full-size and
miniature.
Open: Daily 10am-4pm but telephone
in advance
Cards: No

DIRECTIONS: West from
Llannefydd, first left, signposted
Llansannan. 1½ miles to fork at
bottom of hill, take track on right.

9/962
■ ICE-CREAM

Denbigh Farmhouse Ices
Broadleys Farm, Gwaenynog, Denbigh,
Clwyd LL16 5NU
Tel/Fax: (01745) 814053

Ice-cream in many flavours.
Open: Tue to Sun, Whitsun to Oct
10.30am-5.30pm. Also bank hols
Cards: No

DIRECTIONS: 1½ miles to west of
Denbigh on A543 towards Bylchau.

9/963
■ BAKED GOODS

Alwyn Thomas Bakery
124 Vale Street, Denbigh, Clwyd LL16 3BS
Tel: (01745) 812068

Bread, savouries, fresh cream cakes,
gateaux, sweets.
Open: Daily 8.30am-5pm
Cards: No

DIRECTIONS: On left-hand side
after traffic lights on entering town
from the east.

9/964
● KNITWEAR

Dorie Schreker Designer
Knitwear
Church House, Pont Robert, Meifod,
Powys SY22 6HY
Tel: (01938) 500642

Mohair and pure wool and silk
garments.
Open: By appointment
Cards: No

DIRECTIONS: 10 miles north-west of
Welshpool on A458, take B4389 to
Meifod. After 1 mile at T-junction,
turn left. Signposted to Pont Robert.
Church House (Old Village School)
next to Church Gate.

9/965
● PLANTS

Celyn Vale Eucalyptus Nurseries
Allt-y-Celyn, Carrog, Corwen,
Clwyd LL21 9LD
Tel/Fax: (01490) 430671

Hardy eucalyptus trees.
Open: Mon-Fri 9am-5.15pm. Closed Jan-Feb
Cards: Access, Visa

DIRECTIONS: 1 mile from Carrog village, signposted from the village. Carrog is just off the A5 trunk road and 3 miles east of Corwen.

9/966
■ FISH/SHELLFISH

Forest Hill Trout Farm & Fishery
Downing Road, Whitford, Nr Holywell,
Clwyd CH8 9EQ
Tel: (01745) 560151

Trout.
Open: Apr-Oct 10am-6pm. Nov-Mar 10am-4pm. Closed 25 and 26 Dec
Cards: No

DIRECTIONS: 6 miles from Holywell, 8 miles from Rhyl. Signposted from A548 Flint/Prestatyn coast road and A5026 Chester/Conwy road.

9/967
● CERAMICS

Welshpool Pottery
The Glyn, Cyfronydd, Welshpool,
Powys SY21 9ER
Tel: (01938) 850303
Fax: (01938) 850383

Earthenware pottery and giftware.
Open: Daily 9am-6pm. Closed some bank holiday weekends, best to telephone in advance
Cards: Access, Visa

DIRECTIONS: On A458, 5 miles west of Welshpool. Turn off on to B4392. After 1 mile turn left into narrow lane for 400 yards. Pottery on left in wooded valley.

9/968
■ WINE

Ty Brethyn Meadery
Ty Brethyn, Fron Bache, Llangollen,
Clwyd LL20 7BS
Tel: (01978) 860437
Fax: (01978) 861403

Mead including Brother Cadfael label.
Open: Telephone for appointment
Cards: Access, Switch, Visa

DIRECTIONS: From Shrewsbury along A5 to Llangollen. Turn left in centre, left again and up hill past the Grapes pub. Turn right opposite Plas Newydd Manor House. Up narrow lane, and then follow signposts.

9/969
■ BAKED GOODS

Megan's Kitchen
The Bishop Trevor, Abbey Road,
Llangollen, Clwyd LL20 8SN
Tel/Fax: (01978) 860063

Traditional mixes for 'bake at home' items including Welsh cakes and fruit scones.
Open: Tue-Sun 10am-5.30pm, or by arrangement. Closed Jan-Feb
Cards: No

DIRECTIONS: Facing Llangollen Bridge on Ruabon-Horseshoe Pass road.

9/970
● TEXTILES

Isaf Design Ltd
The Studio, Top Floor, 52 High Street,
Mold, Clwyd CH7 1BH
Tel: (01352) 750908

Hand-painted silks and textile designs, greetings cards.
Open: 9am-5pm, but telephone in advance
Cards: Access, Visa

DIRECTIONS: Opposite church.

9/971
● PLANTS

Oak Cottage Herb Garden
Nesscliffe, Shropshire SY4 1DB
Tel/Fax: (01743) 741262

Culinary and medicinal herb plants,
wild flower and cottage garden plants,
garden open.
Open: Easter-end Sept Mon-Sun
11am-6pm, by appointment in winter
Cards: No

DIRECTIONS: Halfway between
Shrewsbury and Oswestry on A5.
Take lane off A5 opposite Nesscliffe
Hotel.

9/972
■ SMOKED PRODUCE

Blackhurst of Shropshire
Drawwell, Clive, Shrewsbury,
Shropshire SY4 3JN
Tel: (01939) 220329

Smoked fish, poultry, game, ham,
venison and pâté.
Open: Mon-Fri 9am-5pm. Weekends
by arrangement
Cards: No

DIRECTIONS: 8 miles north of
Shrewsbury on A49. Turn left after
Hadnall, signposted Clive. Look for
Clive church spire. The Smokehouse
is opposite the lych gate.

9/973
● ROCKING-HORSES

Greenwoods Rocking Horses
15A Park Road, Tarporley,
Cheshire CW6 0AN
Tel: (01829) 732006

Rocking-horses.
Open: Sat 10am-5pm
Cards: No

DIRECTIONS: In the centre of
Tarporley village, on Park Road
opposite the Swan Hotel.

MAP 10

10/974
✹ MULTIPLE

Llangedwyn Mill
Llangedwyn, Oswestry,
Shropshire SY10 9LD
Tel/Fax: (01691) 780601

Glass, hand-built tandems, clocks,
silversmithing, jewellery, lampshades,
barometers.
Open: Mon-Fri 10am-5pm. Weekends
by appointment
Cards: Access, Visa

DIRECTIONS: Between Welshpool
and Oswestry (A483) turn west at
Llynclys towards Llanrhaeadr on
B4396. Turn left in Llangedwyn. Mill
is opposite, 200 yards on right.

10/975
● CERAMICS

Tickmore Pottery
Treflach Road, Trefonen, Oswestry,
Shropshire SY10 9DZ
Tel: (01691) 661842

Hand-thrown stoneware, decorative
pottery.
Open: Open daily but best to
telephone in advance
Cards: No

DIRECTIONS: From A5 into
Oswestry take left fork towards town.
Cross over at traffic lights carry on for
3 miles – pottery on left just through
village.

10/976
■ SMOKED PRODUCE

Little Cefn Farm Smokehouse
Little Cefn Farm, Hyssington, Churchstoke,
Powys SY15 6EQ
Tel: (01588) 620603

Smoked meat, poultry and game.
Open: Daily 8am-8pm
Cards: No

DIRECTIONS: 19 miles south-west of
Shrewsbury turn off A489 to
Hyssington. Farm is 1 mile north of
village post office.

10/977
● WOOD

A B Woodworking
Unit J, Pentre Wern, Gobowen, Oswestry,
Shropshire SY10 7JZ
Tel: (01691) 670425
Fax: (01691) 670235

Shaker style boxes, wooden hat boxes,
trays, wastepaper bins, sewing and
work boxes.
Open: By appointment only
Cards: No

DIRECTIONS: Take Gobowen Road
off Orthopaedic roundabout on A5
Oswestry bypass. Third set of
buildings on right before Gobowen
village.

10/978
■ DELICATESSEN FOODS

Muffs of Bromborough
3-5 Allport Lane, Bromborough, Wirral,
Merseyside L62 7HH
Tel/Fax: (0151) 3342002

Sausages, black pudding, pies and
cheese.
Open: Daily 9am-5.30pm. Closed
bank hols
Cards: No

DIRECTIONS: Take A141 New
Chester road. Turn into
Bromborough village then Allport
Lane.

10/979
✹ MULTIPLE

**The Old Post Office Craft
Centre**
57 School Lane, Haskayne, Ormskirk,
Lancashire L39 7JE
Tel: (01704) 841066

Crafts, dolls' houses, toys and wood-
turning.
Open: Thur-Sat 9.30am-4.30pm. Extra
opening prior to Christmas. Advisable
to telephone
Cards: Access, Visa

DIRECTIONS: 5 miles west of
Ormskirk going towards Formby. Off
A5147, Southport to Maghull road,
turn west at King's Arms pub. 100
yards on left.

10/980
● CERAMICS

Top Farm Pottery
High Street, Farndon, Cheshire CH3 6PT
Tel: (01978) 364812

Functional stoneware, brush-decorated.
Open: Mon-Fri 9am-5pm, Sat 9am-12 noon, but telephone in advance.
Closed 25 Dec
Cards: No

DIRECTIONS: Between Chester and Wrexham follow signs to Holt.

10/981
● FURNITURE

Silver Lining Workshops
Chester Road, Aldford, Chester, Cheshire CH3 6HJ
Tel: (01244) 620200
Fax: (01244) 620277

Furniture.
Open: Mon-Fri 8am-5.30pm, weekends by appointment only.
Closed 25 Dec-1 Jan
Cards: No

DIRECTIONS: In Aldford on the B5130, 5 miles south of Chester.

10/982
■ FRUIT/VEGETABLES

Ellesmere Road Organic Nursery
Ellesmere Road, Cockshutt, Ellesmere, Shropshire SY12 9AB
Tel: (01939) 270270

Organically grown fruit and vegetables.
Open: Mar-May Mon-Sat 9am-5pm, June-Aug Mon-Sun 9am-6pm, Sept Mon-Wed, Fri-Sat 9am-5pm
Cards: No

DIRECTIONS: 10 miles north of Shrewsbury, 4 miles south of Ellesmere on A528. 400 yards south of Cockshutt village on main road.

10/983
■ PRESERVES

The Hollies Apiary and Farm Shop
The Hollies, Welshampton, Ellesmere, Shropshire SY12 0QA
Tel: (01948) 710253

Pickles, preserves, chutneys and also honey and beeswax products.
Open: Daily
Cards: No

DIRECTIONS: On A495 Ellesmere/Whitchurch road on Whitchurch side of Welshampton.

10/984
■ WINE

Carden Park Vineyard
Carden, Nr Broxton, Chester, Cheshire CH3 9DQ
Tel: (01829) 731000
Fax: (01829) 731133

Wine, tours.
Open: Daily 9am-5.30pm
Cards: Access, Amex, Diners, Visa

DIRECTIONS: M6, A500 exit. A534 Wrexham Road, straight across at Broxton roundabout, for 2 miles, Carden Park entrance on left.

10/985
■ MEAT/POULTRY/GAME

C G Sadd
Main Road, Dorrington, Shrewsbury, Shropshire SY5 7JD
Tel: (01743) 718215

Sausages, pies, cured ham, bacon. Local beef, lamb, pork and poultry.
Open: Tue-Sat 8am-5.30pm. Closed bank hols
Cards: No

DIRECTIONS: On A49 Church Stretton to Shrewsbury road. 6 miles south of Shrewsbury.

10/986
● FURNITURE

Michael Niblett Cabinet Maker

The Lilacs, Hereford Road, Bayston Hill
Common, Bayston Hill, Shrewsbury,
Shropshire SY3 0DZ
Tel: (01743) 872814

Furniture and joinery.
Open: Mon-Sat 9am-5pm, by
appointment
Cards: No

DIRECTIONS: On A49 Shrewsbury
to Leominster road, 3 miles south of
Shrewsbury next door to Compasses
Inn on main road through Bayston
Hill.

10/987
■ PRESERVES

Taylors Original English Mustard Co

Unit 6/7, Barrowmore Estate, Great Barrow,
Nr Tarvin, Cheshire CH3 7JA
Tel: (01829) 740482
Fax: (01829) 741702

English mustard, vinegars and oils.
Open: Mon-Fri 9am-5pm, some Sat
Cards: No

DIRECTIONS: From Chester on the
A51 towards Manchester, turn left at
the first set of lights and follow the
signs for Barrowmore Estate.

10/988
● NEEDLECRAFTS

Eccles Farm Needlecraft Centre

Eccles Lane, Bispham Green, Nr Ormskirk,
Lancashire L40 3SD
Tel: (01257) 463113

Needlecraft, also supplies and
materials.
Open: Wed-Sun 10am-5pm. Closed
bank hols
Cards: Access, Visa

DIRECTIONS: Off B5246 Rufford to
Parbold road. Follow tourist board
signs.

10/989
■ FLOUR

Pimhill (R Mayall & Daughter)

Lea Hall, Harmer Hill, Shrewsbury,
Shropshire SY4 3DY
Tel: (01939) 290342
Fax: (01939) 291156

Flour, meat, cheese, vegetables.
Open: Easter-Sept Wed-Sat 10am-
5pm, Sun 11am-4pm
Cards: Access, Visa

DIRECTIONS: On A528 5 miles
north of Shrewsbury. ½ mile south of
Harmer Hill. Signposted.

10/990
■ MEAT/POULTRY/GAME

Meadow View Quail

Meadow View Farm, Church Lane, Whixall,
Whitchurch, Shropshire SY13 2NA
Tel: (01948) 880300

Quail: pickled and smoked, also
quails' eggs.
Open: 10am-5pm Mon-Sat. Closed
Tue
Cards: No

DIRECTIONS: Off B5476 between
Wem and Whitchurch. Signposted
Whixall and Bostock Hall. 2nd
turning on right 400 yards on right.

10/991
■ MEAT/POULTRY/GAME

Maynards Farm Bacon

The Hough Farm, Weston under Redcastle,
Shrewsbury, Shropshire SY4 5LR
Tel: (01948) 840252

Bacon, sausages.
Open: Wed-Sun 9am-5.30pm. Closed
Mon,Tue and 24 Dec to mid-Jan
Cards: No

DIRECTIONS: A49 from Shrewsbury
for 13 miles. Entrance signposted just
before trees.

10/992
● CERAMICS

Cleehills Crafts
Leasowes, Stanton Long,
Shropshire TF13 6LH
Tel: (01746) 712677

Ceramics, floral terracotta pottery,
garden sculptures and patio chess sets.
Open: Mon-Sun 10.30am-dusk
Cards: No

DIRECTIONS: Signposted 'pottery
and rare breeds' from Shipton on the
B4368 Bridgnorth to Craven Arms
road (Shipton Hall opposite) through
Stanton Long, bear right, signposted
again left ¼ mile on right.

10/993
● CERAMICS

Firs Pottery
Sheppenhall Lane, Aston, Nantwich,
Cheshire CW5 8DE
Tel: (01270) 780345

Functional and decorative stoneware,
thrown and hand-built pottery.
Open: Daily 9am-6pm, but closed
some Thur, telephone in advance to
check
Cards: Access, Visa

DIRECTIONS: On the A530, 4½
miles from Nantwich in the village of
Aston, just past Honda garage.

10/994
● PLANTS

Caddicks Clematis Nurseries
Lymm Road, Thelwall, Warrington,
Cheshire WA13 0UF
Tel: (01925) 757196

Clematis.
Open: 1 Feb-30 Nov, Tue-Sun 10am-
5pm
Cards: Access, Visa

DIRECTIONS: M6 J20, M56 J9; A50
to Warrington, right at first traffic
lights to A56, 4th road on left.
Nursery entrance 80 yards on right.

10/995
● FURNITURE

Ray Read
The Boring Mill, Dale Road, Coalbrookdale,
Shropshire TF8 7DS
Tel: (01952) 433080

Hand-made furniture, french
polishing and restoration.
Open: Mon-Fri 9am-4.30pm, Sat
9am-1.30pm, variable holidays
Cards: No

DIRECTIONS: From Ironbridge head
west through High Street. Turn left
into Dale Road, 500 yards on right,
the workshop is behind Rose Cottage.

10/996
● DRIED FLOWERS

Carolyn's Flowers
Longford Farm, Longford, Market Drayton,
Shropshire TF9 3PW
Tel/Fax: (01630) 638295

Dried flowers.
Open: Mon, Wed-Sat 10am-4pm.
Closed bank hols
Cards: No

DIRECTIONS: On A41 turn right 50
yards north of roundabout at Tern
Hill, 1 mile to Longford, go straight
on at give way sign, 1st farm on right.

10/997
● PLANTS

Stapeley Water Gardens Ltd
London Road, Stapeley, Nantwich,
Cheshire CW5 7LH
Tel: (01270) 623868
Fax: (01270) 624919

Plants, gifts, pots, fish, refreshments,
museum, garden.
Open: summer Mon 9am-6pm, Sat
10am-6pm, Sun 10am-4pm, winter
Mon to Fri 9am-4pm, Sat 10am-5pm,
Sun 10am-4pm
Cards: Access, Switch, Visa

DIRECTIONS: 1 mile south of
Nantwich on the A51, from M6 J16
follow the brown tourist signs.

10/998
■ MEAT/POULTRY/GAME

Dukeshill Ham Co
Hall Farm, Deuxhill, Bridgnorth,
Shropshire WV16 6AF
Tel: (01746) 789519
Fax: (01746) 789533

Home-cured ham.
Open: 9am-6pm but telephone in
advance
Cards: Access, Amex, Visa

DIRECTIONS: Approx 4½ miles out
of Bridgnorth on B4363. Black and
white farm on right.

10/999
✻ MULTIPLE

Maws Craft Centre
Ferry Road, Jackfield, Telford,
Shropshire TF8 7LS
Tel: (01952) 883880

Cakes, ceramics, clothes, dolls,
figurines, furniture, textiles, tiles,
teddy bears, toys, printing, rushwork,
pictures.
Open: 12 noon-5pm by appointment
Cards: No

DIRECTIONS: Take B4373 from
Ironbridge to Broseley. Over new
bridge and turn left following signs
for Jackfield, Tile Museum and Maws
Craft Centre.

10/1000
✻ MULTIPLE

Dagfields Craft Centre
Dagfields Farm, Walgherton, Nr Nantwich,
Cheshire CW5 7LG
Tel: (01270) 841336

24 different craft shops, animal village,
tearoom, antique fairs.
Open: Daily 10.30am-5pm, or longer
Cards: No

DIRECTIONS: On B5071 (off A51)
four miles south-east of Nantwich.
Leave M6 at J16. Follow A500 and
then A51.

10/1001
● LEATHER GOODS

A E Collars
Studio 12, The Mill, Warmingham,
Nr Sandbach, Cheshire CW11 9QW
Tel/Fax: (01270) 526266

Leather decorative dog collars, leads
and harnesses, belts.
Open: Mon-Fri 8am-5pm, Sat-Sun by
appointment, best to telephone in
advance
Cards: No

DIRECTIONS: From M6 J18 go
towards Middlewich, turn left by
lights towards Sandbach.
Warmingham road on right, next door
but one to Bears Paw pub.

10/1002
● PLANTS

Bridgemere Nurseries
Bridgemere, Nr Nantwich,
Cheshire CW5 7QB
Tel: (01270) 520381
Fax: (01270) 520215

Hardy nursery stock plants, jams,
garden compost and fertilisers.
Open: Spring/summer Mon-Sun 9am-
8pm, winter Sun 9am-5pm. Closed
25-26 Dec
Cards: Access, Switch, Visa

DIRECTIONS: On A51, 9 miles south
of Nantwich.

10/1003
■ MEAT/POULTRY/GAME

Holly Tree Farm Shop
Chester Road, Tabley, Knutsford,
Cheshire WA16 0EU
Tel: (01565) 651835

Sausages, bacon, poultry, lamb,
cheeses, jams and pickles.
Open: Tue-Sat 9am-7pm, Sun 10am-
6pm. Closed 25-26 Dec, 1-2 Jan
Cards: No

DIRECTIONS: On A556 Chester to
Manchester road, 500 yards from J19
of the M6, opposite Windmill pub, 2
miles from Knutsford, 4 miles from
Northwich.

10/1004
● PLANTS

Hillview Hardy Plants
Worfield, Nr Bridgnorth,
Shropshire WV15 5NT
Tel: (01746) 716454

Alpine and cottage garden plants.
Open: Mar-mid Oct 10am-5pm,
otherwise telephone in advance
Cards: No

DIRECTIONS: Just off B4176.
Telford 8 miles, Dudley 14 miles, 1½
miles from Royal Oak towards
Telford, turn towards Worfield by
Chesterton Golf course, 300 yards on
right.

10/1005
● CERAMICS

The Potters Barn
Roughwood Lane, Hassall Green,
Sandbach, Cheshire CW11 0XX
Tel: (01270) 884080

Stoneware domestic pottery, terracotta
planters and gardenware.
Open: Mon-Sat 9.30am-6pm, Sun
1pm-5pm. Closed 25-26 Dec
Cards: Access, Visa

DIRECTIONS: From Sandbach
follow A533 Newcastle road over
motorway, first right at the New Inn,
first left in Hassall Green, bear left,
over canal on left.

10/1006
● PLANTS

Ward Fuchsias
5 Pollen Close, Sale, Cheshire M33 3LS
Tel: (0161) 9736467

Fuchsia cuttings and plants,
specialising in hanging baskets and
containers.
Open: 15 Feb-30 June Tue-Sun 9am-
5pm including bank hols
Cards: No

DIRECTIONS: J19 of M6, take A556
to Altrincham and A560 to Stockport.
Turn left at roundabout into Sale then
follow Northenden Road for 100
yards before turning into Derbyshire
Road South. Ward Fuchsias is behind
shops on the right.

10/1007
● PLANTS

David Austin Roses Ltd
Bowling Green Lane, Albrighton,
Shropshire WV7 3HB
Tel: (01902) 373931
Fax: (01902) 372142

Rose hybridisers and breeders.
Open: Mar-Oct Mon-Fri 9am-6pm,
Sat-Sun 10am-6pm, Oct-Mar Mon-
Fri 9am-5pm, Sat 10am-dusk, Sun
12 noon-dusk
Cards: Access, Visa

DIRECTIONS: A41 to
Wolverhampton for 2 miles right to
Albrighton, 2nd right (Bowling Green
Lane) follow through to small lane on
right (Old Worcester Road), entrance
is in this lane.

10/1008
■ CHEESE

Staffordshire Organic Cheese
New House Farm, Acton, Newcastle-under-
Lyme, Staffordshire ST5 4EE
Tel: (01782) 680366

Cows' milk cheese, meat and
vegetables.
Open: Mon 9am-4pm, Fri 9am-
5.30pm, Sat 9am-1pm, or by
appointment. Closed Sun
Cards: No

DIRECTIONS: ¾ mile from A53,
opposite turning from the
Mainwairing Arms, Whitmore,
towards Acton village.

10/1009
■ MEAT/POULTRY/GAME

Mooreland Foods
Vost Farm, Morley Green, Wilmslow,
Cheshire SK9 5NU
Tel: (01625) 548499
Fax: (01625) 548606

Bacon, ham, fish and game, smoked
and cured.
Open: Mon-Fri 9am-5.30pm, Sat
10am-5pm
Cards: Access, Switch, Visa

DIRECTIONS: 5 minutes from J6
M56, take A538 to Wilmslow. After
passing Moat House Hotel on left

look for signs on right for Morley Green. Turn right ½ mile on right.

10/1010
● TEXTILES

The Mill Shop
Quarry Bank Mill, Styal, Wilmslow, Cheshire SK9 4LA
Tel: (01625) 537529
Fax: (01625) 539267

Styal calico – 100% cotton fabric and goods, museum.
Open: Apr-Sept daily 11am-5pm, Oct-Mar daily 11am-5pm except Mon. Closed 24-25 Dec. Open bank hols
Cards: Access, Amex, Switch, Visa

DIRECTIONS: On B5166 2 miles south of Manchester Airport. Signposted from J5 of M56.

10/1011
■ SAUSAGES

Boxley's
20 Windmill Bank, Wombourne, West Midlands WV5 9JD
Tel: (01902) 892359
Fax: (01562) 885569

Home-produced traditional products including pork and leek sausages.
Open: Tue-Fri 7am-5.30pm. Sat 7am-4pm. Closed bank hols
Cards: Access, Switch, Visa

DIRECTIONS: Take A449 from Worcester to Wolverhampton. Turn left at sign for Wombourne at Himley. Overlooking village green.

10/1012
● PAINTS

Colourman Paints
Stockingate, Coton Clanford, Stafford, Staffordshire ST18 9PB
Tel: (01785) 282799
Fax: (01785) 282292

Water-based paints for restoration of houses and furniture. Mainly earth pigments.
Open: 9am-5pm, but telephone in advance
Cards: No

DIRECTIONS: 1 mile from Haughton.

10/1013
■ BAKED GOODS

High Lane Oatcakes
597-599 High Lane, Burslem, Stoke-on-Trent, Staffordshire ST6 7EP
Tel: (01782) 810180

Staffordshire oatcakes. Hot and cold filled oatcakes.
Open: Tue 10.30am-5.30pm, Thur 7am-6pm, Fri 7am-6.30pm, Sat 7am-6pm, Sun 7am-12 noon
Cards: No

DIRECTIONS: Two miles north of Hanley town take B5049 to Chell. 200 yards after Haywood Hospital next to Rileys pub.

10/1014
● PLANTS

Collinwood Nurseries
Mottram St Andrew, Macclesfield, Cheshire SK10 4QR
Tel: (01625) 582272

Chrysanthemums and hanging baskets.
Open: Mon-Sat 8.30am-6pm, Sun 1pm-6pm. Jan-Mar closed Sun, closed 25-26 Dec
Cards: No

DIRECTIONS: A538 Wilmslow to Prestbury Road, 1st right turn after Mottram Hall hotel, then 2nd right.

10/1015
● CERAMICS

Gailey Pottery
Old Church Studios, The Old Church, Watling Street, Gailey, Staffordshire ST19 5PR
Tel: (01902) 790078

One-off pottery ceramic gifts and objects, incorporating a studio/gallery/shop.
Open: Mon-Fri 9.30am-3.30pm, Sat 12 noon-4pm
Cards: Access, Amex, Diners, Visa

DIRECTIONS: Cross road junction of A5-A449, 3 miles south of Pentridge, opposite Spread Eagle pub, in old church.

10/1016
■ MEAT/POULTRY/GAME

Alan Bennett Ltd
100 High Street, Wednesfield,
Wolverhampton, West Midlands WV11 1SZ
Tel: (01902) 732750

Butcher, including pork pies,
sausages, bacon and cooked meat.
Open: Mon-Sat 7.30am-5pm
Cards: No

DIRECTIONS: In High Street, 3
miles from J10 M6.

10/1017
● PLANTS

Barncroft Nurseries
Dunwood Lane, Longsdon, Stoke-on-Trent,
Staffordshire ST9 9QW
Tel/Fax: (01538) 384310

Heathers, conifers, trees, shrubs,
climbers and alpines. Gardens open.
Open: Fri-Sun 9am-dusk. Closed
Christmas
Cards: No

DIRECTIONS: 1 mile along
Dunwood Lane off the A53 Leek to
Stoke-on-Trent road, 3 miles west of
Leek, or 2 miles from Rudyard off the
A523 Leek to Macclesfield road.

10/1018
● CERAMICS

Artisan
3 King Street, Delph, Oldham,
Lancashire OL3 5DL
Tel: (01457) 874506

Handmade ceramics and pottery,
dragons, wizards, fairies and flowers,
castle lamps, mirrors.
Open: Wed-Fri 1pm-5.30pm, Sun and
bank hols, 2pm-5pm. Closed 25 Dec-
1 Jan
Cards: Access, Visa

DIRECTIONS: M62 J21 follow signs
for Oldham, turn left to Huddersfield
and follow to Denshaw crossroads.
Signs for Delph at crossroads, follow
through to village centre. Opposite
Bulls Head pub.

10/1019
● LEATHER GOODS

Walsall Leather Museum
Wisemore, Walsall, West Midlands WS2 8EQ
Tel: (01922) 721153
Fax: (01922) 725827

Leather goods, including wallets,
purses and belts.
Open: Tue-Sat 10am-5pm, Sun
12 noon-5pm, Nov-Mar 12 noon-
4pm. Telephone in advance bank hols
Cards: No

DIRECTIONS: On the Walsall ring
road (Littleton Street) immediately
north of Walsall town centre.

10/1020
■ BAKED GOODS

R & J Lodge Foods
4 Greens End Road, Meltham,
Huddersfield, West Yorkshire HD7 3NW
Tel: (01484) 850571

Pies: pork, game, fidget, turkey, ham.
Open: Tue, Thur, Fri 8.30am-5pm.
Wed 8.30am-1pm. Sat 8.30am-
12.30pm. Closed Sun, Mon, bank
hols
Cards: No

DIRECTIONS: Leave Holmfirth on
A635, after 1 mile at Ford Inn turn
right to Meltham. Church on left.
Shop next door.

10/1021
● CERAMICS

Rookes Pottery
Mill Lane, Hartington, Buxton,
Derbyshire SK17 0AN
Tel: (01298) 84650
Fax: (01298) 84806

Terracotta garden pots.
Open: Mon-Fri 8am-5pm, Sat 10am-
5pm, Sun 11am-5pm. Winter
weekends closing at 4pm. Closed 25
Dec-1 Jan
Cards: Access, Switch, Visa

DIRECTIONS: From A515 or A5012
on B5054 through village and pottery
is clearly marked on the left.

10/1022
■ CHEESE

Ye Old Cheese Shop
Hartington, Buxton, Derbyshire SK17 0AH
Tel: (01298) 84935
Fax: (01298) 84403

Stilton and blue cheeses.
Open: Mon-Fri 9am-5pm. Sat-Sun
9am-4pm. 24 Dec-Mar. Closed on
Mon-Tue
Cards: Access, Switch, Visa

DIRECTIONS: In middle of village
opposite duck pond.

10/1023
● JEWELLERY

Speedwell Cavern Ltd
Winnats Pass, Castleton,
Derbyshire S30 2WA
Tel: (01433) 620512
Fax: (01433) 621888

Gold and silver jewellery set with
Blue John Stone.
Open: Mon-Sun 9.30am-5pm (later in
summer)
Cards: Access, Amex, Diners, Switch,
Visa

DIRECTIONS: Castleton village is on
A625 15 miles west of Sheffield.

10/1024
✳ MULTIPLE

Heart of the Country Centre
Home Farm, Swinfen, Lichfield,
Staffordshire WS14 9QR
Tel: (01543) 481612

Eggs, food hampers, glass, honey,
jewellery, knitwear, patchwork quilts,
picture framing, crêperie.
Open: Tue-Sun 10am-5pm and bank
hols
Cards: No

DIRECTIONS: One mile south of
Lichfield on A38 towards
Birmingham.

10/1025
■ FISH/SHELLFISH

Mayfield Trout
Manor Farm, Mayfield, Ashbourne,
Derbyshire DE6 2JR
Tel: (01335) 342050

Rainbow trout and smoked trout.
Open: Wed, Sat 10am-6pm, Tue,
Thur, Fri 4pm-6pm
Cards: No

DIRECTIONS: From Ashbourne
follow A52 to Leek for 1½ miles.
Turn left on to B5032. At top of hill
turn left and follow road around to
church. Next door to church.

10/1026
● MINERALS

Tideswell Dale Rock Shop
Commercial Road, Tideswell,
Derbyshire SK17 8NU
Tel/Fax: (01298) 871606

Mineral and fossil specimens.
Open: Tue-Sun 10am-5.30pm
Cards: Access, Visa

DIRECTIONS: Off the A623
Chesterfield to Chapel-en-le-Frith
road. Shop is on left on the main road
through the village.

10/1027
■ FARM PRODUCE

**Old Stables Farm Shop &
Bakery**
Packington Moor Farm, Packington,
Lichfield, Staffordshire WS14 9QA
Tel: (01543) 481223/481259

Fresh produce and potatoes,
traditional home-baked products,
cheeses, ice-cream, bacon and bread.
Courtyard café, pick your own
summer fruits from late June to early
August.
Open: Tue-Fri 9.30am-6pm, Sat
9.30am-12.30pm, Sun 9.30am-
12.30pm. Closed Mon
Cards: Access, Visa

DIRECTIONS: Off A51 between
Lichfield and Tamworth near
Whittington army barracks.

10/1028
● GLASS

Derwent Crystal Ltd
Shawcroft Ashbourne, Derbyshire DE6 1GH
Tel: (01335) 345219
Fax: (01335) 300225

English handmade lead crystal.
Open: Mon-Sat 9am-5pm. Closed 24
Dec-1 Jan
Cards: Access, Amex, Diners, Switch,
Visa

DIRECTIONS: 12 miles north-west of
Derby on A52, follow signs to Glass
Craft Centre, the factory fronts on to
the main Shawcroft car park.

10/1029
● FISHING

Steve Woolley Fishing Rod Makers & Vintage Tackle
Adjacent to the Wood Yard, Belle Vue
Road, Ashbourne, Derbyshire DE6 1AT
Tel: (01335) 300095

Split cane fishing rods.
Open: Mon-Sat 8.30am-6pm
Cards: No

DIRECTIONS: Left off Buxton Road
just beyond marketplace coming out
of town. Timber yard on right a few
yards along.

10/1030
● FURNITURE

Steven James Furniture
Vincent Works, Brough, Bradwell,
Derbyshire S30 2HG
Tel: (01433) 620286

Furniture and specialist carpentry.
Open: Mon-Fri 9am-5pm. Sat 10am-
3pm. Open bank hols. Closed 24-27
Dec
Cards: No

DIRECTIONS: On A625 between
Hathersage and Hope. Turn into
Brough Lane opposite Travellers Rest
pub. After ½ mile turn left into
Vincent Works.

10/1031
● GLASS

Tutbury Crystal Glass Ltd
Tutbury Glassworks, Burton Street,
Tutbury, Burton-on-Trent,
Staffordshire DE13 9NG
Tel: (01283) 813281
Fax: (01283) 813228

Handmade full lead crystal glassware,
factory tours.
Open: Mon-Fri 9am-5pm, Sun 11am-
4pm. Closed Christmas
Cards: Access, Switch, Visa

DIRECTIONS: A50 Burton-on-Trent
to Uttoxeter road, 4 miles north-east
of Burton, in the centre of Tutbury,
signposted glassworks off A50.

10/1032
● FURNITURE

Neil Clarke
High Croft, Chapel Lane, Kniveton,
Ashbourne, Derbyshire DE6 1JP
Tel: (01335) 343901

Furniture from native hardwoods,
especially dining-room furniture.
Open: By appointment only
Cards: No

DIRECTIONS: B5035 from
Ashbourne. First turning on right in
Kniveton village, 50 yards along take
first left, keep left along Chapel Lane,
signposted.

10/1033
■ BAKED GOODS

Original Bakewell Pudding Shop
The Square, Bakewell,
Derbyshire DE45 1BT
Tel: (01629) 812193

Bakewell pudding, bread, cakes,
pickles and preserves. Tearoom.
Open: Mon-Fri 9am-9pm. Closed 25
Dec
Cards: No

DIRECTIONS: In town on A6 Buxton
to Matlock road.

10/1034
■ PRESERVES

Connoisseurs of Bakewell
Granby Cottage, Water Lane, Bakewell,
Derbyshire DE45 1LW
Tel: (01629) 814844

Preserves, chutneys, pork pies.
Open: Daily 9am-5.30pm
Cards: No

DIRECTIONS: Main A6 into
Bakewell. Turn down Water Street by
National Westminster bank. Turn
down Water Lane by Red Lion pub.

10/1035
● KNITWEAR

Woollie Pullie
Portland Square, Bakewell,
Derbyshire DE45 1HA
Tel: (01629) 812235

Knitwear.
Open: Mon-Sat 9.45am-5.00pm.
Open bank hols
Cards: Access, Visa

DIRECTIONS: Either A6 or A619 into
Bakewell. Portland Square in centre.

10/1036
● FURNITURE

**Melvyn Tolley – Maker of
English Country Chairs**
The Old Post Office, Bradley, Ashbourne,
Derbyshire DE6 1PG
Tel: (01335) 370112

Traditional Windsor chairs.
Open: Most days 9am-6pm,
appointments advised. Closed 25-26
Dec
Cards: No

DIRECTIONS: Off A517 Ashbourne
to Belper road. About 3 miles from
Ashbourne, take turn signposted
Bradley. Proceed through village past
the church. The workshop is situated
to the left of triangular junction.

10/1037
● FURNITURE

Nova Interiors
Townhead Works, Eyam, Sheffield,
South Yorkshire S30 1RE
Tel: (01433) 631566

Tables, chairs and occasional items
combined with upholstered sofas,
chairs and stools.
Open: Mon-Fri 9am-5pm. Closed
bank hols and 2 weeks over Christmas
Cards: No

DIRECTIONS: At J29 of M1, take
A617 to Chesterfield, A619 to Baslow
and A623 towards Stockport.
Through village of Stoney Middleton,
turn first right and signposted to
Eyam.

10/1038
● FURNITURE

Andrew Lawton Furniture
Goatscliffe Workshops, Grindleford,
Derbyshire S30 1HG
Tel: (01433) 631754

Contemporary furniture. European
and North American woods.
Open: Mon to Sat 9am-5.30pm
Cards: No

DIRECTIONS: On B6001 between
Bakewell and Hathersage. Workshop
on main road at southern end of
Grindleford.

10/1039
● FURNITURE

W K Morley
Main Road, Hulland Ward, Ashbourne,
Derbyshire DE6 3EA
Tel: (01335) 370175

Cabinetmaker.
Open: Variable, please telephone in
advance
Cards: No

DIRECTIONS: On A517 Ashbourne
to Belper road, in Hulland Ward, next
to Nags Head pub.

10/1040
● MUSICAL INSTRUMENTS

Northworthy Musical Instruments
Main Road, Hulland Ward, Ashbourne, Derbyshire DE6 3EA
Tel/Fax: (01335) 370806

Citterns, bozoukis, electric and acoustic guitars, mandolins, mandolas.
Open: Mon-Fri 9.30am-5.30pm by appointment only
Cards: No

DIRECTIONS: 5 miles east of Ashbourne, 7 miles west of Belper, 10 miles north of Derby on A517 Ashbourne to Belper road, above Hulland Motors.

10/1041
● FURNITURE

Ian Saville Furniture
Old Sawmill, Rowsley, Matlock, Derbyshire DE4 2EB
Tel: (01629) 733935

Contemporary furniture and woodwork in hardwoods using traditional techniques.
Open: Mon-Fri 9am-5pm. Occasional weekends, but telephone for appointment
Cards: No

DIRECTIONS: In Rowsley village on A6, 3 miles south of Bakewell, opposite Peacock Hotel, next to Caudwells Mill Craft Centre.

10/1042
● FURNITURE

Nicholas Hobbs
1C Ravenstor Road, off Cromford Road, Wirksworth, Derbyshire DE4 4FY
Tel: (01629) 823445

Furniture from British hardwoods.
Open: Mon-Fri 9.30am-5.30pm. Otherwise by appointment. Advisable to telephone in advance
Cards: No

DIRECTIONS: 15 miles north of Derby on B5023 Duffield to Cromford Road. ¾ mile north of Wirksworth town centre and just below National Stone Centre and High Peak Trail.

10/1043
● GLASS

Hothouse
7 Lumsdale Mill, Lower Lumsdale, Nr Matlock, Derbyshire DE4 5EX
Tel/Fax: (01629) 580821

Recycled crystal perfume bottles, paperweights, vases, bowls, wine glasses and candlesticks.
Open: Mon to Fri 10am-12.30pm, 1.30pm-4.30pm. Open bank hol Sun and Mon. Closed mid-Dec to Easter
Cards: Access, Visa

DIRECTIONS: A615 from Matlock towards Alfreton, turn left 1 mile from town, follow lane for almost 1 mile.

10/1044
● PLANTS

Rileys' Chrysanthemums
Alfreton Nurseries, Ashover Road, Woolley Moor, Derbyshire DE55 6FF
Tel: (01246) 590320

Chrysanthemums (breeders and retailers) for cut, floral art, gardens, exhibitions.
Open: Feb-June Mon-Fri 10am-4pm. Sun in Sept
Cards: No

DIRECTIONS: Nursery situated on B6036, 2 miles from Clay Cross, 6 mile from Matlock and Chesterfield, 20 miles north of Derby.

10/1045
● FORGEWORK

Wentworth Forge
Old Building Yard, Wentworth, Rotherham, South Yorkshire S62 7SB
Tel: (01226) 749234

Forgings, gates, fencing, ornamental ironwork, brackets, signs, garden furniture, security grilles.
Open: Mon-Sat 9am-5pm. Closed bank hols
Cards: No

DIRECTIONS: Through Thorpe Hesley to Wentworth village. Turn right at junction towards Rotherham,

Wentworth Forge is 200 yards on left opposite entrance to Wentworth Woodhouse.

10/1046
■ CONFECTIONERY

Eldanns
10 Valley Road, Bolsover,
Derbyshire S44 6UG
Tel: (01246) 824512

8 varieties of truffles made with Belgian couverture chocolate; also fudge, toffee, dates and cherries dipped in chocolate.
Open: 9am-5.30pm
Cards: Visa

DIRECTIONS: Six miles east of Chesterfield on A632. Valley Road is off Ridgedale Road which is off New Station Road.

MAP 11

11/1047
● FURNITURE
The Old Cheese Factory
Grangemill, Matlock, Derbyshire DE4 4HU
Tel: (01629) 650720

Oak furniture.
Open: Mon-Sat 9am-5pm
Cards: No

DIRECTIONS: From North, take J29 of M1, then A617 Chesterfield, A632 Matlock, A6 Matlock Bath to Cromford road, A5012 signposted Newhaven. 4 miles. Workshop on right by Holly Bush pub.

11/1048
■ FARM PRODUCE
Chatsworth Farm Shop
Stud Farm, Pilsley, Bakewell, Derbyshire DE45 1UF
Tel: (01246) 583392
Fax: (01246) 582514

Farm shop.
Open: Mon-Sat 9am-5pm. Sun 11am-5pm. Closed 25 Dec, 1 Jan
Cards: Access, Amex, Visa

DIRECTIONS: 2 miles from Chatsworth House, signposted from J29 of M1 and other major routes. At the top of Pilsley village.

11/1049
✳ MULTIPLE
Caudwell's Mill and Craft Centre
Caudwell's Mill, Rowsley, Matlock, Derbyshire DE4 2EB
Tel: (01629) 733185

Mill: strong wholemeal and white flour. Craft centre: glass-blowing, ceramics, wood-turning, paintings, furniture-restoring.
Open: Mar-Oct daily 10am-6pm. Nov-Feb 10am-4.30pm
Cards: No

DIRECTIONS: On A6 in centre of Rowsley, opposite Peacock Hotel. Midway between Matlock and Bakewell.

11/1050
● HUNTING ACCESSORIES
Harry Boden
Via Gellia Mill, Bonsall, Matlock, Derbyshire DE4 2AJ
Tel: (01629) 825176

Hunting knives, leather belts and pouches.
Open: Mon-Fri 8.30am-1.30pm and 2.30pm-5pm, Sat 9am-12 noon
Cards: No

DIRECTIONS: A6 to Cromford. Turn to Via Gellia on Buxton Road, ½ mile from Cromford.

11/1051
● RUGS
Tessa Badcock Handweaver
17 High Street, Bonsall, Matlock, Derbyshire DE4 2AS
Tel: (01629) 823774

Hand-woven rugs and wall hangings.
Open: Mon, Wed-Sat 10am-5pm. Telephone call advised
Cards: No

DIRECTIONS: 100 yards up hill from Market Cross.

11/1052
● FURNITURE
Matthew Morris Furniture
Unit A, Markeaton Craft Village, Markeaton Park, Derbyshire DE22 3BG
Tel: (01332) 298460
Fax: (01332) 510722

Furniture in contemporary and classical designs.
Open: Mon-Sat 8am-6pm, some Suns
Cards: No

DIRECTIONS: Take Markeaton Lane off A52, Ashbourne to Derby road. Enter park, 1½ miles further down Markeaton Lane, next to nurseries and farm.

11/1053
● PLANTS

Highgates Alpine Plant Nursery
166A Crich Lane, Belper,
Derbyshire DE56 1EP
Tel: (01773) 822153

Alpine and rockery plants, dwarf rhododendrons.
Open: Mon-Sat 10.30am-4.30pm. Closed mid-Oct-Feb
Cards: No

DIRECTIONS: East off A6 in Belper on to A609, after ½ mile bear left on to B6013. Bear left into Crich Lane after ½ mile, on right.

11/1054
● CERAMICS

Crich Pottery
Market Place, Crich, Derbyshire DE4 5DD
Tel: (01773) 853171
Fax: (01773) 857325

Stoneware pottery in rural floral imagery.
Open: Mon-Sun 10am-6pm, call first on Sun. Closed 25 Dec-1 Jan
Cards: Access, Visa

DIRECTIONS: From M1 J28, A38 to Derby, then take A610 towards Ambergate. Take 2nd right under Bullbridge, up hill to Crich Market Place, opposite bakery.

11/1055
● FURNITURE

Ram Furniture
Cliffside Workshop, Crich, Matlock, Derbyshire DE4 5DP
Tel: (01773) 857092

Handmade oak furniture.
Open: Mon-Sat 8.30am-5pm. Usually open bank hols, except Christmas
Cards: No

DIRECTIONS: Follow signs to National Tramway Museum. Ram Furniture is 300 yards beyond and next to the Cliff Inn pub.

11/1056
■ WINE

Leventhorpe Vineyard
Bullerthorpe Lane, Woodlesford, Leeds, West Yorkshire LS26 8AF
Tel: (01132) 667892

White and red wines, tours.
Open: Sat and Sun 11am-5pm, otherwise by appointment
Cards: No

DIRECTIONS: Take A642 Wakefield to Garforth road, cross river Aire, turn immediately left and vineyard is about 200 yards along road, on left, behind Leventhorpe Cottages.

11/1057
● KNITWEAR

Wingham Wool Work
70 Main Street, Wentworth, Rotherham, South Yorkshire S62 7BR
Tel: (01226) 742926
Fax: (01226) 741166

Fibres for handspinners, carded and blended wools, silks, camel, cashmere. Own knitwear.
Open: Sat 1.30pm-5.30pm, Sun 11.30am-5.30pm, Mon 1.30pm-5.30pm and by appointment
Cards: Access, Visa

DIRECTIONS: On the corner of Wentworth Main Street and Barrowfield Lane, opposite old village church.

11/1058
■ MEAT/POULTRY/GAME

George Stafford Ltd
130 Belper Road, Stanley Common, Derbyshire DE7 6FQ
Tel: (0115) 9325751

Black puddings, sausages, cooked meats.
Open: Tue,Thur, Fri 8.15am-1pm, 2pm-5.30pm. Wed 8.15am-1pm. Sat 7.30am-1.30pm. Closed bank hols
Cards: No

DIRECTIONS: On A609 Belper to Ilkeston road, 3 miles west of Ilkeston. On main road in centre of village, opposite recreation ground.

11/1059
● FISHING

Flies by Wendy & Ray's Rods & Tackle
47 Thorn Drive, Daisy Farm Estate,
Newthorpe Common,
Nottinghamshire NG16 2BH
Tel: (01773) 761645

Framed trout flies and associated gifts.
Flies for fishing, hand-built fly rods,
fishing tackle.
Open: Weekdays by appointment only
Cards: Access, Visa

DIRECTIONS: From J26 of M1, take
A610 towards Ripley. Take 1st exit
which goes underneath A610 and
leads to island. Take last exit on
roundabout under bridge to traffic
lights. Straight on, then left to
Newthorpe Common. Next left into
Daisy Farm Road. Fourth left, Thorn
Drive.

11/1060
● PLANTS

Markham Grange Nurseries
Longlands Lane, Brodsworth, Doncaster,
South Yorkshire DN5 7XB
Tel: (01302) 722390 and 330430
Fax: (01302) 727571

Fuchsias and hanging baskets.
Open: Mon-Sat 9am-6pm, Sun 10am-
4pm. Closed 25-26 Dec
Cards: Access, Switch, Visa

DIRECTIONS: Take exit 38 of the
A1(M), turn back for Brodsworth
village and the nursery is next to the
old Brodsworth colliery site.

11/1061
■ PRESERVES

Womersley Crafts
Womersley Hall, Womersley, Doncaster,
South Yorkshire DN6 9BH
Tel: (01977) 620294

Condiments and herbs.
Open: Mid-Mar to 10 Dec Sat and
bank hols 10.30am-6pm (5pm winter),
Sun 12 noon-6pm (5pm winter), 10
Dec to 24 Dec Mon to Fri 2pm-5pm,
27 Dec to mid-Mar Sun 2pm-5pm.
Other times by appointment
Cards: Access, Visa

DIRECTIONS: 3 miles south-east of
A1/M62 intersection.

11/1062
● JEWELLERY

Rachel Gogerly Jewellery Designer and Manufacturer
The Studio, 60 Eden Close, York, North
Yorkshire YO2 2RD
Tel: (01904) 701670

Professional jeweller specialising in
handmade silver and enamel
jewellery. The above address is a
workshop only, not a shop, although
customers are welcome to discuss
enamel repair work and commissions.
Open: By appointment only Mon-Fri
9.30am-4.30pm
Cards: No

DIRECTIONS: From Leeds on A64,
turn left on to A1237, take first right
signposted Woodthorpe, take third left
into Eden Close.

11/1063
■ WINE

Eglantine Vineyard
Ash Lane, Costock, Nr Loughborough,
Leicestershire LE12 6UX
Tel/Fax: (01509) 852386

English wines, mead, cherry wine,
honey, tours.
Open: Please telephone in advance
Cards: No

DIRECTIONS: A60 from Nottingham
to Loughborough. Ash Lane is to the
west of A60, midway between the
villages of Bunny and Costock. The
vineyard is ½ mile along Ash Lane.

11/1064
● CERAMICS

Carrington Pottery
15 Church Drive, Carrington,
Nottinghamshire NG5 2AS
Tel: (0115) 9603479

Handmade pottery, Carrington cats,
hats, and Nottingham laceware.
Open: Mon to Sat exc Thur 10am-
4pm (6pm Fri). Closed 25 Dec-2 Jan
Cards: No

DIRECTIONS: Leave Nottingham on the A60 Mansfield road, turn left at Church Drive in Carrington. The pottery is at the next crossroads.

11/1065
● CERAMICS
Ravenshead Pottery
23 Milton Drive, Ravenshead,
Nottinghamshire NG15 9BE
Tel: (01623) 793178

Domestic and decorative stoneware pottery.
Open: 10am-6pm by appointment only. Closed Feb
Cards: Access, Visa

DIRECTIONS: In centre of village off the A60 Nottingham to Mansfield road.

11/1066
✱ MULTIPLE
Longdale Craft Centre
Longdale Lane, Ravenshead,
Nottinghamshire NG15 9AH
Tel/Fax: (01623) 794858

Craft village, museum and restaurant.
Open: 9am-6pm. Closed 25-26 Dec
Cards: Access, Visa

DIRECTIONS: Near Newstead Abbey off A60 and A614. J27 of M1. Follow signs to Newstead Abbey. Take road opposite Abbey Gate.

11/1067
● PLANTS
Stillingfleet Lodge Nurseries
Stillingfleet, North Yorkshire YO4 6HW
Tel/Fax: (01904) 728506

Herbaceous plants and foliage, grasses, shrubs and climbing plants. Garden.
Open: 1 Apr-18 Oct Tue, Wed, Fri and Sat 10am-4pm
Cards: No

DIRECTIONS: On the B1222 7 miles south of York. Turn opposite the church in Stillingfleet village ignoring the dead-end sign.

11/1068
● PLANTS
Norden Alpines
Hirst Road, Carlton, Nr Selby,
Humberside DN14 9PX
Tel: (01405) 861348

Rare alpine and rock garden plants, especially campanula, primula and saxifraga.
Open: Mar-Sept weekends and bank hols, or by appointment
Cards: No

DIRECTIONS: A1041 between Selby and Goole, ½ mile along Hirst Road.

11/1069
■ CHEESE
Cropwell Bishop Creamery
Nottingham Road, Cropwell Bishop,
Nottinghamshire NG12 3BQ
Tel: (0115) 9892350
Fax: (0115) 9899046

Cheese: Blue Stilton, Shropshire Blue, Red Leicester, Double Gloucester, Cheddar.
Open: Thur 2pm-3pm, Fri 2pm-3pm. Closed 25-26 Dec
Cards: No

DIRECTIONS: 1 mile off A46, follow signs to Cropwell Bishop. 1st big white building on way into village on the right.

11/1070
■ BAKED GOODS
Mrs Elizabeth King Ltd
Hardigate Road, Cropwell Butler,
Nottinghamshire NG12 3AG
Tel: (0115) 9332252

Pork pies, sausages and pastry products.
Open: Mon-Fri 9am-5pm. Sat 9am-1pm. Closed bank hols
Cards: No

DIRECTIONS: Off A46, south of roundabout with A52. Turn 1st left off A46. Cropwell Butler sign ½ mile. First gateway on right.

11/1071
● CERAMICS
Chris Aston Pottery
4 High Street, Elkesley, Nr Retford,
Nottinghamshire DN22 8AJ
Tel/Fax: (01777) 838391

Domestic and individual pieces, mugs
and plates.
Open: Most days 10am-6pm,
telephone in advance
Cards: No

DIRECTIONS: On A1, 20 miles north
of Newark. In Elkesley on the old
village street near the church.

11/1072
■ CHEESE
**Colston Bassett & District
Dairy Ltd**
Harby Road, Colston Bassett,
Nottinghamshire NG12 3FN
Tel/Fax: (01949) 811322

Blue Stilton cheese.
Open: Mon-Fri 9am-12.30pm,
1.30pm-4pm, Sat 9am-11am. Closed
bank hols
Cards: No

DIRECTIONS: 10 miles south of
Nottingham. 3 miles off A46.

11/1073
● CERAMICS
Grange Farm Pottery
Grange Farm, Granby Lane, Plungar,
Nottinghamshire NG13 0JJ
Tel: (01949) 860630

Pottery and workshop, hand-made
ceramics, oven-to-tableware, garden
planters, wall pots.
Open: Sat and Sun 11am-6pm. Closed
25 Dec-Easter
Cards: No

DIRECTIONS: By the canal in the
village of Plungar, 4 miles south of
Bingham on the A52.

11/1074
● ROCKING-HORSES
The Rocking Horse Shop
Fangfoss, Nr Pocklington, North
Yorkshire YO4 5QH
Tel: (01759) 368737
Fax: (01759) 368194

Makers and restorers of wooden
rocking-horses. Plans, books and kits
for rocking-horses and toy cars.
Open: Mon-Sat 9am-4pm. Closed
bank hols
Cards: Access, Switch, Visa

DIRECTIONS: 12 miles east of York
on A1079, between Pocklington and
Stamford Bridge. By the village green,
next to the old church.

11/1075
■ JUICES/CORDIALS
Belvoir Fruit Farms
Belvoir, Grantham, Lincolnshire NG32 1PB
Tel: (01476) 870286
Fax: (01476) 870114

Fruit cordials: elderflower, ginger,
passion-fruit, strawberry, raspberry,
blackcurrant, lemon. Soft fruits June
to August.
Open: Mon-Sat 9am-7pm
Cards: No

DIRECTIONS: Beneath Belvoir
Castle on road between Belvoir and
Redmile. Belvoir Castle clearly
marked from A52 Nottingham to
Grantham road or A607 Grantham to
Melton Mowbray road.

11/1076
● FURNITURE
Lee Sinclair Furniture
Endon House, Main Street, Laneham,
Nr Retford, Nottinghamshire DN22 0NA
Tel/Fax: (01777) 228303

Modern, solid wood furniture.
Open: Mon-Fri 9am-5pm, otherwise
by appointment
Cards: No

DIRECTIONS: Laneham is 1 mile
north of the A57 between Markham
Moor roundabout (on the A1) and
Lincoln (the Retford side of Dunham

toll bridge). Endon House is on the main street opposite the post office.

11/1077
■ MEAT/POULTRY/GAME

Mrs Potter's Perfect Pork
The Manor House, Gainsborough Road,
Langford, Newark-on-Trent,
Nottinghamshire NG23 7RW
Tel: (01636) 611156

Sausages, bacon, gammon, pork, rare breed meats from free-range Gloucester Old Spot herd.
Open: Mon, Tue, Thur 10am-6pm
Cards: No

DIRECTIONS: On A1123 Gainsborough to Newark road.

11/1078
● CERAMICS

Harvey Wood
The Wharf, Trent Lane, Collingham,
Newark, Nottinghamshire NG23 7LZ
Tel: (01636) 892627
Fax: (01636) 893413

Ceramics and sculpture, portraits.
Open: By appointment
Cards: Visa

DIRECTIONS: From Collingham village green follow signs to river Trent. The Wharf is set back from the road 1½ miles down Trent Lane.

11/1079
■ MEAT/POULTRY/GAME

W E Botterill & Son
Lings View Farm, 10 Middle Street, Croxton
Kerrial, Grantham, Lincolnshire NG32 1QP
Tel/Fax: (01476) 870394

Traditional farm-fresh, free-range geese and bronze turkeys.
Open: June-July 10am-6pm. Oct-Dec telephone for details
Cards: No

DIRECTIONS: On A607 Grantham to Melton Mowbray road, 5 miles west of A1 at Grantham.

11/1080
● FURNITURE

Cobweb Furniture
Old Chapel Workshops, West Street,
West Butterwick, Scunthorpe,
Humberside DN17 3JZ
Tel: (01724) 783888

Reproduction antique furniture in oak and pine, butcher's blocks and accessories.
Open: Mon-Fri 8.30am-5pm, Sat 8.30am-12 noon, Sun by appointment. Closed bank hols
Cards: No

DIRECTIONS: M180 J2, turn right for Belton, take the first left in Belton signposted to West Butterwick. 2 miles on turn 2nd right in the hamlet of Beltoft. 2 miles further on is West Butterwick.

11/1081
● CERAMICS

Jerry Harper Pottery
South Farm Craft Gallery, Staddlethorpe
Lane, Blacktoft, Nr Goole, Humberside
DN14 7XT
Tel: (01430) 441082

Handmade stoneware pottery, refreshments.
Open: Wed-Sat 10am-5pm, Sun and bank hols 11am-5pm. Closed 25-26 Dec, 1 Jan, variable holidays Jan-Feb
Cards: Access, Visa

DIRECTIONS: Brown signs from B1230/A163 and M62 J38. Situated 2 miles south of Gilberdyke village.

11/1082
● METALWORK

T Marshall & Son
Barnby Hall, Barnby in the Willows,
Newark, Nottinghamshire NG24 2SA
Tel: (01636) 626332

Awards, gifts, trophies, mementos in bronze, brass, copper, pewter, silver, gold plate.
Open: By appointment only
Cards: No

DIRECTIONS: From Newark take A17, 3½ miles out of Newark turn right at signpost Barnby. Turn left at

T-junction into Barnby, last property on the left.

11/1083
● PLANTS

Orchard Nurseries
Tow Lane, Foston, Nr Grantham,
Lincolnshire NG32 2LE
Tel: (01400) 281354

Specialist nursery, hellebores, rare snowdrops, hardy geraniums, euphorbia, climbers.
Open: Feb-Sept Mon-Sun
Cards: Access, Visa

DIRECTIONS: ¼ miles off the A1 between Grantham and Newark.

11/1084
✳ MULTIPLE

Manor Stables Craft Workshops
Fulbeck, Grantham, Lincolnshire NG32 7JN
Tel: (01400) 272779

Workshops include ceramics, jewellery, furniture, saddlery, weaving, knitwear, refreshments.
Open: Tue-Sun 10.30am-4.30pm and bank hols. Closed 23 Dec-9 Jan
Cards: Access, Visa

DIRECTIONS: On A607 1 mile south of crossroads with A17.

11/1085
● CERAMICS

Kirton Pottery
36 High Street, Kirton in Lindsey,
Gainsborough, Lincolnshire DN21 4LX
Tel: (01652) 648867

Pottery, majolica and stoneware, domestic and sculptural pieces.
Open: Mon, Wed-Sat 9.30am-5.30pm, Sun 2.30pm-5pm, by appointment on bank hols
Cards: No

DIRECTIONS: Just off the A15, 18 miles north of Lincoln. At the top of village near the market square.

11/1086
● WOOD

Tamcraft Woodworks
Gatehouse Cottage, Caenby,
Lincolnshire LN2 3EE
Tel: (01673) 878634

Wooden toys and children's chairs, carvings of birds, walking sticks.
Open: 9am-4pm. Closed bank hol weekends
Cards: No

DIRECTIONS: From A15 take A631 at Caenby Corner to Blenthom and follow Caenby Road past nursing home. Last house in Caenby.

11/1087
■ CONFECTIONERY

Special Edition Continental Chocolate
59 Honeyholes Lane, Dunholme, Lincoln,
Lincolnshire LN2 3SU
Tel: (01673) 860616

Handmade chocolates.
Open: Mon-Fri 8.30am-5.30pm. Closed first fortnight Sept
Cards: Visa

DIRECTIONS: Off A46, 7 miles north of Lincoln.

11/1088
● TOYS

The Stable Workshop
Snarford, Market Rasen,
Lincolnshire LN8 3SW
Tel: (01673) 885295

Traditional wooden toys.
Open: Most days except Thur, telephone in advance
Cards: No

DIRECTIONS: 9 miles north of Lincoln on A46, not in Snarford village, 1 mile from Leonards Leap Restaurant on left side.

11/1089
■ MEAT/POULTRY/GAME

Three Kings Deer
Three Kings Farm, Mareham
Lane, Threekingham, Sleaford,
Lincolnshire NG34 0BQ
Tel: (01529) 240555

Venison and farmhouse cheeses.
Open: Tue-Sun 10am-5pm (Fri 2pm-5.30pm). Closed 25, 26 Dec
Cards: No

DIRECTIONS: Between Grantham
and Boston on A52. Approx 2 miles
east of Osbournby roundabout, turn
left at Threekingham crossroads.

11/1090
● PLANTS

Potterton & Martin
The Cottage Nursery, Moortown Road,
Nettleton, Nr Caistor, Lincolnshire LN7 6HX
Tel/Fax: (01472) 851792

Dwarf hardy plants, alpines and dwarf
bulbs, ferns, dwarf conifers and
carnivorous plants.
Open: 9am-5pm. Closed 25 Dec
Cards: Access, Visa

DIRECTIONS: At the rear of
Nettleton Manor Nursing Home,
Moortown Road B1205, off the A46 at
Nettleton.

11/1091
● LEATHER GOODS

Pamela Woods Accessories
Unit 3, The Pearoom, Station
Road, Heckington, Sleaford,
Lincolnshire NG34 9JJ
Tel/Fax: (01529) 461501

Leather bags, gloves and belts.
Open: 10am-5pm, but telephone in
advance
Cards: No

DIRECTIONS: Opposite 8-sailed
windmill.

11/1092
● TEXTILES

Timberland Art & Design
12 Church Lane, Timberland,
Lincoln, Lincolnshire LN4 3SB
Tel: (01526) 378222

Prints, tapestries, woodcuts, paintings,
cushions, cards, picture frames, hand-made paper, wool.
Open: Tue-Fri 10am-5pm, Sun and
bank hols 1pm-4pm. Closed over
Christmas for 2 weeks
Cards: No

DIRECTIONS: B1189 from Lincoln
via Metheringham to Timberland
crossroads. Follow brown signs to Art
and Design studios, near village
shop/post office.

11/1093
● GARDEN FURNITURE

Michael Hill Cast Iron Garden Furniture
Cressy Hall, Cawood Lane, Gosberton,
Spalding, Lincolnshire PE11 4JD
Tel: (01775) 840925
Fax: (01775) 840008

Exact copies of antique cast-iron
garden furniture, produced in the
traditional way and finished by hand.
Open: Mon-Fri 9am-5pm, other times
by appointment only
Cards: No

DIRECTIONS: Turn off the A16
Spalding to Boston road in Gosberton
on to the A152, then turn
immediately left on to the B1397
signposted to Bourne. Cawood Lane
is about 1½ miles on the right over a
small bridge with white railings.

11/1094
● PLANTS

Countryside Companions
The Limes, Baumber, Horncastle,
Lincolnshire LN9 5NE
Tel: (01507) 578361
Fax: (01507) 578484

Wildflower seeds and plants.
Greetings cards. Cascading water-barrel gardens.
Open: By appointment only
Cards: No

DIRECTIONS: 4 miles from
Horncastle in the direction of Lincoln
on A158.

11/1095
● PLANTS

The Valley Clematis Nursery
Willingham Road, Hainton,
Lincolnshire LN3 6LN
Tel: (01507) 313398
Fax: (01507) 313705

Clematis.
Open: 10am-5pm. Closed 25 Dec-3
Jan
Cards: Access, Switch, Visa

DIRECTIONS: 400 yards south of the
A517 at Hainton, on the road to South
Willingham.

11/1096
■ MEAT/POULTRY/GAME

F C Phipps
Osborne House, Mareham le Fen, Boston,
Lincolnshire PE22 7RW
Tel: (01507) 568235

Butcher: pies, sausages, haslet, home-
cured hams.
Open: Mon, Tue, Thur, Fri 7am-5pm,
Wed 7am-1pm, Sat 7am-4pm. Closed
bank hols
Cards: No

DIRECTIONS: On A155 from
Sleaford to Skegness, 25 yards from
Royal Oak crossroads.

11/1097
✱ MULTIPLE

Abbeygate Antique & Craft Centre
14 Abbeygate, Grimsby,
Humberside DN31 1JY
Tel: (01472) 361129

Glass, jewellery, needlecrafts,
calligraphy.
Open: Mon-Sat 9.30am-5pm. Closed
bank hols
Cards: No

DIRECTIONS: Off Bethlehem Street
in Grimsby, close to railway station.

11/1098
■ MEAT/POULTRY/GAME

John Pettit & Sons Ltd
33-35 Bethlehem Street, Grimsby,
Humberside DN31 1JQ
Tel: (01472) 349915 and 342724
Fax: (01472) 355917

Aberdeen Angus beef, sausages and
dry-cured bacon.
Open: Mon-Fri 7am-5pm. Thur and
Sat 7am-1pm. Closed bank hols
Cards: No

DIRECTIONS: In town centre.
Entrance in West St Mary's Gate.

11/1099
■ FLOUR

Maud Foster Mill
Willoughby Road, Boston,
Lincolnshire PE21 9EG
Tel: (01205) 352188

Stoneground organic flours.
Wholefood shop.
Open: Wed 10am-5pm, Sun and bank
hols 2pm-5pm. Fri and Sat in Aug.
Closed Christmas and New Year
Cards: No

DIRECTIONS: In Boston town centre
just off A16 Grimsby road.

11/1100
✱ MULTIPLE

Alford Craft Market Shop
New Market Hall, Cornmarket, Louth,
Lincolnshire LN11 9PY
Tel: (01507) 358648

Co-operative of 15 crafts people.
Open: Mon-Sat 9am-5pm. Closed
bank hols
Cards: No

DIRECTIONS: Off A16. Approach
from Cornmarket next to Masons
Arms Hotel, or from Little Eastgate
just past the post office on opposite
side of road.

11/1101
● CERAMICS

Jackpots
The Old Stables, Queen Street Place,
Louth, Lincolnshire LN11 9BD
Tel: (01507) 604656

Hand-thrown domestic earthenware
pottery.
Open: Mon-Sat 10am-4pm, best to
telephone in advance
Cards: No

DIRECTIONS: At rear of Queen
Street car park, signposted.

11/1102
■ SAUSAGES

Swepstones
26/28 High Street, Holbeach,
Lincolnshire PE12 7ED
Tel: (01406) 423283

Lincolnshire pork sausages, cheese
and epicure goods.
Open: Mon,Tue, Sat 7.30am-5pm,
Wed 7.30am-1pm, Thur 7.30am-
5.30pm, Fri 7.30am-7pm. Closed
bank hols
Cards: No

DIRECTIONS: Take A17 Long Sutton
to Fosdyke road. At roundabout take
B1168 to Holbeach. To traffic lights.
Left past front of Woolworth's.
Halfway along High Street on right.

11/1103
● JEWELLERY

Elizabeth Jack Designer Jewellery
Blue Heron Cottage, Muckton, Nr Louth,
Lincolnshire LN11 8NX
Tel: (01507) 480630

Hand-painted wooden earrings,
necklaces, brooches, cufflinks,
hat/lapel pins.
Open: By appointment
Cards: No

DIRECTIONS: Off A16 6 miles south
of Louth, turn left after Burwell
signposted Muckton. Cottage is
opposite T-junction after 2 miles.

11/1104
● DRIED FLOWERS

Candlesby Herbs
Cross Keys Cottage, Candlesby, Spilsby,
Lincolnshire PE23 5SF
Tel: (01754) 890211

Herbs and wildflowers.
Open: Tue-Sun 10am-5pm, open
bank hol Mons
Cards: No

DIRECTIONS: On Skegness to Louth
road, 2 miles north of Gunbey
roundabout.

11/1105
● CERAMICS

Alford Pottery
Commercial Road, Alford,
Lincolnshire LN13 9EY
Tel: (01507) 463342

Pottery, domestic ware and giftware:
dinner services, teasets, pierced and
painted decoration.
Open: Mon-Fri 9am-12.30pm,
1.30pm-5pm. Sat 10am-12.30pm,
1.30pm-5pm. Closed end Sept, 24
Dec-2 Jan
Cards: No

DIRECTIONS: A1104 off A16, main
road into town, well signposted.

11/1106
■ FLOUR

Five Sails Mill
East Street, Alford, Lincolnshire LN13 9EQ
Tel: (01507) 462136

Freshly milled flour.
Open: Sat and bank hols 11am-5pm.
July and Aug Tue, Fri, Sat 1pm-5pm
Cards: No

DIRECTIONS: On A1104
Mablethorpe Road at Alford.

MAP 12

12/1107
■ ICE-CREAM

Hartley's Ice Cream
24 Church Street, Egremont,
Cumbria CA22 2AW
Tel: (01946) 820456

Sorbets and gateaux.
Open: 10am-6pm. Closed in Jan
Cards: No

DIRECTIONS: Near Market Place, St
Mary and St Michael's Church.

12/1108
● DRIED FLOWERS

Pamela Bush Floral Decor
Windermere Building, Peart Road, Derwent
Howe, Workington, Cumbria CA14
Tel/Fax: (01900) 872223

Dried, silk and paper flowers and
displays.
Open: Mon-Fri 8.30am-5.30pm. Sat
9am-2pm, Sun in Dec. Closed
Christmas to New Year
Cards: Access, Visa

DIRECTIONS: Off A697 Whitehaven
to Maryport road. Signposted from
A595 and A596. Near main
supermarkets.

12/1109
■ SAUSAGES

Richard Woodall
Lane End, Waberthwaite, Nr Millom,
Cumbria LA19 5YJ
Tel: (01229) 717237
Fax: (01229) 717007

Dry-curers of Cumberland hams and
bacons. Cumberland sausages.
Open: Mon-Fri 8.30am-12.15pm,
1.15pm-5.30pm. Sat 8.30am-12 noon.
Closed Sun, bank hols and Christmas
Cards: No

DIRECTIONS: 3 miles north of
Bootle and 4 miles south of
Ravenglass just off A595. 300 yards
north of Brown Cow Inn bear left. Go
further 300 yards to corner.

12/1110
■ FLOUR

Muncaster Water Mill
Ravenglass, Cumbria CA18 1ST
Tel: (01229) 717232

Stoneground organic wholemeal flour
and oatmeals.
Open: Sept-Apr Mon-Sun 11am-5pm,
June-Aug Mon-Sun 10.30am-5.30pm
Cards: No

DIRECTIONS: On A595 Barrow-in-
Furness to Workington road, 1 mile
north of Muncaster Castle and 1 mile
north-east of Ravenglass.

12/1111
● TOYS

Pipkin Puppets
Riverside Craft Studio, off Market Place,
Cockermouth, Cumbria CA13 9NP
Tel: (01900) 828867

Puppets for children.
Open: Mon-Sat Mar-Sept 10am-
4.30pm, Oct-Dec 10am-4pm, Jan-Feb
10am-3pm
Cards: No

DIRECTIONS: Off A66, 13 miles
north-west of Keswick. Off Market
Place, 75 yards from Toy Museum
and Information Centre. Overlooking
river Cocker.

12/1112
● CERAMICS

Dalton Pottery
8 Nelson Street, Dalton-in-Furness,
Cumbria LA15 8AF
Tel: (01229) 465313

Thrown and cast terracotta planters.
Open: Advisable to telephone first, but
usually 10am-5pm
Cards: Access, Switch, Visa

DIRECTIONS: Off A590 between
Barrow-in-Furness and Ulverston.
Opposite Merlyn Motors in Dalton.

12/1113
● CERAMICS

Adrian Newnham Ceramics
Sunyn Cottage, Soutergate, Kirkby-in-
Furness, Cumbria LA17 7TW
Tel: (01229) 889517

Ceramics, bowls, vases, plant pots,
decorated in blue, green or pink.
Open: By appointment
Cards: No

DIRECTIONS: On the A595,
Broughton to Barrow road, 1 mile
from Kirkby crossroads with the pub
and village shop. In the centre of
Soutergate on left.

12/1114
● LEATHER GOODS

Leather Mills
Gleaston Water Mill, Gleaston, Ulverston,
Cumbria LA12 0QH
Tel/Fax: (01229) 869077

Leather goods including handbags,
purses, wallets and novelty items.
Open: Tue-Sat 11am-5pm. Sun
1.30pm-5pm. Closed Mon. In winter
close at 4pm
Cards: Access, Visa

DIRECTIONS: Follow coast road
(A5087) from Ulverston and follow
tourist signs for Gleaston Water Mill.

12/1115
● DOLLS' HOUSES

The Dolls' House Man
Furness Galleries, Theatre Street,
Ulverston, Cumbria LA12 7AQ
Tel: (01229) 587657

Dolls' houses, miniatures and
accessories.
Open: Tue-Sat 10.30am-5pm. No
seasonal closures. Closed on bank
hols
Cards: No

DIRECTIONS: A590 Barrow-in-
Furness road, 8 miles west from
Newby Bridge (bottom end of Lake
Windermere) turn right at second set
of traffic lights in Ulverston, third
turning on the right off Queen Street,
well signposted on main road.

12/1116
● GLASS

Heron Glass
54 The Gill, Ulverston, Cumbria LA12 7BL
Tel: (01229) 581121
Fax: (01229) 587530

Ornamental glassware and local crafts.
Open: Mon-Sat 8.30am-5pm. Closed
Christmas
Cards: Access, Visa

DIRECTIONS: 3rd left into Ulverston
one-way system. 50 yards on right.
Turn right by car park.

12/1117
● CERAMICS

Skiddaw Pottery
Rear Lake Road, Keswick,
Cumbria CA12 5DQ
Tel: (017687) 74846

Stoneware pottery.
Open: Reasonable hours, please
telephone in advance
Cards: No

DIRECTIONS: Overlooking the
central car park in centre of Keswick.

12/1118
● DOLLS

Vrons Dolls
Daresfield, Chestnut Hill, Keswick,
Cumbria CA12 4LS
Tel: (01768) 772531

Dolls.
Open: All reasonable hours. Closed
Christmas/New Year. Telephone in
advance
Cards: No

DIRECTIONS: On A591 1 mile from
town centre. 100 yards above junction
with Penrith Road.

12/1119
● TEXTILES

Coniston Woollen Mill Ltd
Lake Road, Coniston, Cumbria LA21 8EW
Tel: (015394) 41360
Fax: (015394) 41143

Knitwear and embroidery.
Open: Mon-Sat 9am-5pm

Cards: Access, Amex, Diners, Switch, Visa

DIRECTIONS: In centre of village. Follow signs for gondola. Mill by lake.

12/1120
● TEXTILES
Countryman John & Co Ltd
The Rural Workshops, Lake Road, Coniston, Cumbria LA21 8EW
Tel: (015394) 41129

Wildlife designs printed on fabrics for roller blinds, and table linen, napkins, mats, cushions etc.
Open: Mon-Fri 10am-5.30pm Sat 10am-4pm. Closed Sun and bank hols
Cards: No

DIRECTIONS: From Coniston centre turn down Lake Road (signposted for Gondola Steam Pier). Workshop is one of a group where road bends left.

12/1121
● WOOD
Lathe and Chisel
Dander Cottage, Bouth, Ulverston, Cumbria LA12 8JB
Tel: (01229) 861269

Wood-turning, carving, sculpture, including rocking-horses and animal sculptures.
Open: Mon-Fri 9am-5pm, or telephone
Cards: No

DIRECTIONS: Off main Kendal to Ulverston road, 5 miles from Ulverston. Studio signposted in village.

12/1122
● WOOD
Maurice Mullins
Whelpo Farm, Caldbeck, Wigton, Cumbria CA7 8HQ
Tel: (016974) 78645

Wooden boxes, bowls, decorative platters and semi-sculptural forms.
Open: Mar-Dec Tue-Sat 2pm-5pm. Bank hols 1pm-6pm. Advisable to telephone first
Cards: No

DIRECTIONS: Take Uldale/Keswick road from Caldbeck for 1 mile. Whelpo Farm is on left opposite stone bridge over river Caldbeck. From J41, M6, take B5305 to Wigton. After 6 miles turn left for Caldbeck.

12/1123
● STONE
Kirkstone Galleries
Skelwith Bridge, Ambleside, Cumbria LA22 9NN
Tel: (015394) 34002
Fax: (015394) 34006

Carved stone crafts and work tops.
Open: Apr-Oct Mon-Fri 10am-6pm. Nov-Mar 10am-5pm. Closed 24-26 Dec and 30 Jan-3 Feb
Cards: Access, Switch, Visa

DIRECTIONS: At Skelwith Bridge, 3 miles west of Ambleside on A593 to Coniston.

12/1124
● TEXTILES
Fibrecrafts
Barnhowe, Elterwater, Ambleside, Cumbria LA22 9HW
Tel: (015394) 37346

Spinning and weaving equipment, fleece and fibres, dyes, yarns and literature.
Open: Easter-Nov Mon-Sat 10am-5pm, call first in winter
Cards: Access, Visa

DIRECTIONS: On B5343 to Langdale, just before Elterwater village, the track on the right.

12/1125
● SADDLERY GOODS
Hide & Horn
Dixons Court, 101 Lake Road, Ambleside, Cumbria LA22 0DB
Tel/Fax: (015394) 33052

Saddler, horn craftsman, leather goods.
Open: Mon-Wed, Fri-Sat 9am-5pm
Cards: No

DIRECTIONS: In Ambleside in alley opposite the Old Lake Road.

12/1126
● GLASS

Adrian Sankey Glass
Rydal Road, Ambleside, Cumbria LA22 9AN
Tel: (015394) 33039
Fax: (015394) 31139

Studio glass-makers, handmade lead
crystal, wine glasses, bowls, perfume
bottles and lighting.
Open: Mon-Sun 9am-5.30pm. Closed
25-26 Dec
Cards: Access, Amex, Switch, Visa

DIRECTIONS: On the northern side
of Ambleside, directly behind Bridge
House.

12/1127
● CERAMICS

Spiral Pottery
Zeffirelli's Arcade, Compston Road,
Ambleside, Cumbria LA22 9AD
Tel/Fax: (015394) 41305

Handmade stoneware pottery.
Open: Mon-Sat 10am-5pm, some
Sun. Closed holidays
Cards: Access, Amex, Diners, Visa

DIRECTIONS: Follow Compston
Road on the one-way system in
Ambleside, Zeffirelli's arcade is by the
traffic lights.

12/1128
● FURNITURE

Country Furniture
Bark House, Witherslack, Grange-over-
Sands, Cumbria LA11 6RX
Tel: (015395) 52566

Stools and chairs from coppice
hardwoods.
Open: By appointment only
Cards: No

DIRECTIONS: From J36 M6 follow
signs to Barrow (A590). Take right
turn to Witherslack, then 3 first lefts.
Workshop is 100 yards along.

12/1129
● CERAMICS

John Kershaw Studio Pottery
40 Main Road, Windermere,
Cumbria LA23 1DY
Tel: (015394) 44844

Stoneware pottery, mainly wheel-
thrown, some hand-built, some raku.
Open: Mon-Sat 9.30am-5.30pm
Cards: Access, Visa

DIRECTIONS: In the centre of
Windermere, down a passageway
opposite Simpsons newsagents.

12/1130
● JEWELLERY

Sue Kane Designs
The Gem Den, Whitbarrow Village, Berrier,
Penrith, Cumbria CA11 0XB
Tel: (01768) 483797

Semi-precious stones and gemstone
jewellery.
Open: Mon-Fri 9.30am-3pm
Cards: Access, Visa

DIRECTIONS: 2 minutes off A66
midway between Penrith and Keswick
at Hutton Roof junction close to
Sportsmans Inn. Follow signs to
Whitbarrow on Berrier to Greystoke
road.

12/1131
● CERAMICS

William Plumptre Pottery
Pool Bank, Witherslack, Grange-over-
Sands, Cumbria LA11 6SB
Tel/Fax: (015395) 68750

Ceramic earthenware pots, bowls and
vases.
Open: By appointment
Cards: No

DIRECTIONS: A591 to Kendal
bypass, A590 towards Barrow, turning
to Witherslack. Follow Boland Bridge
sign from Witherslack village for 4
miles.

12/1144
● CERAMICS

Jim Malone Pottery
Hagget House, Towngate, Ainstable,
Carlisle, Cumbria CA4 9RE
Tel: (01768) 896444

Pottery using local Cumbrian
minerals.
Open: Summer Mon-Sun 10am-8pm,
winter Mon-Sun 10am-4pm. Closed
25-26 Dec
Cards: No

DIRECTIONS: On A6 halfway
between Carlisle and Penrith, take
turn to Armathwaite. At Armathwaite
turn right at the Duke's Head and
follow road to Ainstable for 1½ miles.

12/1145
✳ MULTIPLE

**Brougham Hall Craft
Workshops**
Brougham Hall, Penrith, Cumbria CA10 2DE
Tel: (01768) 868184

Chocolates, soft furnishings,
metalwork, stone, smoked foods,
tearoom.
Open: Summer daily 9am-5pm.
Winter Mon-Fri 10am-4pm. Closed
25 Dec
Cards: No

DIRECTIONS: On B6262 between A6
and A66, 1½ miles south of Penrith
(M6 J40).

12/1146
● TOYS

Croglin Toys
The Old School, Lazonby,
Cumbria CA4 9LU
Tel: (01768) 896475

Wooden toys of original designs.
Open: Mon, Wed, Fri 10am-4pm.
Otherwise by appointment
Cards: No

DIRECTIONS: On A6 north of
Penrith at Plumpton take B6413 to
Lazonby.

12/1147
● DOLLS' HOUSES

Carol Black Miniatures
Sun Hill, Great Strickland, Penrith,
Cumbria CA10 3DF
Tel/Fax: (01931) 712330

Dolls' house miniatures for collectors.
Open: By appointment only
Cards: Access, Visa

DIRECTIONS: 1 mile off A6 Penrith
road, opposite church in Great
Strickland.

12/1148
● CERAMICS

Wetheriggs Country Pottery
Clifton Dykes, Penrith, Cumbria CA10 2DH
Tel: (01768) 892733
Fax: (01768) 892722

Pottery.
Open: Daily 9am-6pm. Closed 25, 26
Dec
Cards: Visa

DIRECTIONS: 4 miles south of
Penrith off A6 on Cliburn Road.
Alternatively, 5 minutes from J40 M6
and follow A6 signs.

12/1149
■ MEAT/POULTRY/GAME

C R & J Towers
70 Main Street, Hornby, Lancaster,
Lancashire LA2 8JT
Tel: (015242) 21248

Baked pies, sweet and savoury.
Sausages and oven-ready products.
Open: Tue-Fri 8am-6pm. Sat 8am-3pm
Cards: No

DIRECTIONS: 8 miles north-east of
Lancaster. Take A683 from J34 on M6
to Kirkby Lonsdale. In Hornby next
door to the church on Main Street.

12/1150
● PHOTOGRAPHY

Ian Johnson Photography
Punchbowl House, Grayrigg, Nr Kendal,
Cumbria LA8 9BU
Tel: (0539) 824345

Landscape photographs of the Lake
District.

Open: Normal hours but advisable to telephone first
Cards: No

DIRECTIONS: On A685 between Kendal and M6 (J38). Punchbowl House is on main road in centre of village.

12/1151
■ CONFECTIONERY

Kennedys Fine Chocolates Ltd
1A Silver Yard, Orton, Penrith, Cumbria CA10 3RQ
Tel/Fax: (015396) 24781

Chocolates.
Open: Mon-Sat 9am-5pm, Sun 1pm-4.30pm but advisable to telephone first
Cards: No

DIRECTIONS: On B6260 from Tebay to Appleby, Silver Yard is located beside the main road through the village of Orton, on the right.

12/1152
■ MEAT/POULTRY/GAME

M F & D J Slack
Newlands Farm, Raisbeck, Orton, Penrith, Cumbria CA10 3SG
Tel: (015396) 24667

Home-cured bacon and sausages.
Open: Mon-Fri 9am-1pm, 2pm-5.30pm. Sat 9am-12.30pm, 2pm-5pm. Wed 9am-12.30pm
Cards: No

DIRECTIONS: At M6, J38 take B6260 to Orton, fork left at George Hotel. 100 yards on left.

12/1153
■ BAKED GOODS

Lakeland Gateaux
Rayson Hall, Townhead, Ousby, Penrith, Cumbria CA10 1QB
Tel: (01768) 881686
Fax: (01768) 881799

Continental patisseries, cheesecake, puddings, cakes.
Open: Mon-Thur 8.30am-5pm. Fri 8.30am-1.30pm. Sat and Sun by appointment. Closed bank hols
Cards: No

DIRECTIONS: From A686 towards Alston, after 6 miles turn right to Ousby. Take 2nd left, 2nd right, and then ½ mile on right.

12/1154
■ BAKED GOODS

The Village Bakery
Melmerby, Penrith, Cumbria CA10 1HE
Tel: (01768) 881515
Fax: (01768) 881848

Organic breads and confectionery from a wood-fired brick oven.
Open: Mon-Sat 8.30am-5pm, Sun 9.30am-5pm. Jan-Feb Mon-Fri 8.30am-2.30pm
Cards: Access, Diners, Switch, Visa

DIRECTIONS: Alston road A686 to Melmerby, turn left immediately after sharp left-hand bend, 50 yards on right.

12/1155
● CERAMICS

Bentham Pottery
Oysterber Farm, Low Bentham, Lancaster LA2 7ET
Tel: (015242) 61567

Domestic stoneware pottery. Pottery courses.
Open: Easter-end Oct, Mon-Sat 8.30am-5pm, Nov-March, Mon-Fri 8.30am-5pm. Closed 25 Dec, 1 Jan
Cards: No

DIRECTIONS: From the A65 turn-off for Burton-in-Consdale, take the road signposted to Bentham, down the hill and over the bridge. Go straight up hill and over crossroads, 300 yards on right.

12/1156
● CLOTHES

Farfield
Farfield Mill, Sedbergh, Cumbria LA10 5LW
Tel/Fax: (01539) 620169

Casual clothing.
Open: Mon-Fri 8am-6pm, Apr-Sept Sat-Sun 1pm-5pm
Cards: Access, Visa

DIRECTIONS: On A684 Sedbergh to Hawes road, ¼ mile from town centre, next to Oakdean Guest House.

12/1157
● TOYS

Michael Frost
Hillcroft Farm, Kelleth, Tebay, Penrith, Cumbria CA10 3UG
Tel: (015396) 23248

Traditional wooden toys.
Open: Usually open all year
Cards: No

DIRECTIONS: From J38 on M6 take the Brough road. After 1½ miles turn left and follow sign to Kelleth.

12/1158
● CERAMICS

Ingleton Pottery
Ingleton, Via Carnforth, Lancashire LA6 3HB
Tel/Fax: (015242) 41363

Hand-thrown, high-fired stoneware pottery.
Open: Mon-Sun 9.30am-5pm. May be closed Jan-Feb, advisable to telephone first
Cards: No

DIRECTIONS: Off A68 between Kendal and Skipton, under the viaduct down by the river in Ingleton.

12/1159
● ROCKING-HORSES

Heirlooms
Dufton Hall, Dufton, Appleby, Cumbria CA16 6DD
Tel/Fax: (01768) 353353

Rocking-horses.
Open: Mon-Fri 9am-5pm. Closed 24 Dec-2 Jan
Cards: No

DIRECTIONS: 3 miles from A66 Appleby exit on Fellside road. Top of village green opposite car park.

12/1160
● WOOD

John J Rudd & Sons
Sawmills, Dufton, Appleby, Cumbria CA16 6DF
Tel: (017683) 51880

Handmade wooden hay rakes.
Open: Mon-Fri 7.30am-5pm. Closed early Aug and bank hols
Cards: No

DIRECTIONS: From north: leave A66 10 miles east of Penrith. Follow signs to Dufton 3 miles. From south: leave Appleby on Penrith road at edge of town, pass under railway bridge and follow signs to Dufton (3 miles).

12/1161
✱ MULTIPLE

Dent Crafts Centre
Helmside, Dent, Sedbergh, Cumbria LA10 5SY
Tel: (015396) 25400

Pottery, jewellery.
Open: Mar-Nov daily 9.30am-5.30pm. Nov-Jan 10.30am-5pm. Jan/Feb weekends only
Cards: Access, Amex, Visa

DIRECTIONS: 8 miles from M6 J37 between Sedbergh and Dent.

12/1162
● PLANTS

Weasdale Nurseries
Newbiggin on Lune, Kirkby Stephen, Cumbria CA17 4LX
Tel: (015396) 23246
Fax: (015396) 23277

Trees and shrubs.
Open: Mon-Fri 8am-5pm. Closed Nov-Apr
Cards: No

DIRECTIONS: 7 miles from J38 M6 off A685 Tebay to Brough. Take Weasdale road from A685 at western limit of Newbiggin on Lune. Follow signposts.

12/1163
● PLANTS

Hartside Nursery Garden
Nr Alston, Cumbria CA9 3BL
Tel: (01434) 381372

Alpine plants, hardy ferns, dwarf
shrubs and conifers.
Open: Mar-Oct Mon-Fri 9am-5pm,
Sat and bank hols 10am-4pm, Sun
12.30pm-4pm, Nov-Feb by
appointment
Cards: Access, Amex, Visa

DIRECTIONS: 1½ miles from Alston
on A686 Alston to Penrith road.

12/1164
● PLANTS

Pinks & Carnations
22 Chetwyn Avenue, Bromley Cross,
Bolton, Lancashire BL7 9BN
Tel/Fax: (01204) 306273

Pinks and carnations.
Open: By appointment
Cards: Access, Visa

DIRECTIONS: 1 mile off A666
Bolton to Blackburn road, 3 miles
north of Bolton.

12/1165
■ SAUSAGES

Cowman's Famous Sausage Shop
13 Castle Street, Clitheroe,
Lancashire BB7 2BT
Tel: (01200) 23842

Sausages, dry-cured bacon, venison
and wild boar.
Open: Mon-Sat 7.30am-5.30pm. Wed
8am-12 noon
Cards: No

DIRECTIONS: Turn off A59 to
Clitheroe. Follow town centre signs.
Near the castle.

12/1166
● MUSICAL INSTRUMENTS

Dennis Woolley Harpsichords
Tubhole Barn, Dent, Sedbergh, West
Yorkshire LA10 5RE
Tel: (015396) 25361

Fortepianos, harpsichords,
clavichords.

Open: By appointment only
Cards: No

DIRECTIONS: Tubhole Barn is 2
miles east of Dent village on back
lane, take right fork in village by
George and Dragon pub.

12/1167
● CERAMICS

Hutton Lodge Pottery
Soulby, Kirkby Stephen, Cumbria CA17 4PL
Tel: (017683) 71396

Hand-thrown stoneware pots for
everyday use, from egg cups to bread
crocks.
Open: Mon-Sun 9am-9pm. Closed
25-26 Dec, 1 Jan
Cards: Visa

DIRECTIONS: At Kirkby Stephen
follow sign to Soulby. In village cross
bridge, 1st left follow Crosby Garrett
for 350 yards, 2nd on left at no
through road sign.

12/1168
● PLANTS

Holden Clough Nursery
Holden, Bolton-by-Bowland, Nr Clitheroe,
Lancashire BB7 4PF
Tel: (01200) 447615

Alpines, perennials, shrubs and
woodland plants.
Open: Mar-Sept Mon-Thur 1pm-
5pm, Sat 9am-5pm, Sun Apr-May
only. Oct-Feb Mon-Sat 9am-5pm.
Closed 25 Dec-1 Jan
Cards: Access, Visa

DIRECTIONS: Leave A59 at Sawley,
after 2 miles turn left at Copy Nook,
fork left after ½ mile.

12/1169
● HUNTING ACCESSORIES

Ivy Cottage Gun Cabinets & Walking Sticks
Ivy Cottage, Stone House, Cowgill, Dent,
Sedbergh, Cumbria LA10 5RL
Tel: (015396) 25481

Hardwood and metal gun cabinets,
walking sticks, shepherds' crooks and
all stick-making accessories.
Open: By appointment only

Cards: No

DIRECTIONS: Between Dent and Hawes.

12/1170
● METALWORK

Heredities Limited
Crossfield Mill, Kirkby Stephen,
Cumbria CA17 4QY
Tel: (017683) 71543
Fax: (017683) 72041

Bronze cold-cast figurines.
Open: Mon-Fri 9am-5pm. Closed bank hols, Christmas and Easter
Cards: Access, Visa

DIRECTIONS: In Kirkby Stephen. Turn into Redmayne Road at Johnstone's Garage (right from west, left from east) then first right into Hobsons Lane and follow road round into yard.

12/1171
● PRESERVES

Island Cottage Crafts
Island Cottage, Nentsberry, Alston,
Cumbria CA9 3LW
Tel/Fax: (01434) 381860

Truffles, fudge, preserves, chutneys, saltdough magnets and figures, textile novelties.
Open: Mon-Fri 10am-4pm
Cards: No

DIRECTIONS: 3½ miles south-east of Alston on A689 Stanhope to Durham road. Island Cottage sign on roadside.

12/1172
● SLATE

Slate Age (Fence) Ltd
Fence Gate, Fence, Nr Burnley,
Lancashire BB12 9EG
Tel: (01282) 616952
Fax: (01282) 619058

Slate giftware: clocks, barometers, placemats, egg-timers.
Open: Mon-Fri 8am-4.30pm, Sat 9am-1pm. Closed bank hols, 1 week at Christmas
Cards: Access, Visa

DIRECTIONS: On A6068 between Padiham and Nelson, 3 miles north-east of Padiham. The works are opposite turn off for Burnley, next to Fence Gate Inn.

12/1173
● FORGEWORK

Barley Forge
Barley, Burnley, Lancashire BB12 9JZ
Tel: (01282) 603919

Wrought iron for house and garden.
Open: Mon-Fri 8am-5pm, varied holidays
Cards: No

DIRECTIONS: 5 miles from Nelson on Gisburn road. Forge in middle of the village.

12/1174
● SADDLERY GOODS

M Miller Saddler and Harnessmaker
624 Burnley Road, East Whitewell Bottom,
Rossendale, Lancashire BB4 9NT
Tel: (01706) 226983

Saddlery and harnesses.
Open: Mon-Sat 9am-6pm. Closed bank hols, 25 Dec-2 Jan
Cards: Access, Visa

DIRECTIONS: From Burnley town centre on the A671, right along B2638 for 3 miles, on the right opposite post office.

12/1175
● ROPE

W R Outhwaite & Son
Town Foot, Hawes, North Yorkshire DL8 3NT
Tel: (01969) 667487
Fax: (01969) 667576

Traditional ropemaking. Dog leads, halters. Demonstrations.
Open: Mon-Fri 9am-5.30pm. Bank hols, Sat in July 10am-5.30pm.
Cards: No

DIRECTIONS: On A684, next to old station car park.

12/1176
● TOYS

Jigajog Toys
The Penn House, off Market Place, Hawes,
North Yorkshire DL8 3NT
Tel: (01969) 667008

Wooden toys.
Open: Mon-Sat 10am-5pm, also Sun
in summer 2pm-5pm, telephone call
advised
Cards: Access, Visa

DIRECTIONS: In the centre of
Hawes, in courtyard next to the
market hall, behind the Spar
supermarket.

12/1177
● CERAMICS

Yorkshire Flowerpots
Unit 2C, Brunt Acres Industrial Estate,
Hawes, North Yorkshire DL8 3UZ
Tel: (01969) 667464

Hand-thrown quality terracotta
gardenware, flowerpots, planters,
wallpots.
Open: Mon-Fri 9am-5pm, Sat 10am-
4.30pm
Cards: No

DIRECTIONS: On the Hardaw road
just outside Hawes (100 yards from
Town Foot). The estate is clearly
signposted.

12/1178
■ ICE-CREAM

Sweet Clough Dairy Ice Cream
Higher Town House Farm, Southfield,
Nr Burnley, Lancashire BB10 3RH
Tel: (01282) 612682/865880

Dairy ice-cream using milk and cream
from farm.
Open: Any reasonable hours. Closed
25-26 Dec
Cards: No

DIRECTIONS: A56 out of Nelson
turn right at Hour Glass pub. After
1½ miles turn left at traffic island.
Farm is ½ mile up the road on right.

12/1179
● WOOD

David Tippey
Victoria Lodge, Kirkby Malham, Nr Skipton,
North Yorkshire BD23 4BS
Tel: (01729) 830547

Hand-carved and painted birds.
Open: Mon-Sat 10am-4pm, weekends
by appointment, best to call first
Cards: Access, Visa

DIRECTIONS: Take A65 Skipton to
Kendal road from Skipton. 4 miles
west of Skipton turn right at Gargrave
towards Malham, about 4½ miles
north is village of Kirkby Malham.
Situated opposite Victoria Inn.

12/1180
● CERAMICS

Askrigg Pottery
Old School House, West End, Askrigg,
Leyburn, North Yorkshire DL8 3HN
Tel: (01969) 650548

High-fired stoneware and porcelain,
decorated by hand.
Open: Mon-Fri 10am-5pm but
appointment advisable
Cards: No

DIRECTIONS: In Askrigg, behind the
church.

12/1181
● GARDEN FURNITURE

Freegate Metal Products
Freegate Mill, Ickornshaw, Cowling,
Keighley, North Yorkshire BD22 0DJ
Tel/Fax: (01535) 632723

Reproduction Victorian garden
furniture and decorative castings.
Open: Daily 7.30am-4.30pm. Closed
bank hols
Cards: No

DIRECTIONS: Between Cowling and
Keighley in Ickornshaw behind the
Black Gull, in an old mill.

12/1182
● CERAMICS

Mill Pottery

Bridge Mill Workshops, St George's Square,
Hebden Bridge, West Yorkshire HX7 8ET
Tel: (01422) 844559

Hand-thrown domestic stoneware.
Open: Mon-Fri 9.30am-5pm, Sat
11am-5pm, some Suns 2pm-5pm,
variable holidays
Cards: No

DIRECTIONS: Bridge Mill is on the
corner of St George's Square and the
road bridge over the river, next to the
White Lion pub. The pottery is on the
top floor of the mill.

12/1183
● JEWELLERY

Gemini Studios

51a Main Street, Grassington, Skipton,
North Yorkshire BD23 5AA
Tel: (01756) 752605

Silver and gold jewellery.
Open: Mon-Sun 10.30am-5.30pm
Cards: No

DIRECTIONS: A65 to Skipton, 10
miles north on B6265 to Pateley
Bridge.

12/1184
● CERAMICS

Jim Cooper Pottery & Forge

105 Oldham Road, Ripponden, Halifax,
West Yorkshire HX6 4EB
Tel: (01422) 822728

Pottery, from porcelain busts to
terracotta milkbottle covers.
Traditional ironwork.
Open: Any reasonable hours
Cards: No

DIRECTIONS: J22 M62, 5 miles
towards Halifax on the right, just past
Besom pub and opposite dentist.

12/1185
● CERAMICS

Throstle Nest Pottery & Gallery

Old Lindley, Holywell Green, Halifax,
West Yorkshire HX4 9DF
Tel: (01422) 374388

Ceramics and paintings.
Open: Mon-Sun 10am-5pm. Closed
25-26 Dec
Cards: No

DIRECTIONS: A640 Rochdale road,
first right after Wappy Spring pub and
¾ mile down country lane on right
behind car park.

12/1186
● TEXTILES

Helyg Pottery and Textiles Workshops and Gallery

2 Bolton Road, Addingham, Nr Ilkley, West
Yorkshire LS29 0NR
Tel: (01943) 830165

Handmade stoneware pottery, mainly
functional, and hand-woven tapestry.
Open: Mon-Sat 9am-5pm, but Sun
sometimes, call in advance.
Cards: No

DIRECTIONS: Off the A65 between
Ilkley and Skipton, just off
Addingham village main street,
behind Crown Inn.

12/1187
● WOOD

Oakleaf Reproductions Ltd

Ling Bob Mill, Main Street, Wilsden,
Bradford, West Yorkshire BD15 0JP
Tel: (01535) 272878

Hand-stained simulated wood
mouldings in cellular resin.
Open: Mon-Fri 9am-5pm
Cards: No

DIRECTIONS: At junction of A629
Bradford to Haworth road and Main
Street, Wilsden.

12/1188
● CERAMICS

The Teapottery
Leyburn Business Park,
North Yorkshire DL8 5QA
Tel: (01969) 23839
Fax: (01969) 24079

Handmade novelty teapots.
Showroom, shop, demonstrations.
Open: Mon-Sun 9am-5pm. Closed 25
Dec
Cards: Access, Visa

DIRECTIONS: ½ mile from Leyburn
market place in Leyburn Business
Park.

12/1189
● GLASS

Tana Stained Glass
7 Railway Street, Leyburn,
North Yorkshire DL8 5EH
Tel: (01969) 24312
Fax: (01969) 23206

Stained glass windows, lights, mirrors
and interior design fitments. Design,
manufacture and restoration.
Open: Mon-Sat 9am-5pm. Closed 25
Dec
Cards: Access, Visa

DIRECTIONS: Entrance to Leyburn
on Bedale road, next to cinema.
Opposite St Matthews church and the
Sandpiper pub.

12/1190
● JEWELLERY

D H Howarth Goldsmith
114 Huddersfield Road, Mirfield,
West Yorkshire WF14 8XB
Tel/Fax: (01924) 492153

General and precious jewellery.
Open: Wed-Fri 9.30am-5pm. Sat
9.30am-2pm. Closed bank hols
Cards: Access, Visa

DIRECTIONS: First-floor workshop
in centre of Mirfield on A644.

12/1191
■ FLOUR

Village Craft Flour
Thorpe Mill, Grewelthorpe, Ripon,
North Yorkshire HG4 3BS
Tel: (01765) 658534

Organic, wholemeal flour.
Open: Mon-Fri 8am-5pm. Sat 8am-
12.30pm. Closed bank hols
Cards: No

DIRECTIONS: 6 miles north-west of
Ripon on road to Kirkby (minor road
with no A or B number). Past the
pond on right opposite chapel.

12/1192
● CERAMICS

Masham Pottery
Kings Head Yard, Market Square, Masham,
North Yorkshire HG4 4EF
Tel: (01765) 689765

Domestic stoneware gifts and crafts.
Open: Tue-Sat 10am-5pm. Closed
Jan-Mar
Cards: No

DIRECTIONS: On Masham market
square, pass through archway next to
Kings Head Hotel, 20 yards on right.

12/1193
■ MEAT/POULTRY/GAME

J B Cockburn & Sons
12 Market Place, Bedale,
North Yorkshire DL8 1EQ
Tel: (01677) 422126

Home-made pies, sausages from
locally produced meat.
Open: Mon-Sat 8am-5.30pm. Closed
bank hols
Cards: No

DIRECTIONS: 1 mile off A1M at
Leeming Motel, signposted Bedale. In
centre of village off Market Place.

12/1194
■ MEAT/POULTRY/GAME

Allisons of Ferryhill
8 Market Street, Ferryhill,
Co Durham DL17 8JN
Tel: (01740) 651321

Sausages, cooked meats, pies.
Open: Mon, Tue, Thur, Fri 8am-5pm.
Wed, Sat 8am-12.30pm
Cards: No

DIRECTIONS: At Ferryhill on A167
between Darlington and Durham.

12/1195
■ FRUIT/VEGETABLES

Harewood Bridge Fruit Farm
Wharfedale Grange, Harewood, Leeds,
West Yorkshire LS17 9LW
Tel: (0113) 2886320
Fax: (0113) 2886206

Soft fruits, vegetables, asparagus,
flowers and herbs.
Open: End June-mid Aug Mon-Fri
9am-6pm
Cards: No

DIRECTIONS: On A61 between
Leeds and Harrogate. First farm on
left, 400 yards north of Harewood
Bridge. Opposite red brick house.

MAP 13

13/1196
● FURNITURE

Bear Chairs

1 Frankham Farm Cottages, Fourstones,
Hexham, Northumberland NE47 5DL
Tel: (01434) 674343

Windsor chairs, coffee tables, spinning
wheels.
Open: By appointment only
Cards: No

DIRECTIONS: A69 Newcastle to
Carlisle road, B6319 from Haydon
Bridge to Newbrough and
Fourstones. At T-junction turn right,
after 100 yards take first left. First
house on left up bank.

13/1197
● DOLLS' HOUSES

Longbarn Enterprises

Low Mill, Bainbridge, Leyburn, North
Yorkshire DL8 3EF
Tel: (01969) 650416

Dolls' houses.
Open: July to Sept Wed and Fri 2pm-
5pm, otherwise by appointment
Cards: No

DIRECTIONS: Junction 37 off M6,
A684 to Bainbridge.

13/1198
● KNITWEAR

Swaledale Woollens Limited

Strawbeck, Muker, Richmond, North
Yorkshire DL11 6QG
Tel/Fax: (01748) 886251

Hand-knitted, crochet and other
woollen items.
Open: Mon-Sat 10am-5.30pm. Sun
1pm-5.30pm. Closed Mon in Jan-Mar
Cards: Access, Amex, Switch, Visa

DIRECTIONS: 20 miles from
Richmond on B6270.

13/1199
● HERBS

Hexham Herbs

Chesters Walled Garden, Chollerford,
Hexham, Northumberland NE46 4BQ
Tel: (01434) 681483

Herbs and unusual plants, herbal gift
shop and dried flowers.
Open: Mar-Oct daily 10am-5pm,
reduced off-season hours, phone for
details
Cards: No

DIRECTIONS: 6 miles north of
Hexham, ½ mile west of Chollerford
roundabout, next to Chester's Roman
fort, just off B6318.

13/1200
■ BEER

Hexhamshire Brewery

Leafields, Ordley, Hexham,
Northumberland NE46 1SX
Tel: (0434) 673031

Micro brewer.
Open: Not fixed – dependent upon
brewing. Closed 25 Dec
Cards: No

DIRECTIONS: 2 miles south of
Hexham between Newbiggin and
Whitley Chapel.

13/1201
● CERAMICS

The Potting Shed

1/3 Broadgates, Hexham,
Northumberland NE46 1QN
Tel: (01434) 606811

Terracotta garden pots.
Open: Mon-Sat 10am-5pm
Cards: No

DIRECTIONS: Travelling west on
main through road in Hexham take
first left after bus station then 50
yards.

13/1202
■ SHELLFISH

Kilnsey Park & Trout Farm
Kilnsey, Nr Skipton, North
Yorkshire BD23 5PS
Tel: (01756) 752150
Fax: (01756) 752224

Trout products and game. Local
cheeses, sausages and smoked foods.
Open: Daily 9am-5.30pm. (Dusk in
winter.) Closed 25 Dec
Cards: Access, Switch, Visa

DIRECTIONS: On B6160 between
Threshfield and Kettlewell. 10 miles
north of Skipton.

13/1203
● CERAMICS

Swaledale Pottery
Low Row, Richmond, North
Yorkshire DL11 6PF
Tel: (01748) 886377
Fax: (01748) 884555

Domestic stoneware.
Open: Mar-Oct daily 9am-5.30pm.
Closed Nov-Feb
Cards: Access, Visa

DIRECTIONS: From Richmond take
B6270 to Reeth. Continue up
Swaledale to Low Row for 2½ miles.
Take road on right past Punchbowl
pub.

13/1204
● CERAMICS

The Cat Pottery – Moorside Design
West Burton, Leyburn, North
Yorkshire DL8 4JW
Tel: (01969) 663273

Ceramic and reconstituted stone cats
for house and garden.
Open: Mon-Fri 9am-5pm, best to
telephone in advance
Cards: Access, Visa

DIRECTIONS: Just off B6160 which
leads south from A684 between
Leyburn and Hawes.

13/1205
● CERAMICS

Shire Pottery
Unit 3, Station Yard, Corbridge,
Northumberland NE45 5AZ
Tel/Fax: (01434) 633503

Hand-thrown, hand-finished,
terracotta gardenware.
Open: Mon-Fri 9am-6pm, Sat 10am-
4pm
Cards: No

DIRECTIONS: 1 mile south of
Corbridge in Riding Mill direction.
Take first left immediately after
Corbridge railway station. Pottery is
in goods yard opposite side of the line
from the station.

13/1206
● CERAMICS

Nexus Designs
Inspiration Works, 1 & 2 Station Yard,
Corbridge, Northumberland NE45 5AY
Tel/Fax: (01434) 633811

China plates and mugs, cards,
stationery and posters.
Open: Mon-Fri 10am-4pm. Closed
Christmas/New Year. Advisable to
telephone in advance
Cards: No

DIRECTIONS: ½ mile from
Corbridge. Head south over river
Tyne, left at roundabout at end of
bridge, road climbs crossing railway
line, then sharp left.

13/1207
● WOOD

Fine Grain
2 Bakery Yard, Princes Street, Corbridge,
Northumberland NE45 5AE
Tel: (01434) 633155

Solid wood furniture and traditional
rocking-horses. Also lamps and bowls.
Open: Mon-Sat 8.45am-6pm. Some
Sundays. Closed Christmas to New
Year
Cards: Amex

DIRECTIONS: In centre of Corbridge
village near the Angel Hotel.

13/1208
● FURNITURE

Philip Bastow Cabinet Maker
The Workshop, Back Lane, Reeth,
Richmond, North Yorkshire DL11 6TJ
Tel/Fax: (01748) 884555

Furniture using mainly oak, ash, elm
and sycamore.
Open: Mon-Fri 9am-6pm, Sat 9am-
12 noon, July-Aug also Sun 10am-
4pm
Cards: No

DIRECTIONS: From Richmond
follow B6270 signposted Reeth, once
over bridge into Reeth take first lane
on left.

13/1209
● CERAMICS

Stef's Models
Bagshaw's Yard, Anvil Square, Reeth,
Richmond, North Yorkshire DL11 6TB
Tel: (01748) 884498
Fax: (01748) 884334

Model animals: sheep, dogs, ponies,
cattle. Also wall plaques.
Open: Mon-Fri 9am-4pm. Closed 24
Dec to 1 Jan
Cards: Access, Visa

DIRECTIONS: 10 miles west of
Richmond on B6270. Enter Reeth and
bear left at village green. Pass Barclays
Bank into Anvil Square.

13/1210
● NEEDLECRAFTS

Jennifer Davies
2 Bridge Terrace, Reeth, Richmond, North
Yorkshire DL11 6TP
Tel: (01748) 884572

Patchwork quilts, waistcoats, mats,
wallets, cushions and other items.
Open: Mon-Fri 9am-5pm, Sat 9am-
12 noon
Cards: No

DIRECTIONS: Take B6270 to Reeth.
Over bridge take first left before the
paper shop. Showroom is just beyond
the line of stone cottages.

13/1211
● CERAMICS

Garden House Pottery
The Green, Reeth, Richmond, North
Yorkshire DL11 6AB
Tel: (01748) 884648

Stoneware ceramics including garden
pots, wall planters and other garden
ornaments.
Open: Mar to mid-Oct 10am-5pm.
Closed Sun and Good Friday. Other
times by appointment
Cards: No

DIRECTIONS: Take B6270 out of
Richmond to Reeth. Studio on Green
next to Congregational church.

13/1212
■ SMOKED PRODUCE

Teesdale Trencherman
Startforth Hall, Barnard Castle, County
Durham DL12 9RA
Tel/Fax: (01833) 638370

Smoked fish and meat, and cheeses.
Open: Mon-Sat 10am-4pm, but
telephone for appointment
Cards: Access, Visa

DIRECTIONS: ½ mile west of
Barnard Castle on B6277.

13/1213
● STENCILS

The Stencil Library
Stocksfield Hall, Stocksfield,
Northumberland NE43 7TN
Tel: (01661) 844844

Design and manufacture of interior
decoration stencils and related
products.
Open: Mon-Sat 9.30am-5.30pm, Sun
by appointment
Cards: Access, Visa

DIRECTIONS: From A69 take the
B6309 to Stocksfield. Follow road
until it crosses the river Tyne at
Bywell (about 2 miles). Stocksfield
Hall is first left over the bridge.

13/1214
● CUSHIONS

Fingers & Thumbs

Fellside House, 80 New Ridley Road,
Stocksfield, Northumberland NE43 7EF
Tel: (01661) 843608

Quilted picture and geometric
cushion covers, cushion pads and
perfumed mini-cushions.
Open: Telephone for appointment
Cards: Access, Visa

DIRECTIONS: From A695 Blaydon
to Hexham road, 2 miles west of
Prudhoe at Branch End follow New
Ridley road for ¼ mile.

13/1215
● CANDLES

White Rose Candles

Wensley Mill, Wensley, Leyburn, North
Yorkshire DL8 4HR
Tel: (01969) 23544

Hand-dipped candles.
Open: Jun-Nov, bank hols and Easter
10am-5pm. Closed Wed and Sat. Dec,
Sun only. Closed Jan-Easter
Cards: No

DIRECTIONS: On A684 1½ miles
west of Leyburn in village of Wensley.

13/1216
● ENGRAVING

The Bewick Studios, Printmaking Workshop and Museum

Mickley Square, Stocksfield,
Northumberland NE43 7DB
Tel/Fax: (01661) 844055

Hand-printed historic pictures,
etchings, engravings and wood blocks.
Stationery.
Open: Tue-Sat 10am-12 noon,
1pm-5.30pm. Closed Christmas for 2
weeks
Cards: No

DIRECTIONS: On A695 Newcastle
to Hexham roads, 11 miles west of
Newcastle, 2 miles west of Prudhoe.
Old co-op building at crossroads in
Mickley Square.

13/1217   ● CERAMICS

Cottage Pottery

Vine Cottage, Bellerby, Nr Leyburn, North
Yorkshire DL8 5QP
Tel/Fax: (01969) 622184

Fragrance pottery gifts.
Open: Mon-Fri 9am-6pm, Sat-Sun
9.30am-5pm but telephone in
advance. Closed 25 Dec-1 Jan
Cards: Access

DIRECTIONS: A1 turn off Bedale to
Leyburn A684. Leyburn to Richmond
road A6108, 1½ miles north of
Leyburn on the village green in
Bellerby.

13/1218
● WOOD/HORN

Northumbria Horncraft

The Old Telephone Exchange, Manor
House Dairy, Whalton Village, Morpeth,
Northumberland
Tel: (01670) 519174

Horn-handled, plain and decorative
walking sticks, crooks, thumbsticks,
horncraft, spoons, buttons.
Open: Most days 11am-4pm but
telephone in advance
Cards: No

DIRECTIONS: A6087 Morpeth to
Belsay road, 6 miles west of Morpeth.

13/1219
■ PRESERVES

Rosebud Preserves

Rosebud Farm, Healey, Ripon, North
Yorkshire HG4 4LH
Tel/Fax: (01765) 689174

Chutneys, relishes, pickles, herb
jellies, jams, marmalade and lemon
curd.
Open: Mon-Fri 9am-5.30pm.
Weekends by appointment
Cards: No

DIRECTIONS: 9 miles north-west of
Ripon on A6108 at Masham. Take left
turn for Healey directly opposite
animal auction mart buildings.
Second on left in village.

13/1220
● FURNITURE
M C Clayson
11 Whitefields Gate, Richmond, North
Yorkshire DL10 7DD
Tel: (01748) 822631

Cabinet making, furniture restoration,
wooden toys, toy boxes, trains, hobby
horses and stilts.
Open: Daily by appointment
Cards: No

DIRECTIONS: 4 miles south-west of
Scotch Corner (A1). 2nd left on
entering Richmond, then 1st right
(cul de sac).

13/1221
● ART
Margaret Morrison
35 Collingwood Crescent, Ponteland,
Northumberland NE20 9DZ
Tel: (01661) 872007

Watercolour and pastel paintings,
greetings cards and calendars. Limited
edition prints.
Open: By appointment Mon-Sat
10am-5pm
Cards: No

DIRECTIONS: A696 to Ponteland
traffic lights. Turn to Darras Hall to
mini-roundabout. Bear right into
Middle Drive. After 250 yards take
2nd right.

13/1222
● GLASS
Uredale Glass
42 Market Place, Masham, Nr Ripon,
North Yorkshire HG4 4EF
Tel/Fax: (01765) 689780

Handmade coloured glassware.
Open: Easter-31 Oct daily 10am-5pm,
Nov-Easter Tue-Sat 10am-4.30pm.
Closed Jan
Cards: Access, Visa

DIRECTIONS: From the market
square walk underneath the King's
Head archway and 50 yards further.

13/1223
● GLASS
Jane Charles Studio Glass
Premier Workshops, Units 19&20,
Whitehouse Road, Scotswood, Newcastle-
upon-Tyne, Tyne & Wear NE15 6EP
Tel: (0191) 2280152
Fax: (0191) 2749378

Studio glass – decorative, bowls,
dishes and vases.
Open: Mon-Sat 10am-6pm, but
telephone in advance
Cards: No

DIRECTIONS: From Newcastle take
Scotswood road. At mini-roundabout
turn right into White House road. At
end turn right.

13/1224
● CERAMICS
Shire Pottery
Scruton, Northallerton, North
Yorkshire DL7 0RD
Tel: (01609) 748225

Domestic and decorative reduced
stoneware pottery.
Open: Sat-Sun 10am-4pm. Weekdays
by appointment
Cards: No

DIRECTIONS: Scruton village is
situated off the A684 Northallerton to
Bedale road, 3 miles east of the A1.
Shire Pottery overlooks the village
green.

13/1225
■ MEAT PRODUCTS
T Appleton & Sons
6 Market Place, Ripon, North
Yorkshire HG4 1BP
Tel: (01765) 603198

Pies, sausages, hams, dry salt-cured
bacon.
Open: Mon, Tue, Thur, Fri 8am-
5.30pm. Wed, Sat 8am-5pm. Closed
bank hols
Cards: No

DIRECTIONS: East side of Ripon
Market Square, next door to
Morrisons supermarket.

13/1226
● CERAMICS

Alan Ball
Biddick Farm Pottery, Washington Arts Centre, Biddick Lane, Washington, Tyne & Wear NE38 8AB
Tel: (0191) 4177508

Ceramic bowls, vases and commemorative plates.
Open: Mon-Fri 9am-4pm. Sat 10am-12 noon. First Sat in each month 10am-4pm
Cards: No

DIRECTIONS: Turn off A1M at Washington services on A195. Turn right at second roundabout signposted Fatfield.

13/1227
■ SAUSAGES

Whites Butchers
Morton on Swale, Northallerton, North Yorkshire DL7 9RF
Tel: (01609) 772855

Sausages, beef, lamb.
Open: Mon-Fri 8am-5.30pm. Sat 8am-5pm. Closed bank hols
Cards: No

DIRECTIONS: 3 miles from Northallerton in Frost Street.

13/1228
● TEXTILES

Northumbria Weavers
71 Stanley Street, Blyth, Northumberland NE24 3BX
Tel: (01670) 355643

Hand-woven tweed.
Open: Mon-Sat 9am-5pm. Closed Christmas
Cards: No

DIRECTIONS: In Blyth town centre 200 yards from Royal Tavern.

13/1229
● GLASS

Custom Display Cases
Wayside, Skelton on Ure, Ripon, North Yorkshire HG4 5AG
Tel: (01423) 322633

Display cases.
Open: Mon-Fri 9am-5.30pm, Sat 9am-1pm, variable holidays
Cards: No

DIRECTIONS: 2 miles west of A1 off the B6265. Follow signs for Newby hall. Workshop situated north end of village.

13/1230
■ MEAT/POULTRY/GAME

Smithy Farmshop
Baldersby, Thirsk, North Yorkshire YO7 4PN
Tel: (01765) 640676

Bacon, meat, pâté, puddings.
Open: Mon-Sat 9.30am-5.30pm. Closed Sun
Cards: No

DIRECTIONS: In centre of Baldersby village.

13/1231
■ MEAT/POULTRY/GAME

Twizell's
Gilly Flatts Farm, Bishopton, Stockton-on-Tees, Cleveland TS21 1HH
Tel: (01740) 630139

Farmhouse sausages, dry-cured bacon.
Open: Mon-Thur 9am-4pm. Closed bank hols
Cards: No

DIRECTIONS: Gilly Flatts is ½ mile out of Bishopton on the Darlington Road.

13/1232
● CERAMICS

Sedgefield Pottery
The Old Smithy, Cross Street, Sedgefield, Stockton-on-Tees, Cleveland TS21 3AH
Tel: (01740) 621998

Hand-thrown stoneware and terracotta.

Open: Mon, Tue, Thur-Sat 9am-5.30pm, Wed 9am-12 noon
Cards: No

DIRECTIONS: From the A1M take the A689, at the first roundabout turn off for Sedgefield. The pottery is near the church and opposite the Dun Cow pub.

13/1233
■ CHEESE

Shepherd's Purse Speciality Cheeses
Leachfield Grange, Newsham, Thirsk, North Yorkshire YO7 4DL
Tel/Fax: (01845) 587220

Sheep's milk, cows' and goats' milk cheeses.
Open: Mon-Fri 8am-5pm, telephone at weekends
Cards: No

DIRECTIONS: 4 miles from Thirsk on A168 to Thornton le Moor, then 250 yards to farm turning.

13/1234
● FURNITURE

A P Bulmer
Mill Yard, Catton Lane, Topcliffe, Nr Thirsk, North Yorkshire YO7 3RZ
Tel: (01845) 578172

English hardwood furniture, chairs and tables.
Open: Mon-Sat 10am-5pm. Sun by appointment. Closed bank hols
Cards: No

DIRECTIONS: Turn off A19 for Topcliffe. Opposite Angel pub turn right. At junction with Swan pub, mill on left, then first right down track.

13/1235
● FURNITURE

The Treske Shop
Station Maltings, Thirsk, North Yorkshire YO7 4NY
Tel: (01845) 522770
Fax: (01845) 522692

Handcrafted wood furniture and wooden gifts, factory tours.
Open: Mon-Sun 10am-5pm. Closed 23 Dec-3 Jan

Cards: Access, Switch, Visa

DIRECTIONS: On the A61 Thirsk to Ripon road beside Thirsk railway station.

13/1236
● LEATHER GOODS

Brownie
Base 17, Foyle Street, Sunderland, Tyne & Wear SR1 1LE
Tel: (0191) 5651514

Leather goods and accessories.
Open: By appointment only
Cards: Access, Visa

DIRECTIONS: In town centre near museum and railway station.

13/1237
● WOOD

The Wrens Nest
12 Finkle Street, Thirsk, North Yorkshire YO7 1DA
Tel: (01845) 526232

Oak furniture and gifts bearing a hand-carved wren.
Open: Mon-Fri 10am-3.15pm (closed Wed). Sat 10am-4pm. Other times by appointment. Closed bank hols
Cards: No

DIRECTIONS: Finkle Street is a one-way street into Thirsk Marketplace.

13/1238
● FURNITURE

Albert Jeffray Woodcarver and Cabinet Maker
Sessay, Thirsk, North Yorkshire YO7 3BE
Tel: (01845) 501323

Hand-carved furniture in solid woods. English oak a speciality.
Open: Mon-Fri 8am-5pm. Sat, Sun and bank hols by appointment
Cards: No

DIRECTIONS: 2 miles from A19 between Thirsk and Easingwold. 6 miles from A1 using A168 junction.

13/1239
■ MEAT/POULTRY/GAME

Holme Farmed Venison (Produce) Ltd
Thorpe Underwood, York, North
Yorkshire YO5 9SRG
Tel: (01423) 331212
Fax: (01423) 330855

Fresh, smoked, cured venison and
pies and pâtés.
Open: Daily 9am-5pm
Cards: Access, Visa

DIRECTIONS: On York to Harrogate
road. Turn right at Borsbridge to
Little Ouseburn. Then right to
Thorpe Underwood. First left after
¼ mile.

13/1240
● FURNITURE

Penhalagon Cabinet Maker
School House, Boltby, Thirsk, North
Yorkshire YO7 2DY
Tel: (01845) 537670

Furniture in English hardwoods.
Open: Mon-Sat 10am-5pm
Cards: No

DIRECTIONS: Off A1, take A61 to
Thirsk. A170 to Scarborough, after ½
mile take left-hand turn to Felixkirk-
Boltby.

13/1241
● FURNITURE

Gordon Hodgson Handmade Furniture
Cross Lane, Ingleby Cross, Northallerton,
North Yorkshire DL6 3NQ
Tel: (01609) 882414

Handmade solid wood furniture.
Open: Mon-Fri 9am-5pm, Sat 1pm-
5pm
Cards: No

DIRECTIONS: 7 miles north-east of
Northallerton and 1 mile north of
Cleveland Tontine, between A19 and
A172 opposite the village green.

13/1242
● FURNITURE

Robert Thompsons Craftsmen Ltd
Kilburn, York, North Yorkshire YO6 4AH
Tel: (01347) 868218
Fax: (01347) 868400

Handmade domestic, church and
boardroom furniture in English oak.
Also carvings and smaller items.
Open: Mon-Fri 8am-5pm. Sat 10am-
12 noon. Closed 2 weeks at Christmas
Cards: Access, Switch, Visa

DIRECTIONS: Take A170
Scarborough Road from Thirsk. Turn
right after 2 miles and follow road to
Kilburn. Turn right at T-junction in
village.

13/1243
● CERAMICS

Coxwold Pottery
Coxwold, York, North Yorkshire YO6 4AA
Tel: (01347) 868344

Pottery in stoneware and earthenware.
Open: Tue-Fri 2pm-5.30pm, also Sun
June-Aug. Closed 25 Dec-1 Jan
Cards: No

DIRECTIONS: On the main street at
lower end of the village.

13/1244
● FURNITURE

John Harrison Interiors
16 High Street, Great Ayton, North
Yorkshire TS9 6NJ
Tel: (01642) 724784

Furniture manufacturers, dining
tables, bookcases and chairs in English
hardwoods.
Open: Tue-Fri 10am-5pm, Sat 10am-
4.30pm. Closed 25 Dec-1 Jan
Cards: Access, Visa

DIRECTIONS: From the A173 turn
into the High Street by the river, shop
is 100 yards on the right.

13/1245
● CERAMICS

Great Ayton Pottery
Park Rise, Great Ayton, North
Yorkshire TS9 6ND
Tel: (01642) 722641

Pottery and ceramics in strong
colours.
Open: Thur-Sat 10am-1pm, 2pm-
5pm. Closed 24 Dec-10 Jan
Cards: No

DIRECTIONS: Behind Royal Oak in
Great Ayton. 8 miles south of
Middlesbrough.

13/1246
● ART

Daisy Barns Watercolours
Holly House Studio, Main Street,
Wombleton, York, North Yorkshire YO6 5RX
Tel: (01751) 431429

Original watercolours and limited
edition prints.
Open: 10am-5pm but telephone in
advance
Cards: Access, Visa

DIRECTIONS: At bottom end of
main street.

13/1247
● CERAMICS

Holtby Pottery
Arnup Studios, Holtby Pottery, Holtby,
York, North Yorkshire YO1 3UA
Tel: (01904) 489377

Traditional stoneware studio pottery,
plates and bowls, letters and signs,
bird and animal sculpture.
Open: Mon-Sun 10am-6pm. Closed
25 Dec
Cards: No

DIRECTIONS: 6 miles east of York on
A166 (Bridlington).

13/1248
● MINIATURES

Margaret Rose Collectables
3 High Street, Skelton, Saltburn,
Cleveland TS12 2EF
Tel: (01287) 650357

Miniatures of original buildings, ruins
and artefacts.
Open: Daily 9am-4pm
Cards: No

DIRECTIONS: Take A173 through
Guisborough to Skelton.

13/1249
● GLASS

Jorvik Glass
Castle Howard, York, North
Yorkshire YO6 7DA
Tel: (01653) 648555

Hand-blown glassware from giftware
to gallery pieces.
Open: Daily 10am-4.30pm from 18
Mar-31 Oct. Rest of year Mon-Fri.
Telephone in advance. Closed Jan
Cards: Access, Amex, Diners, Switch,
Visa

DIRECTIONS: 15 miles from York off
A64 near Malton.

13/1250
● GLASS

Gillies-Jones – Rosedale Glass
The Old Forge, Rosedale Abbey, North
Yorkshire YO18 8SA
Tel: (01751) 417550
Fax: (01751) 417124

Contemporary functional glass –
decanters, vases and bowls.
Open: Tue-Sat 10am-5pm, Sun 2pm-
5pm. Closed Mon. Telephone in
advance
Cards: No

DIRECTIONS: Off A170 Helmsley to
Pickering road at Wrelton, then 7
miles north.

13/1251
● SILVERWARE

Wolds Silver
Rothay Cottage, Leppington, Malton, North
Yorkshire YO17 9RL
Tel: (01653) 658485

Handmade jewellery and small articles
in silver.
Open: Mon-Sat 9am-5.30pm. Closed
25 Dec, and end of Mar each year
Cards: No

DIRECTIONS: From York take A166
through Stamford Bridge. After 1½
mile turn left to Malton. After 1 mile
right to Malton, in 1½ miles turn
right into Leppington. Wolds Silver is
opposite telephone kiosk.

13/1252
● CERAMICS

Forge Pottery
Forge House, Lealholm, Whitby, North
Yorkshire YO21 2AQ
Tel: (01947) 897457

Stoneware pottery.
Open: Mon-Sat 10am-3.30pm.
Summer Sun 2pm-4pm
Cards: No

DIRECTIONS: On main street
through Lealholm to Danby.

13/1253
● NEEDLECRAFTS

The World Embroidery Shop
13-15 Commercial Street, Norton, Malton,
North Yorkshire YO17 9HX
Tel: (01653) 697179

Textiles, crafts and craft materials.
Open: Mon-Sat 9.30am-4.30pm.
Closed Sun, bank hols
Cards: No

DIRECTIONS: On A64 York to
Scarborough road.

13/1254
■ MEAT/POULTRY/GAME

Derek Fox
25 Market Place, Malton, North
Yorkshire YO17 0LP
Tel: (01653) 600338

Butcher, game dealer and delicatessen.

Open: Mon-Sat 8am-5pm. Closed
bank hols
Cards: No

DIRECTIONS: On A64 between York
and Scarborough.

13/1255
● NEEDLECRAFTS

Catherine Fields
Upholstery Workshop, 3 Coopers Yard,
Southgate, Pickering, North
Yorkshire YO18 8BL
Tel: (01751) 477064

Upholstered chairs and stools,
cushions.
Open: Mon-Fri 10am-4pm. Closed
Wed. Other times by appointment.
Closed bank hols and Christmas
Cards: No

DIRECTIONS: At Pickering
roundabout take A170 towards
Helmsley. 50 yards past traffic lights
turn left at antique shop into Coopers
Yard.

13/1256
● CERAMICS

Rock Cottage Crafts
Rock Cottage, New Bridge, Pickering,
North Yorkshire YO18 8JJ
Tel: (01751) 475323

Ceramics.
Open: Daily 8.30am-8.30pm
Cards: No

DIRECTIONS: Take A169 from
Malton to Pickering. Take Newton-
on-Rawcliffe road and after ¼ mile
turn left through Trout Farm car
park. Rock Cottage on right over
railway line.

13/1257
● CERAMICS

Runtons Pottery
7 Castle Road, Pickering, North
Yorkshire YO18 7BA
Tel: (01751) 472377

Ceramic tableware.
Open: Daily 10am-6pm. Closed Sun
in winter and 24 Dec-2 Jan
Cards: Access, Visa

DIRECTIONS: On A170 Scarborough to Thirsk road. Next to Pickering Castle on northern edge of town.

13/1258
● CERAMICS

Deerholme Pottery
High Marishes, Malton, North Yorkshire YO17 0UQ
Tel: (01653) 668228

Manufacture of functional decorative stoneware pots, individually hand-decorated with richly coloured glazes and patterns.
Open: Mon-Fri 10am-6pm. Sun by appointment only. Closed 24 Dec-7 Jan
Cards: No

DIRECTIONS: Turn off the A169 Malton to Pickering road at turning sign posted High Marishes and Thornton Dale, follow pottery signs.

13/1259
● FORGEWORK

James Godbold – Blacksmith
Mount Pleasant, Egton, Whitby, North Yorkshire YO21 1UE
Tel: (01947) 895514
Fax: (01947) 895562

Wrought ironwork and general blacksmithing.
Open: Daily 8am-5pm, but advisable to telephone in advance
Cards: No

DIRECTIONS: Take A171 Middlesbrough to Whitby road. Turn right signposted Egton and Grosmont. At T-Junction turn right in village, then first left, signposted Grosmont Steam Railway. Last house on left.

13/1260
● GLASS

The Stained Glass Workshop
The Studio, High Street, Lythe, North Yorkshire YO21 3RT
Tel: (01947) 893246/810101

Stained glass, leaded lights, Tiffany lampshades.
Open: Mon-Sat 9am-5pm. Closed bank hols
Cards: No

DIRECTIONS: On A174 on coastal Whitby to Saltburn road. Workshop is situated opposite the garage/fire station.

13/1261
● NEEDLECRAFTS

All Sewn Up
29 Wydale Rise, Snainton, Scarborough, North Yorkshire YO13 9AQ
Tel: (01723) 859152

Hand-embroidered bibs, aprons, samplers.
Open: Mon-Fri 10am-4pm
Cards: No

DIRECTIONS: Off A64 behind Snainton School.

13/1262
■ SMOKED PRODUCE

Fortunes
22 Henrietta Street, Whitby, North Yorkshire YO21 4DW
Tel: (01947) 601659

Kippers.
Open: Apr-Oct Mon-Sat 9am-4.30pm, Sun 9am-4pm. Nov-Mar Mon-Sat 9am-4pm, Sun 9am-12 noon
Cards: No

DIRECTIONS: From west side of Whitby Harbour cross swing bridge. Turn left up cobbled area of Church Street then 100 yards up Henrietta Street.

13/1263
● NEEDLECRAFTS

Artefacts of Whitby
159 Church Street, Whitby, North Yorkshire YO22 4AS
Tel: (01947) 820682

Needlecraft and materials.
Open: Easter to Oct daily 10am-5pm. Winter Fri-Mon 10am-5pm
Cards: No

DIRECTIONS: On east side of Whitby, over swing bridge down main road to the right. Next door to Hadleys restaurant.

13/1264
● CERAMICS

E Bailey Earthenware
The Workshop, White Horse Yard, Church Street, Whitby, North Yorkshire YO22 4BW
Tel: (01947) 601225

Earthenware pottery.
Open: By appointment only
Cards: Access, Visa

DIRECTIONS: Just off right-hand side of Church Street in Whitby.

13/1265
● GLASS

R R Bruce Stained Glass
13 Park Terrace, Whitby, North Yorkshire YO21 1PN
Tel: (01947) 600513

Windows, door panels, lampshades and mirrors.
Open: By appointment only
Cards: No

DIRECTIONS: From Whitby town centre turn right down Windsor Terrace, continue up hill. Third road on left.

13/1266
● WOOD

Readmans Distinctive Woodcraft
7 Newlands Avenue, Whitby, North Yorkshire YO21 3DX
Tel: (01947) 820245

Hardwood items.
Open: By appointment only
Cards: No

DIRECTIONS: On A174 at Upgang Lane, Whitby, turn into Fieldhouse Road, then first left into Newlands Avenue.

13/1267
● FORGEWORK .

David Athey Blacksmith
The Smithy, West End Works, Garton-on-the-Wolds, Driffield, Humberside YO25 0EU
Tel: (01377) 241723

Decorative and architectural blacksmith including weathervanes, garden and conservatory furniture.

Open: Mon-Fri 8am-6pm, Sat 8am-12 noon. Closed Christmas-New Year
Cards: No

DIRECTIONS: On A166 Driffield to York road, 3 miles west of Driffield. Next to Venture Inn.

13/1268
● TEXTILES

Ankaret Cresswell
Wykeham, Scarborough, North Yorkshire YO13 9QB
Tel: (01723) 864406
Fax: (01723) 864041

Woven fabric and clothes to measure and off the peg.
Open: Mon-Fri 10am-5pm, otherwise by arrangement, best to telephone first in summer
Cards: Access, Switch, Visa

DIRECTIONS: On A170 6 miles from Scarborough on left of road, just past St Helens caravan park after entering Wykeham. Approaching from Pickering, on right just after Downe Arms.

13/1269
■ HONEY

Sneatondale Honey Farm
Racecourse Road, East Ayton, Scarborough, North Yorkshire YO13 9HP
Tel: (01723) 864001
Fax: (01723) 862455

Honey and all bee-related products.
Open: Daily 9am-6pm
Cards: No

DIRECTIONS: On A170 Scarborough to Pickering road.

13/1270
● PLANTS

J & D Marston Fern Specialists
Culag Green Lane, Nafferton, Driffield, East Yorkshire YO25 0LF
Tel: (01377) 254487

Ferns and garden ornaments.
Open: Easter-mid-Sept Sat-Sun 1.30pm-4.30pm, weekdays by appointment
Cards: No

DIRECTIONS: From Driffield take the road to Nafferton from the centre of town, out past the Alfred Bean Hospital. Down the first lane on the left.

13/1271
● CERAMICS

Park Rose Pottery and Leisure Park

Carnaby Covert Lane, Carnaby,
Bridlington, Humberside YO15 3QF
Tel: (01262) 602823
Fax: (01262) 400202

Pottery and giftware.
Open: Mon-Sun 10am-5pm. Closed Christmas week
Cards: Access, Visa

DIRECTIONS: 2 miles south of Bridlington between the A166 York to Bridlington road and the A165 Hull to Bridlington road.

13/1272
● KNITWEAR

Flamborough Marine Ltd

The Manor House, Flamborough,
Bridlington, Humberside YO15 1PD
Tel: (01262) 850943

Knitwear, hand-knitted ganseys, knitting kits and British wool.
Open: Mon-Sun 9.30am-5.30pm. Closed 25 Dec
Cards: Access, Amex, Visa

DIRECTIONS: From Bridlington take B1255 to Flamborough and follow signs to lighthouse, past the parish church on right. Shop is on the next corner (Tower Street and Lighthouse Road).

MAP 14

14/1273
■ FISH/SHELLFISH

Isle of Colonsay Oysters
Poll Gorm, Isle of Colonsay,
Strathclyde PA61 7YR
Tel/Fax: (01951) 2365

Pacific oysters, honey.
Open: 9am-5pm
Cards: No

DIRECTIONS: On beach between
islands of Colonsay and Oronsay.

14/1274
■ CHEESE

Isle of Mull Cheese
Sgriob-Ruadh Farm, Tobermory, Isle of
Mull, Strathclyde PA75 6QD
Tel: (01688) 302235
Fax: (01688) 302546

Traditional farmhouse cheese.
Open: Mon-Fri, Sun 10am-4pm.
Closed Nov-Mar
Cards: Access, Visa

DIRECTIONS: 300 yards up the
Glengorm Road on the left, over cattle
grid. Farm track into yard and
buildings.

14/1275
■ FISH/SHELLFISH

R & M George
Salen, Acharacle, Highland PH36 4JN
Tel: (01967) 431212 and 431628
Fax: (01967) 431332

Lobster and crab. Sometimes oysters,
mussels and scallops.
Open: Mon-Sat 9am-5pm, sometimes
later
Cards: No

DIRECTIONS: 1 mile west of Salen
Hotel on Loch Sunart north shore.

14/1276
■ SMOKED PRODUCE

Macdonalds Smoked Produce
Glenuig, Lochailort, Highland PH38 4NG
Tel: (01687) 470266
Fax: (01687) 470311

Smoked foods including cream cheese,
alligator, ostrich, fish, shellfish.

Open: Mon-Thur and Sat 9am-5pm.
Closed Fri, Sun. Closed 23 Dec-10
Jan
Cards: Access, Visa

DIRECTIONS: Turn off A830 (Road
to the Isles) Fort William-Mallaig at
Lochailort. After 8 miles to Glenuig,
Smokehouse is white building with
four chimneys.

14/1277
■ FISH/SHELLFISH

Scallop Kings Plc
The Boatyard, Crinan, Strathclyde PA31 8SP
Tel: (01546) 83282
Fax: (01546) 83281

Prime scallops.
Open: Mon-Sat 8am-5.30pm. Closed
Christmas and New Year
Cards: No

DIRECTIONS: Take A82 Glasgow to
Inveraray road, then A83 to
Lochgilphead. Follow A816 to Oban
for about 5 miles, then B841 to
Crinan.

14/1278
■ SMOKED PRODUCE

Colfin Smokehouse
Portpatrick, Stranraer, Dumfries & Galloway
DG9 9BN
Tel: (01776) 820622

Scottish smoked salmon.
Open: Mon-Sat 9am-5pm. Sun 10am-
3pm. Closed Christmas and New
Year
Cards: Access, Visa

DIRECTIONS: On A77 Stranraer to
Portpatrick road. 2 miles on from
Lochans village on left. Follow signs
to Smokehouse.

14/1279
● LEATHER GOODS

A D Mackenzie Leather Goods
Cladach, Brodick, Isle of Arran,
Strathclyde KA27 8DF
Tel: (01770) 302311

Leather bags, briefcases and luggage.
Open: Mon-Fri 10.30am-5pm
Cards: Amex, Visa

DIRECTIONS: 1 mile outside Brodick on Corrie road. Turn left at Sawmill and just before main entrance to National Trust.

14/1280
■ CHEESE

Island Cheese Co Ltd
Home Farm, Brodick, Isle of Arran,
Strathclyde KA27 8DD
Tel/Fax: (01770) 302788

Cheese.
Open: Summer 10am-5pm. Closed Jan, Feb
Cards: Access, Visa

DIRECTIONS: 1 mile north of Brodick on road to Corrie. On right-hand side of road.

14/1281
■ SMOKED PRODUCE

Inverawe Smokehouses
Taynuilt, Strathclyde PA35 1HU
Tel: (01866) 822446
Fax: (01866) 822274

Smoked fish and meats.
Open: Mon-Sat 8.30am-6pm. Closed bank hols
Cards: Access, Switch, Visa

DIRECTIONS: On A85 between Dalmally and Oban. From Dalmally go through Lochawe village. After 5 miles on right beyond Esso station.

14/1282
■ SMOKED PRODUCE

Ritchies of Rothesay
111 Montague Street, Rothesay, Isle of Bute, Strathclyde PA20 9OJ
Tel/Fax: (01700) 505414

Smoked fish products: wild salmon, kippers, trout and haddock.

DIRECTIONS: In Rothesay main street.

14/1283
■ SMOKED PRODUCE

Crannog Scottish Seafoods
Unit 5B1, Blar Mhor, Fort William, Highland PH33 7NG
Tel: (01397) 703919
Fax: (0397) 705026

Smoked salmon, trout, mussels. Fresh langoustine.
Open: May-Sept Mon-Fri 9am-5pm. Sat and Sun 9am-12 noon. Oct-Apr Sat 10am-12 noon. Closed Sun, and 24 Dec-4 Jan
Cards: Access, Amex, Visa

DIRECTIONS: In Blar Mhor Industrial Estate on A82 Fort William to Mallaig road. About 3 miles from Fort William.

14/1284
■ FISH/SHELLFISH

Loch Fyne Oysters Ltd
Clachan Farm, Cairndow,
Strathclyde PA26 8BH
Tel: (01499) 600264
Fax: (01499) 600234

Shellfish and smoked fish. Oyster bar.
Open: Apr-Oct 9am-8pm. Oct-Apr 9am-6pm. Closed Christmas and New Year
Cards: Access, Switch, Visa

DIRECTIONS: Well signposted 12 miles on from Tarbet. On right at top of Loch Fyne.

14/1285
■ MEAT/POULTRY/GAME

Letterfinlay Game Services
The Boathouse, Letterfinlay, Spean Bridge, Highland PH34 4DZ
Tel: (01397) 712626
Fax: (01397) 712510

Venison, game, salmon, cheese, smoked fish and meats.
Open: May-Sept Mon-Sat 9am-6pm
Cards: No

DIRECTIONS: From Spean Bridge, north on A82, 7 miles on left. From Invergarry, south on A82, 6 miles on right. On shores of Loch Lochy.

14/1286
● TOYS

Dormouse Designs
The Old Drapery, Faith Avenue, Quarriers
Village, Bridge of Weir, Strathclyde
PA11 3SX
Tel: (01505) 690435
Fax: (01505) 702163

Traditional teddy bears and
Dormouse range of soft toys.
Open: Mon-Fri 9.30am-4.30pm.
Closed bank hols
Cards: Access, Amex, Visa

DIRECTIONS: 6 miles west of
Paisley, take A737 then A761 to
Bridge of Weir. Turn left opposite
Gryffe Inn into Torr Road, then first
on right to Quarriers Village.

14/1287
● CLOTHES

Cocoon Coats
Lomond Industrial Estate, Loch Lomond,
Alexandria, Central G83 0TL
Tel/Fax: (01389) 755511

Rainwear.
Open: Mon-Fri 9am-5pm, Sat-Sun
11am-5pm. Closed bank hols
Cards: Access, Amex, Visa

DIRECTIONS: On Alexandria bypass
(A82) turn off on to A811 (Stirling
road). At first roundabout turn right
and follow signs for Lomond
Industrial Estate.

14/1288
■ SMOKED PRODUCE

Galloway Smokehouse
Carsluith, Newton Stewart, Dumfries &
Galloway DG8 7DN
Tel: (01671) 820354
Fax: (01671) 820545

Smoked salmon, fresh fish, shellfish
and game.
Open: Daily 9am-5.30pm. Closed 1
week at Christmas
Cards: Access, Visa

DIRECTIONS: On A75 3 miles east of
Creetown.

14/1289
● PLANTS

Blairhoyle Nursery
East Lodge, Blairhoyle, Port of Menteith,
Central FK8 3LF
Tel: (01877) 385669

Small nursery growing heathers,
conifers, unusual alpines.
Open: Mon, Thur, Fri, Sat 10am-5pm.
Wed and Sun 1pm-5pm. Closed all
day Tue and Nov-Mar
Cards: No

DIRECTIONS: On A873 Stirling to
Aberfoyle road, 6 miles east of
Aberfoyle.

14/1290
■ BAKED GOODS

Alexander Taylor at the
Waterside Bakery
10/11 Waterside Street, Strathaven,
Strathclyde ML10 6AW
Tel: (01357) 21260
Fax: (01357) 22774

Continental-style bakery.
Open: Mon-Fri 8am-5.30pm. Sat
7am-5.30pm. Closed 25 and 26 Dec, 1
Jan
Cards: No

DIRECTIONS: Near the castle in
Strathaven, just off Stonehouse Road.

14/1291
■ SMOKED PRODUCE

Swanswater Smokehouse
Sauchieburn, Stirling, Central FK7 9QB
Tel/Fax: (01786) 814805

Smoked salmon, trout, haddock,
kippers, chicken, duck and game.
Open: Daily 8am-5pm
Cards: No

DIRECTIONS: From J9 of M9/M8 –
Stirling Service roundabout, take road
to Stirling for Bannockburn Heritage
Centre. Turn left just before centre to
Chartershall. At end of road turn right
for Swanswater.

14/1292
● SILVERWARE

Graham Stewart
91-95 High Street, Dunblane,
Central FK15 0ER
Tel: (01786) 825244
Fax: (01786) 825993

Gold and silversmith: candlesticks,
coffee pots and fine jewellery.
Open: Mon-Sat 9am-5pm. Closed
Sun
Cards: Access, Amex, Visa

DIRECTIONS: Entering Dunblane at
roundabout take exit signed for
Cathedral, 100 yards on right, red
17th-century cottage with outside
staircase.

14/1293
● CERAMICS

Will Levi Marshall
Orchardton Pottery, Auchencairn, Castle
Douglas, Dumfries & Galloway DG7 1QL
Tel: (01556) 640399

Domestic stoneware and stools or
plant stands.
Open: By appointment only
Cards: No

DIRECTIONS: Take left turn to
Auchencairn on Solway coast road.
One mile after Palnakie signpost to
Orchardton House on left (not
tower). Pottery is in basement.

14/1294
■ MEAT/POULTRY/GAME

Ramsay of Carluke Ltd
22 Mount Stewart Street, Carluke,
Strathclyde ML8 5ED
Tel: (01555) 772277
Fax: (01555) 750686

Ayrshire bacon.
Open: Mon-Fri 8am-12 noon, 1pm-
4.30pm. Sat 8am-12.30pm
Cards: No

DIRECTIONS: On A73 between
Lanark and Wishaw. Mount Stewart
Street is off the Cross in centre.
Halfway up on right opposite fire
station.

14/1295
■ DAIRY PRODUCE

Loch Arthur Creamery
Camphill Village Trust, Beeswing, Dumfries,
Dumfries & Galloway DG2 8JQ
Tel: (01387) 760296
Fax: (01387) 760618

Cheeses, yoghurt and butter from
Ayrshire cows' milk.
Open: Mon-Fri 9am-5.30pm
Cards: No

DIRECTIONS: From Dumfries, take
A711 to Dalbeattie. After about 5
miles turn left at church in Beeswing
towards New Abbey.

14/1296
■ DELICATESSEN FOODS

Rothiemurchus Fish Farm Shop
Rothiemurchus Estate, Ski Road, by
Aviemore, Highland PH22 1QH
Tel: (01479) 810703
Fax: (01479) 811778

A Highland delicatessen specialising
in home-produced fresh and smoked
trout and venison, cheeses, pickles,
condiments, mustards, preserves and
confectionery.
Open: Mar-Oct 9am-6pm, Nov-Feb
9am-5pm
Cards: Access, Visa

DIRECTIONS: From the south turn
off the A9 into Aviemore, turn right at
junction into Cairngorm Ski Road,
shop entrance is ¼ mile on left, well
signposted.

14/1297
■ CHEESE

H J Errington & Co
Walston Braehead Farm, Carnwath,
Lanarkshire ML11 8NF
Tel/Fax: (01899) 81257

Ewes'-milk and cows'-milk cheese,
Lanarkshire blue and Dunsyre blue.
Open: Mon-Fri 7am-4pm, Sat 7am-
11am, also Apr-July Sun 7am-11am
Cards: Access, Amex, Diners, Switch,
Visa

DIRECTIONS: Located 1 mile off
A721, 1½ miles east of Newbigging, 2
miles west of Elsrickle, take turning

signposted for Walston (also
signposted Blue Cheese Farm).

14/1298
■ CONFECTIONERY
E Blacklock (Moffat) Ltd
Toffee Shop, High Street, Moffat, Dumfries
& Galloway DG10 9DL
Tel: (01683) 20032

Toffee, fudge, tablet, truffles.
Open: Mon-Sat 9am-6pm. Sun 10am-
6pm. Closed 25 Dec, 1 Jan
Cards: No

DIRECTIONS: In town centre by the
war memorial.

14/1299
■ PRESERVES
Scone Palace
The Administrator, Scone Palace, Perth,
Tayside PH2 6BD
Tel: (01738) 552300
Fax: (01738) 552588

Cakes, soda bread, chutney and
marmalades.
Open: Good Friday to mid-Oct daily
9.30am-5pm
Cards: Access, Amex, Visa

DIRECTIONS: 2 miles north-east of
Perth on A93 Braemar road.

14/1300
● TOYS
Sam Samson
Sibbaldbie School, Lockerbie, Dumfries
& Galloway DG11 2JU
Tel: (01576) 610345
Fax: (01576) 204220

Traditional toys, steam engines,
aeroplanes and cars from salvaged
wood and antique wool bobbins.
Lamps and candlesticks.
Open: By appointment
Cards: No

DIRECTIONS: 4 miles north of
Lockerbie on B723 signposted to
Boreland and Eskdalemuir.

14/1301
■ MEAT/POULTRY/GAME
G Gronbach & Sons
198-202 High Street, Cowdenbeath,
Fife KY4 9NP
Tel: (01383) 510906

Haggis, sausages, pies, meat products.
Open: Mon-Sat 8am-5pm. Closed
1pm-2pm. Mon and Wed 8am-1pm
Cards: No

DIRECTIONS: On M90 5 miles north
of Forth Bridge. Take Fife regional
road to Kirkcaldy, turn off at signs for
Cowdenbeath.

14/1302
● CERAMICS
Paul Scott
2 Holly Cottage, Blencogo, Wigton,
Cumbria CA7 0BZ
Tel/Fax: (016973) 61706

Porcelain tiles and forms.
Open: Mon-Fri 10am-5pm, but
telephone first
Cards: No

DIRECTIONS: 3 miles west of
Wigton in Blencogo. Off main A596
Carlisle to Workington road.

14/1303
■ MEAT/POULTRY/GAME
Ian Miller's Organic Meat
Jamesfield Farm, Newburgh, Fife KY14 6EW
Tel: (01738) 850498
Fax: (01738) 850741

Organic beef and lamp, poultry, pork,
bacon and vegetables.
Open: Fri-Sun 10am-5pm. Closed
Christmas and New Year
Cards: Access, Visa

DIRECTIONS: Turn off M90 at J9.
Turn south on A912. Drive 1 mile
turn left (A913). Go through
Abernethy. After 1 mile look for signs.
Turn left.

14/1304
■ FISH/SHELLFISH

George Campbell & Sons
The Smoke House, West Harbour Road,
Granton, Edinburgh EH5 1RF
Tel: (0131) 5520376
Fax: (0131) 5511149

Fishmongers, smoked salmon, poultry
and game.
Open: Mon 7am-12 noon. Tue-Fri
7am-4pm. Sat 8am-12 noon. Closed
25 Dec, 1 Jan
Cards: Access, Amex, Visa

DIRECTIONS: On West Harbour
Road to west of Granton Square.

14/1305
■ MEAT/POULTRY/GAME

Fletchers of Auchtermuchty
Reediehill Deer Farm, Auchtermuchty,
Fife KY14 7HS
Tel: (01337) 828369
Fax: (01337) 827001

Free-range farm venison.
Open: 9am-7pm (other times by
appointment). Closed bank hols
Cards: Access, Visa

DIRECTIONS: Take A91 to
Auchtermuchty. North on B936, bear
left at White House in Auchtermuchty
at 'Venison' sign. 2 miles up and over
hill.

14/1306
● PLANTS

Glendoick Gardens Ltd
Glendoick, Perth, Tayside PH2 7NS
Tel: (017388) 860260
Fax: (017388) 860735

Rhododendrons, primulas, azaleas,
ericas and meconopsis. Garden centre.
Open: Summer Mon-Sun 9am-6pm,
winter Mon-Sun 9am-5pm
Cards: Access, Switch, Visa

DIRECTIONS: On A90 Perth to
Dundee, signpost to Glendoick.

14/1307
● JEWELLERY

Jewellery by Michael King
Oakleigh, Todd Close, Curthwaite, Wigton,
Cumbria CA7 8BE
Tel: (01228) 710756

Handmade gold and silver jewellery
set with precious and semi-precious
stones.
Open: Tue-Sat 9.30am-5.30pm.
Closed 25-26 Dec, 1 Jan
Cards: No

DIRECTIONS: From A595 take
Curthwaite turning at Thursby
roundabout, approx 8 miles south of
Carlisle. Workshop is just above the
village on south side. From B5305
turn at Rosley to Curthwaite.

14/1308
● FURNITURE

Ian Laval – Cabinet Maker
Meadow Bank Farm, Curthwaite, Wigton,
Cumbria CA7 8BG
Tel: (01228) 710409

Furniture in Cumbrian hardwoods
with inlays and sawn veneers.
Open: Mon-Sat 10am-5pm. Closed
bank hols
Cards: Access, Visa

DIRECTIONS: 5 miles from Carlisle,
25 miles from Keswick via the A595
and 14 miles along the B5305 from
the M6 J41. Meadowbank farm is in
middle of village.

14/1309
■ CHEESE

Thornby Moor Dairy
Crofton Hall, Crofton, Thursby,
Cumbria CA5 6QB
Tel/Fax: (016973) 45555

Cows'- and goats'-milk cheeses.
Open: Mon-Fri 9am-5pm, Sat 10am-
1.30pm. Closed 25-26 Dec, 1 Jan
Cards: No

DIRECTIONS: 7 miles west of
Carlisle on A595, signposted from
Thursby roundabout. 1 mile Crofton
Arch on right, 1st left opposite the
lake.

14/1310
■ CONFECTIONERY
Dee Valley Confectioners
Station Square, Ballater,
Grampian AB35 5RB
Tel: (013397) 55499
Fax: (013397) 55110

Boiled confectionery.
Open: Daily 9am-5pm. Peak season
9am-8pm
Cards: Access

DIRECTIONS: On A93 Aberdeen to
Braemar road, beside old railway
station.

14/1311
■ BAKED GOODS
Goodfellow & Steven
81-83 Gray Street, Broughty Ferry, Dundee,
Tayside DD5 2BQ
Tel: (01382) 730181
Fax: (01382) 736041

Bread, rolls, savoury and cream goods.
Open: Mon-Sat 8am-5pm. Closed
bank hols
Cards: No

DIRECTIONS: 4 miles east of
Dundee city centre. Cross railway into
Broughty Ferry town centre. Gray
Street crosses Brook Street. Shop just
south of Brook Street.

14/1312
● TEXTILES
Eden Valley Woollen Mill
Armathwaite, Carlisle, Cumbria CA4 9PB
Tel/Fax: (016974) 72457

Cloth, clothing and accessories.
Open: Mon-Sat 9.30am-5.30pm, Sun
12 noon-5pm. Closed Oct-Dec on
Sun and Jan-Easter on Sun, Tue, Wed
Cards: Access, Visa

DIRECTIONS: Between Penrith and
Carlisle 1½ miles off A6, in
Armathwaite village, opposite post
office.

14/1313
● WOOD
Three Horse Shoes Wood Crafts
Three Horse Shoes, Irthington, Carlisle,
Cumbria CA6 4PT
Tel/Fax: (01228) 75657

Decorative and functional wood-
turning.
Open: 10am-4pm. Evenings by
arrangement. Advisable to telephone
in advance
Cards: Access, Visa

DIRECTIONS: From south/east/west
take A69 Carlisle to Newcastle road to
Brampton. Take A6071 for 4 miles.
Turn at Three Horse Shoes to
crossroads. Workshop behind
cottages. From north take A6071 from
Longtown.

14/1314
■ BAKED GOODS
Shirra Bakery
14 Market Place, Selkirk, Borders TD7 4BT
Tel: (01750) 20690

Shortbread.
Open: Advisable to telephone first
Cards: No

DIRECTIONS: Into centre of Selkirk
via A7 from Hawick, or the A708. Up
lane between Borthwicks chemist and
Spar. 50 yards on left.

14/1315
■ BAKED GOODS
Houstons Bakers
16 Bourtree Place, Hawick,
Borders TD9 9HW
Tel: (01450) 370075
Fax: (01450) 370343

Baked goods, including Selkirk
bannocks.
Open: Mon-Sat 6am-5pm, Tue and
Sat only to 1pm. Closed 25 Dec, 1 Jan
Cards: No

DIRECTIONS: On A7 Carlisle to
Hawick road. Turn right at horse
monument on A698. Shop is 50 yards
on right.

14/1316
● GLASS

Lindean Mill Glass
Lindean, Galashiels, Borders TD1 3PE
Tel: (01750) 20173
Fax: (01750) 21794

Glass workshop and studio,
handmade glasses, bowls,
candleholders and vases in 24% lead
crystal.
Open: Mon-Fri 9am-12 noon, 1pm-
5pm, weekends by appointment
Cards: Access, Visa

DIRECTIONS: 2 miles north of
Selkirk on A7 Edinburgh to Carlisle
road.

14/1317
■ BAKED GOODS

Alex Dalgetty & Sons
21 Island Street, Galashiels,
Borders TD1 1NZ
Tel: (01896) 752508
Fax: (01896) 750452

Selkirk bannocks.
Open: Mon-Sat 8am-5pm. Closed
Christmas and New Year
Cards: No

DIRECTIONS: 33 miles south of
Edinburgh on A7.

14/1318
■ FISH/SHELLFISH

New Mills Trout Farm
Brampton, Cumbria CA8 2QS
Tel: (016977) 2384
Fax: (016977) 41300

Fresh and smoked trout, salmon,
shellfish, game, pâtés, dairy products
and preserves.
Open: Daily 10am-5pm. Closed Mon
and Christmas/New Year
Cards: Access, Visa

DIRECTIONS: On A6071, 1 mile east
of Brampton, just off A69 Newcastle
to Carlisle road.

14/1319
● PLANTS

Angus Heathers
10 Guthrie Street, Letham, By Forfar,
Tayside DD8 2PS
Tel: (01307) 818504
Fax: (01307) 818055

Over 130 varieties of heathers.
Gentians.
Open: Mon-Sun 9am-5pm
Cards: No

DIRECTIONS: Entrance in West
Hemming Street off Market Square,
towards Forfar and signposted.

14/1320
● WOOD

Peter Lloyd
The Old School House, Hallbankgate,
Brampton, Cumbria CA8 2NW
Tel: (016977) 46698

Jewellery boxes, writing slopes and
workboxes made from oak, elm and
sycamore.
Open: By appointment
Cards: No

DIRECTIONS: From A69 take A689
to Alston. In centre of Hallbankgate
take road signposted to Talkin. Old
School House is 30 yards on right.

14/1321
● FURNITURE

Clock House Furniture
The Old Stables, Over Hailes, Haddington,
East Lothian EH41 3SB
Tel: (01620) 860968
Fax: (01620) 860984

Footstools and fireside stools covered
in tapestry, old kilims or fine fabrics.
Open: Mon-Sat 8.30am-4.30pm. Sat
9.30am-1pm. Closed New Year
Cards: Access, Amex, Visa

DIRECTIONS: On A1 4 miles east of
Haddington. Turning at top of hill
signposted to Over Hailes.

14/1322
■ CHEESE

Easter Weens Enterprises
Bonchester Bridge, Hawick,
Borders TD9 8JQ
Tel/Fax: (0145) 0860635

Cheesemakers: Bonchester,
Teviotdale and Belle d'Ecosse.
Open: Mon-Sun at any time
Cards: No

DIRECTIONS: 1 mile from
Bonchester Bridge on the B6357
towards Jedburgh.

14/1323
■ FARM PRODUCE

Knowes Farm Shop
Knowes Farm, East Linton, Dunbar,
East Lothian EH42 1XJ
Tel: (01620) 860010
Fax: (01620) 860221

Soups, preserves, pâté and farm
produce.
Open: All week 10am-4.30pm. Closed
Christmas: 2 days. New Year: 3 days
Cards: No

DIRECTIONS: 1 mile east of East
Linton. Signposted exit on north side
of A1. Alternative access from Dunbar
or North Berwick signposted on
A198, near A1 junction.

14/1324
■ MEAT/POULTRY/GAME

David Palmer
3 High Street, Jedburgh,
Borders TD8 6AQ
Tel: (01835) 863276

Meat, sausages and haggis.
Open: Mon-Thur 7am-5.30pm. Fri
7am-6pm. Sat 6.30am-5pm. Closed
Christmas and New Year and 2nd
Fri/Sat July
Cards: Access, Amex, Diners, Switch,
Visa

DIRECTIONS: On main A68
Edinburgh-Newcastle road. In main
street opposite zebra crossing.

14/1325
● CERAMICS

Alston Pottery and Ceramics
The Old Brewery, Alston,
Cumbria CA9 3RP
Tel: (01434) 382080

Pottery and ceramic tiles. Handmade
vases, jugs, bowls and planters in
decorative white earthenware.
Open: Most days 10am-7.30pm,
advisable to telephone first
Cards: No

DIRECTIONS: Leave Alston village
on A686 Penrith road. Cross the
bridge over the South Tyne river, turn
right on the Carlisle road and
immediately right again down the
track marked Pennine Way. The
pottery faces the car park.

14/1326
■ SMOKED PRODUCE

The Teviot Game Fare Smokery Ltd
Kirkbank House, Kelso, Borders TD5 8LE
Tel/Fax: (01835) 850253

Smoked salmon, trout, eels, chicken,
pheasant, cheese. Coffee shop and
water gardens.
Open: Mon-Fri 10am-4.30pm. Sun
(Apr-Sept) 11am-4pm. Closed
Christmas
Cards: No

DIRECTIONS: Midway between
Kelso and Jedburgh on A698.

14/1327
■ BAKED GOODS

R T Hossack
50 Horsemarket, Kelso, Borders TD5 7AE
Tel: (01573) 224139

Range includes bannocks and spice
cake.
Open: Daily 6am-5pm, except Wed:
6am-1.30pm
Cards: No

DIRECTIONS: On A696 22 miles
west of Berwick-upon-Tweed, 22
miles east of Hawick.

14/1328
■ DAIRY PRODUCE

Stichill Jerseys
Garden Cottage Farm, Stichill, Kelso,
Borders TD5 7TL
Tel: (01573) 470263

Cheeses, butter and cream.
Open: Telephone first
Cards: No

DIRECTIONS: Take Edinburgh road
from Kelso to Stichill. At St Boswells
turn right to Stichill. ½ mile up lane,
turn left (no signpost). After ½ mile
gate on right. Go through and follow
lane for 1 mile.

14/1329
● JEWELLERY

Malcolm Appleby
Crathes Station, Banchory,
Grampian AB31 3JN
Tel/Fax: (01330) 844642

Gold, platinum, silver and iron
jewellery.
Open: By appointment 9am-9pm daily
Cards: No

DIRECTIONS: By Crathes village
hall.

14/1330
● WOOD

Carr Shield Decorative Accessories
Whiteley Shield, Carr Shield, Hexham,
Northumberland NE47 8AB
Tel: (01434) 345344

Hand-turned and painted table lamps,
candlesticks, wine-coasters and other
accessories.
Open: Strictly by appointment
Cards: No

DIRECTIONS: 17 miles south-west of
Hexham, off A686 to Alston or A689
Alston to Stanhope road.

14/1331
● GLASS

Stained Glass by Jenny Hammond
High Greenleycleugh, Ninebanks, Hexham,
Northumberland NE47 8DE
Tel/Fax: (01434) 345307

Stained glass windows, panels and
lampshades.
Open: By arrangement
Cards: No

DIRECTIONS: Off A686 on road
from Ninebanks to Carr Shield.
About 1½ miles above Ninebanks off
the road on left. Wire strand fence on
right.

14/1332
● CLOTHES

Packman Crafts
1 Kings Street, Bellingham,
Northumberland NE48 2BW
Tel: (01434) 220006

Padded jackets, cushions, fabric
doorstops.
Open: Easter-May Mon-Sat 10am-
5pm, June-Sept Mon-Sun 10am-5pm,
Oct-Christmas Mon-Sat 10am-5pm
Cards: Access, Visa

DIRECTIONS: Off the A68, 8 miles
along the Keilder turn off, or on the
B6320 Hexham to Bellingham. The
shop is next door to the Cheviot
Hotel.

14/1333
● WOOD

Tarset Toys
The Old Dairy, Highgreen, Tarset,
Bellingham, Northumberland NE48 1RP
Tel: (01434) 240405

Wooden toys, puzzles and bookends.
Open: By appointment only
Cards: No

DIRECTIONS: A68 from Corbridge
to 1 mile north of A68/B6320
(Otterburn/Bellingham) crossing. Left
on to minor road signposted
Highgreen 4 miles.

14/1334
■ FLOUR

Heatherslaw Corn Mill
Cornhill on Tweed, Northumberland
TD12 4TJ
Tel: (01890) 820338
Fax: (01890) 820384

Flour, cakes, biscuits and crafts.
Open: Apr-Oct daily 10am-6pm.
Closed Nov-Mar
Cards: No

DIRECTIONS: Signposted from A697
north of Wooler. 12 miles south-west
of Berwick-upon-Tweed on B6354.

14/1335
● ART

Mary Ann Rogers
Leam Cottage, West Woodburn, Hexham,
Northumberland NE48 2SE
Tel: (01434) 270216

Water-colour artist of rural subjects.
Open: Strictly by appointment only
Cards: No

DIRECTIONS: Turn left to
Bellingham, head north on A68 in
West Woodburn. After ¼ mile turn
right to Leam Cottage.

14/1336
● FORGEWORK

S Farrell & Co Ltd
Industrial Estate (Townhead) Otterburn,
Newcastle upon Tyne NE19 1NP
Tel: (01830) 520431

Wrought iron, copper and brass work.
Open: Mon-Sun 9am-4pm
Cards: No

DIRECTIONS: 12 miles south of
Scotland on the A68.

14/1337
■ CHEESE

Redesdale Farmhouse Pantry
Soppitt Farm, Otterburn, Elsdon,
Northumberland NE19 1AF
Tel: (01830) 520276

Cheeses, farm shop.
Open: Apr-Oct Mon-Sun 10.30am-
5.30pm, Nov-Mar Sat-Sun 10.30am-
5.30pm. Closed 25 Dec, 1 Jan

Cards: No

DIRECTIONS: From A696 1 mile
south of Otterburn, take B6341
signposted to Rothbury. After 1½
miles farm is signposted to left.

14/1338
● FURNITURE

Erroll Hut Woodwork
Letham Hill, Etal, Cornhill on Tweed,
Northumberland TD12 4TP
Tel: (01890) 820317

Hardwood furniture from local
timber.
Open: Mon-Sun 10am-5pm. Closed
25 Dec, 1 Jan
Cards: No

DIRECTIONS: Situated on Ford and
Etal estates on B6354, 10 miles south
of Berwick-upon-Tweed

14/1339
● LEATHER GOODS

**Belt Up (Dave Downie
Enterprises)**
Letham Hill, Cornhill on Tweed,
Northumberland TD12 4TP
Tel: (01890) 820227

Cow hide belts, hand-sewn handbags
and briefcases, Celtic designs.
Open: Mainly 9am-5pm but flexible.
Closed 25-26 Dec, 1 Jan
Cards: No

DIRECTIONS: On Ford and Etal
Estate, just off the B6354 near Etal,
next to the blacksmith.

14/1340
● FURNITURE

S W Taylor and A Green
The Old Power House, Etal, Cornhill on
Tweed, Northumberland TD12 4TW
Tel: (01890) 820376

Handmade furniture in traditional
and contemporary designs in
softwood and English hardwoods.
Open: Mon-Fri 8.30am-5pm,
weekends by appointment
Cards: Access, Visa

DIRECTIONS: On Ford and Etal
estate on the B6354, 10 miles south of

Berwick-upon-Tweed and 10 miles
north of Wooler.

14/1341
■ HONEY
Chain Bridge Honey Farm
Horncliffe, Berwick-upon-Tweed,
Northumberland TD15 2XT
Tel: (01289) 386362
Fax: (01289) 386763

Honey, candles, cosmestics and
polish.
Open: Mon-Sat 11am-5pm, Sun 2pm-
5pm. Closed Christmas to Easter
Cards: No

DIRECTIONS: Take A6988 from
Berwick to Cornhill and 1 mile from
A1 follow sign for Horncliffe. Honey
Farm signposted from this road.

14/1342
● TOYS
Pictoys
33 High Street, Ayton, Borders TD14 5QW
Tel: (018907) 81387

Wooden toy farmyards and buildings.
Open: Tue-Fri 10am-5pm, Sat 10am-
1pm
Cards: No

DIRECTIONS: In centre of village off
A1, 8 miles north of Berwick-upon-
Tweed.

14/1343
● PLANTS
Northumbria Nurseries
Castle Gardens, Ford, Berwick-upon-
Tweed, Northumberland TD15 2PZ
Tel: (01890) 820379
Fax: (01890) 820594

Hardy ornamental plant nursery,
shrubs perennials, ground cover and
alpines.
Open: Mar-Oct Mon-Fri 9am-6pm,
Sat-Sun 10am-6pm, Nov-Feb Mon-
Fri 9am-5pm
Cards: Access, Visa

DIRECTIONS: In Ford, 10 miles
south-west of Berwick-upon-Tweed.

14/1344
■ FISH/SHELLFISH
John Waddell & Son
Mason's Wynd, Eyemouth,
Borders TD14 5JH
Tel: (018907) 50392

Fish, smoked products, including
salmon.
Open: Mon-Fri 8am-5pm, Sat 8am-
12.30pm. Closed 26 Dec-9 Jan
Cards: No

DIRECTIONS: 2 miles from A1 – exit
7 miles north of Berwick-upon-
Tweed.

14/1345
● CERAMICS
Studio Pottery
56 High Street, Wooler,
Northumberland NE71 6BG
Tel: (01668) 281623

Handmade ceramics, tableware,
mocha ware, stoneware and
earthenware.
Open: Tue-Sat 10am-5pm
Cards: No

DIRECTIONS: In Wooler High Street
off the A697.

14/1346
■ PRESERVES
Oxford Farm Shop
Oxford Farm, Ancroft, Berwick-upon-
Tweed, Northumberland TD15 2TA
Tel: (01289) 387253

Jams and marmalades, strawberries
and raspberries in season.
Open: Nov-April Tue-Sat, May-Oct
Tue-Sun
Cards: No

DIRECTIONS: On B6525, just off A1,
south of Berwick-upon-Tweed.

14/1347
● CERAMICS

Tower House Pottery

Tower Road, Tweedmouth, Berwick-upon-
Tweed, Northumberland TD15 2BD
Tel: (01289) 307314

Handmade decorative earthenware,
mostly pots and tile panels.
Showroom.
Open: 10am-4pm most days
Cards: No

DIRECTIONS: On south side of river
near docks.

14/1348
● ART

Windmill Hole Studio

9 Railway Street, Berwick-upon-Tweed,
Northumberland TD15 1NF
Tel: (01289) 307135

Etchings and woodcuts, paintings and
other crafts.
Open: Tue and Fri 11am-4pm, or by
appointment
Cards: No

DIRECTIONS: 200 yards up hill from
railway station.

14/1349
● CERAMICS

Westfield Farm Pottery and Gallery

Westfield House Farm, Thropton, Rothbury,
Northumberland NE65 7LB
Tel: (01669) 640263

Wood-fired domestic and kitchen
stoneware.
Open: Easter-Christmas Tue-Sat
10am-5pm. Otherwise telephone for
appointment. Closed Christmas-
Easter
Cards: Access, Visa

DIRECTIONS: 3 miles west of
Rothbury, ¾ mile west of Thropton
on B6341.

14/1350
■ FARM PRODUCE

Roseden Farm Shop

Wooperton, Alnwick,
Northumberland NE66 4XU
Tel: (01668) 217271
Fax: (01668) 217348

All home produce: sausages, meat,
butter, pies, preserves, cakes.
Restaurant.
Open: Oct-Easter Tue-Sat 10am-5pm.
Easter-end Sept Tue-Sun 10am-5pm.
Closed 2 weeks in October
Cards: Access, Visa

DIRECTIONS: On A697, 5 miles
south of Wooler, 3 miles north of
Powburn.

14/1351
● WOOD

Ian Taylor Creative Woodwork

46 Main Street, Lowick, Berwick-upon-
Tweed, Northumberland TD15 2UA
Tel: (01289) 388389

Wooden products from jewel boxes
and clocks to blanket chests and
dining tables.
Open: By appointment only
Cards: Access, Visa

DIRECTIONS: Midway between
Berwick and Wooler on B6353.

14/1352
● TEXTILES

Shepherd's Cottage

Lemmington Hill Head, Edlingham,
Alnwick, Northumberland NE66 2BS
Tel: (01665) 574431

Yarn and sheepskins from rare breed
sheep.
Open: By appointment only
Cards: No

DIRECTIONS: On A697 north of
Newcastle upon Tyne take B6341
towards Alnwick at Cragside
crossroads. Turn left through
Edlingham and follow road for 2
miles.

14/1353
● CERAMICS

Harehope Forge Pottery
Harehope Farm, Eglingham, Alnwick,
Northumberland NE66 2DW
Tel: (01668) 217347

Handmade frostproof terracotta
gardenware, fired in a wood-burning
kiln.
Open: 9.30am-5.30pm, Mon-Sat
Cards: No

DIRECTIONS: 8 miles north-west of
Alnwick, 1 mile from Eglingham on
the B6346.

14/1354
● MUSICAL INSTRUMENTS

**D G Burleigh – Northumbrian
Smallpipes**
Rothbury Road, Longframlington, Morpeth,
Northumberland NE65 8HU
Tel: (01665) 570635

Northumbrian smallpipes and
musical instruments.
Open: Mon-Fri 8am-12 noon,
1.30pm-4pm. Closed 24 Dec-2 Jan
Cards: No

DIRECTIONS: 10 miles north of
Morpeth on the A697, turn left into
Rothbury road, in centre of village
next to Mace store.

14/1355
● CERAMICS

Norselands Gallery/Studio Two
The Old School, Warenford, Belford,
Northumberland NE70 7HY
Tel: (01668) 213465

Ceramic figurines, gallery.
Open: Mon-Sun 9am-5pm, summer
9am-9pm. Closed 25 Dec-1 Jan
Cards: Access, Visa

DIRECTIONS: Off A1 Newcastle to
Edinburgh, 12 miles north of
Alnwick.

14/1356
● JEWELLERY

**Christine Greenhaugh
Designer Jewellery**
Bolland House, Pottery Bank, Morpeth,
Northumberland NE61 1DE
Tel: (01670) 516513

Mixed metal, mixed media jewellery
and mirrors.
Open: All reasonable hours, best to
telephone in advance
Cards: No

DIRECTIONS: Follow road north out
of Morpeth town centre. The road
curves left going uphill, the stone
building on right with double black
wooden gates.

14/1357
■ FISH/SHELLFISH

Robertson's Prime
Unit 1D, Willowtree Industrial Estate,
Alnwick, Northumberland NE66 2HA
Tel/Fax: (01665) 604386

Scottish fresh and smoked salmon,
smoked products, shellfish, white fish,
game.
Open: Mon-Sat 9am-5pm. Closed
bank hols
Cards: No

DIRECTIONS: Heading north from
Newcastle to Berwick on A1, take slip
road to Alnwick. Turn right at service
station into estate.

14/1358
● CLOTHES

House of Hardy
Willowburn, Alnwick,
Northumberland NE66 2PF
Tel: (01665) 510027
Fax: (01665) 602389

Country clothing, bags, accessories
and fishing tackle.
Open: Mon-Fri 9am-5pm, Sat 10am-
5pm. Mar-Oct Sun 1.30pm-5pm.
Closed Christmas to New Year
Cards: Access, Amex, Visa

DIRECTIONS: From north take 2nd
exit for Alnwick. Turn right at
crossroads, 300 yards after junction on
right. From south, take 1st exit for

Alnwick, 400 yards along road, on right.

14/1359
● ART

Rookwood Studio Gallery
Gull Hall, Rock South, Alnwick,
Northumberland NE66 2LG
Tel: (01665) 579275

Landscape water-colours.
Open: 1 Mar-24 Dec daily 10am-6pm.
Otherwise by appointment
Cards: Access, Visa

DIRECTIONS: Turn right off A1
approx 3 miles north of Alnwick.
Signposted Rock South Farm.

14/1360
■ FISH/SHELLFISH

Swallow Fish Ltd
Fisherman's Kitchen, 2 South Street,
Seahouses, Northumberland NE68 7RP
Tel: (01665) 721052

Fish merchants and curers.
Open: May to Sept Mon-Fri 9am-
5pm, Sat 9am-4pm, Oct-Apr
Mon/Tue/Thur/Fri 9am-4.30pm,
Wed/Sat 9am-1pm
Cards: Access, Visa

DIRECTIONS: Turn off A1
approximately 6 miles north of
Alnwick. Follow signs to Seahouses.

14/1361
● FURNITURE

Karva Furniture
Widdrington Station, Morpeth,
Northumberland NE61 5DW
Tel/Fax: (01670) 790325

Solid wood dining-room and
bedroom furniture in mahogany and
oak.
Open: Mon-Fri 9am-5.30pm. Sat and
Sun 12 noon-5pm
Cards: Access, Visa

DIRECTIONS: Take B1337 from
Morpeth to Warkworth (just before
Widdrington Station if coming from
Morpeth travelling north).

14/1362
● GLASS

Iona Art Glass
Woodlands, Warkworth, Northumberland
NE65 0SY
Tel: (01665) 711533

Stained glass design, ecclesiastical and
domestic restoration, lampshades.
Open: By appointment only
Cards: Access, Visa

DIRECTIONS: On A1068, 6 miles
south of Alnwick, opposite
Warkworth Castle car park entrance.

14/1363
✱ MULTIPLE

Dial Gallery
5 Dial Place, Warkworth, Northumberland
NE65 0UR
Tel: (01665) 710822

Crafts, paintings.
Open: Tue-Sun 11am-5.30pm. Closed
Mon and 25 and 26 Dec
Cards: Access, Amex, Visa

DIRECTIONS: On A1068 (coast
route) from A1 Seaton Burn to
Alnwick. In village square.

14/1364
✱ MULTIPLE

Fenwick Gallery
21 Castle Street, Warkworth, Morpeth,
Northumberland NE65 0UW
Tel: (01665) 711136

Ceramics, clocks, découpage, glass,
jewellery, paintings, silk, textiles,
wood carving.
Open: Tue-Sun 10am-5pm. Closed
bank hols
Cards: Access, Amex, Visa

DIRECTIONS: In centre of village at
southern end of Northumberland
coastal route on A1068.

14/1365
■ SMOKED PRODUCE

Gourmet Goodies Ltd
Peppermoor Farm, Longhoughton,
Alnwick, Northumberland NE66 3AB
Tel: (01665) 577255
Fax: (01665) 575213

Smoked local products.
Open: Mon-Sat 10am-5pm. Closed
Christmas and Easter
Cards: No

DIRECTIONS: Leave A1 just north of
Alnwick on to B1340. Through
Denwick, turn right for
Longhoughton, RAF Boulmer.
Continue 1½ miles to crossroads.
Signposted left, then 300 yards on
right.

14/1366
● GLASS

Corrib Crafts
53 Beverley Drive, Wansbeck Estate,
Choppington, Northumberland NE62 5YA
Tel: (01670) 815534

Hand-engraved glassware and crystal.
Open: By appointment only
Cards: No

DIRECTIONS: 10 miles north of
Newcastle. Join the A196 Ashington
road at the Guide Post roundabout, go
½ mile east towards Stakeford then
turn left at Cherry Tree pub.

14/1367
● RUGS

The Matmaking Workshop
Woodhorn Colliery Museum, Ashington,
Northumberland NE63 9YF
Tel: (01670) 523331
Fax: (01912) 619230

Rugs and wall-hangings.
Open: Summer Wed, Thur, Sun
11am-5pm, winter 10am-4pm. Or by
appointment
Cards: No

DIRECTIONS: Museum signposted
on A189.

14/1368
■ FISH/SHELLFISH

**Border Lairds Quality Foods
Ltd**
Amble Industrial Estate, Amble, Morpeth,
Northumberland NE65 0LH
Tel: (01665) 712390
Fax: (01665) 711551

Fresh fish and seafood.
Open: Mon-Fri 8am-4.30pm. Sat
8am-12 noon. Closed 23 Dec-3 Jan
Cards: No

DIRECTIONS: On A1068 9 miles
south of Alnwick. Take A1 to
Morpeth and follow signs for Coastal
Route. ½ mile south of Amble on
right-hand side.

MAP 15

15/1369
■ FISH/SHELLFISH

Mermaid Fish Supplies
Clachan, Lochmaddy, North Uist,
Western Isles HS6 5ET
Tel: (01876) 580209
Fax: (01876) 580323

Peat-smoked salmon. Fish and
shellfish in season.
Open: Mon-Sat 9am-6pm, and some
evenings to 10pm
Cards: Access, Switch, Visa

DIRECTIONS: At junction of A865
and A867 at Clachan turn west and go
¼ mile round bay.

15/1370
● TOYS

Changelings
3 Mishigarry, Sollas, North Uist,
Western Isles PA82 5BT
Tel: (01876) 560240

Teddy bears, rabbits, dolls and
'pooks'.
Open: Daily 10am-6pm
Cards: No

DIRECTIONS: 7 miles on Sollas Road
from Lochmaddy.

15/1371
■ DAIRY PRODUCE

West Highland Dairy
Achmore, Stromeferry, by Kyle,
Highland IV53 8UW
Tel: (01599) 577203

Cheese, yoghurts, ice-cream.
Open: Mar-Oct, dawn to dusk. Nov-
Feb advisable to telephone first
Cards: No

DIRECTIONS: Off A890 on Plockton
trail. In village take road to Fernaig.
Dairy is 800 yards down lane.

15/1372
■ SMOKED PRODUCE

Summer Isles Foods Ltd
The Smokehouse, Achiltibuie, Ullapool,
Highland IV26 2YG
Tel: (01854) 622353
Fax: (01854) 622357

Oak-smoked salmon, trout, eels,
haddock, kippers.
Open: Mon-Fri 9.30am-5pm. Also Sat
from Easter to End Sept
Cards: Access, Visa

DIRECTIONS: Approach Achiltibuie
on single track road heading west of
A835 Ullapool/Lochinver road. At
junction by Achnahaird Bay turn right
for 6 miles to Alltan Dubh.
Smokehouse beside road overlooking
Alltan Dubh Bay.

15/1373
■ FISH/SHELLFISH

Kinlochbervie Seafoods
4 Bervie Road, Kinlochbervie, by Lairg,
Highland IV27 4RP
Tel: (01971) 521303

Fresh white fish, salmon, smoked
haddock, mackerel and kippers.
Open: Mon-Fri 7am-11.30pm. Sat
7am-2pm. Closed 22 Dec-12 Jan
Cards: No

DIRECTIONS: Take A838 from Lairg
to Laxford Bridge, then Kinlochbervie
Road. Premises in village opposite
hotel.

15/1374
● PLANTS

Highland Liliums
Kiltarlity, by Beauly, Highland IV4 7JQ
Tel: (01463) 741365
Fax: (01463) 741272

Hardy perennials.
Open: Mon-Sat 9am-5pm. Closed 25
Dec-9 Jan, and 1st Thur in Aug
Cards: Access, Switch, Visa

DIRECTIONS: 12 miles west of
Inverness on the A833 Beauly to
Drumnadrochit road, signposted from
post office in Kiltarlity.

15/1375
● KNITWEAR

Lynda Usher Knitwear & Yarns
50 High Street, Beauly, Inverness,
Highland IV4 7BX
Tel: (01463) 783017

Knitwear, yarns and textile design.
Open: July-Sept: Mon-Sat 10am-8pm,
Sun 12 noon-5pm, Oct-June: Mon-
Wed, Fri-Sat 10am-5pm. Closed 25
Dec-3 Jan
Cards: Access, Visa

DIRECTIONS: 11 miles west of
Inverness on A8562. In centre of
Beauly opposite Priory and car park.

15/1376
■ WINE

Highland Wineries
Moniack Castle, Kirkhill, Inverness,
Highland IV5 7PQ
Tel: (01463) 831283
Fax: (01463) 831419

Wines, liqueurs and preserves.
Open: Mon-Sat 10am-5pm. Closed
Sun, 25 Dec
Cards: Access, Visa

DIRECTIONS: 7 miles from
Inverness on A862.

15/1377
■ HONEY

Struan Apiaries
Burnside Lane, Conon Bridge,
Highland IV7 8EX
Tel/Fax: (01349) 861427

Honey products including
combinations with marmalade and
malt whisky.
Open: Mon-Fri 9am-6pm
Cards: Access, Switch, Visa

DIRECTIONS: A9 to Tore
roundabout beyond Inverness. A835
to Conon Bridge exit. In village
Burnside Lane on left halfway down
the hill, opposite post office. At foot
of the lane.

15/1378
■ SMOKED PRODUCE

Sargasso Ltd
Sargasso Buildings, Units 1-3, Alness
Industrial Estate, Alness, Highland IV17 0XS
Tel: (01349) 883954
Fax: (01349) 883015

Smoked Scottish eel and kabayaki (a
Japanese delicacy).
Open: Mon-Fri 11am to 4pm. Closed
Christmas
Cards: Access, Visa

DIRECTIONS: Follow A9 north from
Inverness to Wick. Take Furning to
Alness Industrial Estate to left after 15
miles north of Inverness. Take second
road on left into the industrial estate
(after ½ mile). Sargasso Buildings are
on the right.

15/1379
● HERBS

Poyntzfield Herb Nursery
Black Isle, Nr Balblair, Dingwall,
Highland IV7 8LX
Tel/Fax: (01381) 610352

Culinary, aromatic and medicinal
herb plants and seeds.
Open: 1 Mar-30 Sept Mon-Sat 1pm-
5pm
Cards: No

DIRECTIONS: Five miles west of
Cromarty on B9163.

15/1380
■ CHEESE

Highland Fine Cheeses Ltd
Knockbreck, Tain, Highland IV19 1LZ
Tel: (01862) 892034
Fax: (01862) 894289

Cheeses, including Caboc, Gruth
Dhu and wild garlic.
Open: Mon-Sat 9am-5pm. Closed 25
Dec, 1 Jan
Cards: Access, Visa

DIRECTIONS: Tain is 37 miles north
of Inverness. Go through Tain along
High Street and turn right past St
Duthus Hotel, down Shore Road.
Keep high wall on left, which curves
left, and keep straight on. Signposted.

15/1381
● STONE

Orcadian Stone Company Ltd
Main Street, Golspie, Highland KW10 6RH
Tel: (01408) 633483

Stone giftware from local stone.
Mineral display.
Open: Mon-Sat 9am-5.30pm. Also
Sun Apr-Sept
Cards: Access, Visa

DIRECTIONS: Between post office
and churchyard.

15/1382
● TEXTILES

Hunters of Brora
Station Square, Brora, Highland KW9 6NA
Tel: (01408) 621023

Tweeds, knitwear, accessories.
Open: Apr-Oct 9am-5.30pm. Nov-
Mar 10am-5pm. Closed 1pm-2pm
Cards: Access, Visa

DIRECTIONS: Next to railway
station.

15/1383
■ MEAT/POULTRY/GAME

MacBeth's
20 Tolbooth Street, Forres,
Grampian IV36 0DB
Tel/Fax: (01309) 672254

Traditional matured beef, lamb, pork
and game.
Open: Mon, Wed 9am-1pm. Tue,
Thur, Fri, Sat 9am-5pm
Cards: Access, Visa

DIRECTIONS: Tolbooth Street is off
High Street. Macbeth's is next to
Newmarket Bar.

15/1384
● TEXTILES

Johnston's of Elgin
New Mill, Elgin, Moray, Grampian IV30 2AF
Tel: (01343) 554000
Fax: (01343) 554055

Cloth, scarves, rugs.
Open: Oct-Jun Mon-Sat 9am-5.30pm
July-Sept Mon-Sat 9am-6pm. Sun,
July-Aug, 11am-4pm
Cards: Access, Amex, Switch, Visa

DIRECTIONS: In Elgin near
cathedral. Signposted.

15/1385
● KNITWEAR

Brough Knitwear Workshops
Ivy Cottage, Brough, Thurso, Caithness,
Highland KW14 8YE
Tel: (01847) 851695

Knitwear and tweed.
Open: Advisable to telephone first
Cards: Access, Visa

DIRECTIONS: Off A836 for Dunnet
Head, then signposted.

15/1386
■ BAKED GOODS

Walkers Shortbread Ltd
Aberlour on Spey, Grampian AB38 9PD
Tel: (01340) 871555
Fax: (01340) 871055

Shortbread, oatcakes, cakes, biscuits
and meringues.
Open: Mon-Thur 8.30am-5pm. Fri
8.30am-4pm. Closed 3 days at
Christmas and 3 days at New Year
Cards: Access, Switch, Visa

DIRECTIONS: On outskirts of
Aberlour on A95 between Elgin and
Grantown.

15/1387
● CERAMICS

John O'Groats Pottery
Unit 3, John O'Groats, Wick,
Highland KW1 4YR
Tel: (01955) 611284

Ceramics – particularly puffin jugs,
mugs, bowls and teapots.
Open: Summer daily 9am-6pm.
Winter Mon-Sat 9am-5pm. Closed 24
Dec-4 Jan
Cards: Access, Visa

DIRECTIONS: Take A9 to John
O'Groats. On south side of main car
park.

15/1388
● KNITWEAR
Barrack Knitwear
Unit 2, John O'Groats, Wick,
Highland KW1 4YR
Tel: (01955) 611440

Knitwear.
Open: Mon-Sat 9am-5pm. Also Sun,
Easter-Oct 12.30pm-5pm
Cards: Access, Visa

DIRECTIONS: By main car park.

15/1389
● GIFTWARE
Fripperies
Unit 4, John O'Groats Business Centre,
John O'Groats, Wick,
Highland KW1 4YR
Tel: (01955) 611445

Bridal giftware, tartan giftware and
fragant gifts.
Open: Daily 9.30am-5pm
Cards: Access, Visa

DIRECTIONS: By main car park.

15/1390
● CANDLES
Caithness Candles
John O'Groats, Wick, Highland KW1 4YR
Tel: (01955) 611238

Candles.
Open: Winter Mon-Fri 10am-5pm,
summer daily
Cards: Access, Switch, Visa

DIRECTIONS: By main car park.

15/1391
■ FLOUR
A MacDonald & Son
The Oatmeal of Alford, Montgarrie Mills,
Alford, Grampian AB33 8AP
Tel: (01975) 562209
Fax: (01975) 562295

Oatmeal millers.
Open: Mon-Fri 7am-5pm. Sat 8am-
12 noon. Closed Christmas-New Year
and first Mon in Apr, May, Jun, Aug,
Oct
Cards: No

DIRECTIONS: At Alldays shop in
Alford (A944) turn into Montgarrie
Road. Past golf course. Cross river
Don into Montgarrie Mill Road.
Signposted on left.

15/1392
■ BAKED GOODS
Mr McKenzie Biscuits
41 Main Street, Turriff, Grampian AB53 5GB
Tel: (01888) 562425
Fax: (01888) 562459

Bakery. Sweet biscuits, shortbread,
oatcakes and black bun.
Open: Mon-Sat 8am-5pm. Closed
bank hols
Cards: No

DIRECTIONS: Turriff is on A947.

MAP 16

16/1393
● TEXTILES

Tait & Style
Brae Studio, Old Academy, Back Road,
Stromness, Orkney KW16 3AW
Tel: (01856) 851186
Fax: (01856) 851190

Embroidered and felted woollen
textiles – hats, shawls, scarves and
cushion covers.
Open: Mon-Fri 10am-1pm, 2pm-
4pm. Sat 10am-2pm. Closed bank
hols
Cards: Access, Visa

DIRECTIONS: Up Back Road from
town. Left down to Old Academy.
Overlooking sea.

16/1394
● SADDLERY GOODS

Orkney Saddlery
57 John Street, Stromness,
Orkney KW16 3AD
Tel: (01856) 851147

Saddlery, belts and other leather
goods.
Open: Mon-Sat 11am-1pm, 2pm-5pm
Cards: No

DIRECTIONS: Off Victoria Street, a
few 100 yards on left.

16/1395
■ FISH/SHELLFISH

Orkney Herring Co Ltd
Garson Industrial Estate, Stromness,
Orkney KW16 3JU
Tel: (01856) 850514
Fax: (01856) 850568

Sweet marinated herring in 6 flavours.
Open: Daily 7.30am-4pm. Closed 23
Dec-6 Jan
Cards: No

DIRECTIONS: Up Ferry Road. Turn
right at crossroads, turn right at foot
of hill, past Stromness Academy.
Green building first left.

16/1396
● SILVERWARE

Orkneyinga Silversmiths
Holland Cottage, Marwick, Birsay,
Orkney KW17 2NB
Tel/Fax: (01856) 721359

From bookmarks to candle snuffers.
Also jewellery.
Open: Usually open, but advisable to
telephone first
Cards: Access, Visa

DIRECTIONS: On B9056 Stromness
to Birsay road between Skaill Bay and
Marwick Head. Take 2nd driveway on
right after the Howe Road turn off.

16/1397
● HATS

Tangle Designs
Tangles, Stenness, Orkney KW16 3JY
Tel: (01856) 851065

Soft fabric hats.
Open: Easter to Oct 11am-5pm most
days. Closed Oct to Easter
Cards: No

DIRECTIONS: About 4 miles from
Stromness on A965. In village near
garage and sub post office.

16/1398
● CERAMICS

Fursbreck Pottery
Harray, Orkney KW17 2JR
Tel: (01856) 771419

Pottery and craft shop.
Open: 10am-6pm
Cards: Access, Visa

DIRECTIONS: A 965 Stromness to
Kirkwall road. Turn on to A986 at
Harray turn off. After 2 miles the
pottery is on left.

16/1399
● STONE

Frances Pelly Stone
Costa Schoolhouse, Evie,
Orkney KW17 2NJ
Tel: (01856) 751326

Commemorative work in stone,
hand-cut lettering and relief work.
Open: By appointment

Cards: No

DIRECTIONS: 17 miles from
Kirkwall on A966. 2½ miles from
Mistra shop/pub on Birsay Road.

16/1400
■ FISH/SHELLFISH

Orkney Seafayre
Marsdene, Grimbister, Firth,
Orkney KW15 1TU
Tel/Fax: (01856) 761544

Shellfish and oysters.
Open: Mon-Fri 8am-6pm. Closed
Christmas-New Year
Cards: No

DIRECTIONS: Halfway between
Kirkwall and Stromness on A965.

16/1401
● FURNITURE

Robert H Towers
Rosegarth House, St Ola, Kirkwall,
Orkney KW15 1SE
Tel/Fax: (01856) 873521

Straw-backed Orkney chairs in pine
and walnut.
Open: Mon-Fri 8.30am-1pm, 2pm-
5pm, or by appointment. Closed last
week of Sept and 21 Dec-10 Jan
Cards: No

DIRECTIONS: Take A964 from
Kirkwall for 1½ miles. Workshop on
left.

16/1402
● CERAMICS

Elli Pearson Pottery
Hestily, Windwick, St Margaret's Hope,
Orkney KW17 2RN
Tel: (01856) 831355

Pottery.
Open: Mon-Sat 9am-6pm
Cards: No

DIRECTIONS: Take A961 from
Kirkwall to South Ronaldsay (approx
12 miles). Drive past St Margaret's
Hope (5 miles). Turn left at
Windwick and follow signs to pottery.

16/1403
✳ MULTIPLE

Wheems
Eastside, South Ronaldsay,
Orkney KW17 2TJ
Tel: (01856) 831537

Hand-felted rugs and wall-hangings,
naturally coloured fleece, organic
vegetables, cheeses.
Open: Any reasonable hour, but
advised to telephone first. Closed
Nov-Apr
Cards: No

DIRECTIONS: At St Margaret's Hope
turn left to Eastside at war memorial.
1½ miles. Across crossroads. First
farm on left.

16/1404
■ FISH/SHELLFISH

Banks Sea Farms
The Pier, St Margaret's Hope,
Orkney KW17 2SW
Tel: (01856) 831226
Fax: (01856) 831614

Fresh, frozen and smoked salmon.
Open: Mon-Fri 8am-5pm
Cards: No

DIRECTIONS: From St Margaret's
Hope out along Pier Road to pier
buildings.

16/1405
● KNITWEAR

Stéphane Jaeger
Littlequoy, Burray, Orkney KW17 2SX
Tel/Fax: (01856) 731228

Handspun knitwear using home-
grown wools and cashmere.
Open: 9am-9pm
Cards: Access, Visa

DIRECTIONS: Take Kirkwall to
South Ronaldsay road (A961) then
first road to the right after Echnaloch
in Burray. Last farmhouse down road
(2½ miles).

16/1406
● KNITWEAR

Judith Glue
25 Broad Street, Kirkwall,
Orkney KW15 1DH
Tel: (01856) 876263
Fax: (01856) 874225

Knitwear, crafts.
Open: Winter 9.30am-5.30pm.
Summer 9am-6pm
Cards: Access, Amex, Switch, Visa

DIRECTIONS: Opposite cathedral.

16/1407
● STRAWCRAFT

Scapa Crafts
Cantara, 12 Scapa Court, Kirkwall,
Orkney KW15 1BJ
Tel: (01856) 872517

Straw backs for Orkney chairs,
cubbies, flower baskets, stools.
Open: All day
Cards: No

DIRECTIONS: In centre of Kirkwall.

16/1408
● FURNITURE

Traditional Orkney Crafts
Mariveg, Rope Walk, Kirkwall,
Orkney KW15 1XJ
Tel: (01856) 875110

Straw-backed chairs and stools.
Open: All day all week
Cards: Access, Visa

DIRECTIONS: In Kirkwall on A960.

16/1409
● FURNITURE

Orcadian Crafts
8 Bridge Street, Kirkwall,
Orkney KW15 1HR
Tel: (01856) 872846

Straw-backed Orkney chairs, sea grass
stools and knitwear.
Open: Mon-Sat 10am-5pm
Cards: Access, Visa

DIRECTIONS: In main shopping area
approximately 30 yards up street from
pier.

16/1410
● JEWELLERY

Ortak Jewellery
Hatston, Kirkwall, Orkney KW15 1RH
Tel: (01856) 872224
Fax: (01856) 875165

Gold, silver and pewter jewellery.
Open: Mon-Fri 9am-1pm, 2pm-5pm.
Sat-Sun: seasonal
Cards: Access, Amex, Switch, Visa

DIRECTIONS: On main Kirkwall to
Stromness road adjacent to Hatston
Industrial Estate.

16/1411
■ FISH/SHELLFISH

Scott's Fish Shop
3 Bridge Street, Kirkwall, Orkney KW15 1HR
Tel: (01856) 873170

Local fresh fish, shellfish, oak-smoked
salmon and farm cheese.
Open: Mon-Sat 9am-5pm. Early
closing Wed 1pm
Cards: No

DIRECTIONS: In centre of town,
near pier.

16/1412
● GIFTWARE

Joker Jewellery
The East School, Holm, Orkney KW17 2SD
Tel/Fax: (01856) 781336

Ceramic giftware: brooches, clocks,
mirrors, games, mobiles, jigsaws.
Open: Mon-Fri 9am-5pm and by
appointment. Closed 24 Dec-6 Jan
Cards: No

DIRECTIONS: 7 miles out of
Kirkwall, turn to Toab at end of St
Mary's. Turn right at war memorial,
then turn to Cornquoy. First building
on left.

16/1413
● JEWELLERY

Sheila Fleet Jewellery
Old Schoolhouse, Tankerness,
Orkney KW17 2QT
Tel/Fax: (01856) 861203

Silver and gold jewellery.

Open: Daily 9am-5pm. Evenings by appointment
Cards: Access, Visa

DIRECTIONS: First turn left after airport on A960. Take first turning to right after about 2 miles. Continue for ¼ mile and follow sign.

16/1414
● FURNITURE
Sui Generis
Redbanks, Isle of Eday, Orkney KW17 2AA
Tel: (01857) 622219
Fax: (01857) 622254

Furniture maker and designer. Upholstery, leatherwork, marquetry, carving, bookbinding.
Open: By appointment only
Cards: No

DIRECTIONS: 14 miles north east of Kirkwall. Access to Eday daily by ferry except Sundays in winter.

16/1415
● KNITWEAR
Eday Spinners
Isle of Eday, Orkney KW17 2AB
Tel: (01857) 622248
Fax: (01857) 622254

Hand-spun knitwear.
Open: Daily 10am-dusk
Cards: No

DIRECTIONS: North end of Eday (7 miles from ferry) in Carrick Bay. Turn left by coastguard's hut and follow road to two houses. Sign at gate.

16/1416
● SADDLERY GOODS
Shetland Leather Centre
Millhaugh, Sandness, Shetland ZE2 9PL
Tel: (01595) 870243

Saddlery, harness and general leather goods.
Open: Tue-Sun 10am-6pm
Cards: No

DIRECTIONS: In Sandness turn right into Bousta Road. Shop is at first croft on left.

16/1417
■ SMOKED PRODUCE
The Shetland Smokehouse
Skeld, Shetland ZE2 9NS
Tel: (01595) 860251
Fax: (01595) 860203

Smoked and marinated seafoods.
Open: Daily 7.30am-6.30pm. Closed Christmas, New Year and bank hols
Cards: Access, Visa

DIRECTIONS: Take road north from Lerwick. West past Tingwall. Head for Bixter then turn left at sign for Skeld. Follow signs for Wester Skeld and opposite village hall.

16/1418
● KNITWEAR
Shetland Collection
Orcadia, Virkie, Shetland ZE3 9JS
Tel: (01950) 460340

Traditional Fair Isle range of knitwear.
Open: By appointment or Mon-Sat 9am-6pm
Cards: No

DIRECTIONS: 1 mile north of Sumburgh airport, next to Meadowvale Hotel.

16/1419
● KNITWEAR
Spirit of Shetland
5 Cauldhame, Trondra, Shetland ZE1 0XL
Tel: (01595) 880437

Hand-knitted jumpers, gloves, waistcoats and cardigans.
Open: Daily 9am-9pm
Cards: No

DIRECTIONS: About 8 miles from Lerwick, Trondra is small island off mainland connected by bridge. Cauldhame is a small settlement.

16/1420
● GLASS
Shetland Glass
Units 1&2, Blydoit Industrial Estate, Scalloway, Shetland ZE1 0UG
Tel/Fax: (01595) 880432

Hand-blown and decorative glass.

Open: Mon-Fri 9am-5pm, Sat
10.30am-5pm, Sun 1pm-4pm. Closed
25 Dec to 3 Jan
Cards: Access, Visa

DIRECTIONS: Take A970 to
Scalloway, turn left towards Burra on
B9074. Take first left to workshop.

16/1421
● KNITWEAR

Gunna's
Anderson's Building, Main Street,
Scalloway, Shetland ZE1 0TR
Tel: (01595) 880840

Crafts and knitwear.
Open: Mon-Fri 9.30am-5pm. Sat
10am-5pm. Closed Sun
Cards: Access, Visa

DIRECTIONS: Next to post office.

16/1422
● KNITWEAR

Shetland Knitwear Associates
31 King Harald Street, Lerwick,
Shetland ZE1 0EQ
Tel: (01595) 692746

Hand-knitted or hand-framed
knitwear by designers.
Open: Mon-Fri 9am-3.30pm. Closed
Christmas/New Year
Cards: Access, Visa

DIRECTIONS: On A970 south
entrance to Lerwick. Junction of
Scalloway road (A970) and King
Harald Street.

16/1423
● SCULPTURE

Shetland Workshop Gallery
4 & 6 Burns Lane, Lerwick,
Shetland ZE1 0EJ
Tel: (01595) 693343
Fax: (01950) 477550

Animal figurines (puffins, Shetland
ponies, cats, seals etc) cast from
original stone carvings.
Open: Mon-Fri 9.30am-1pm, 2pm-
5pm
Cards: Access, Visa

DIRECTIONS: Just off main street, 10
yards up from jewellers.

INDEX

● **ART**

2/137 Simon Drew Gallery, DARTMOUTH

2/138 John Gillo Gallery, DARTMOUTH

2/150 Anna Fraser Fine Art, WINSFORD

2/175 Sona Bennett, STOGUMBER

2/178 Richard Pocock Printmaker, RUNNINGTON

2/183 Marilyn Ewens, CROWCOMBE

2/218 John Morgan's Fantastica, WATERGORE

2/262 Jim Woods, CASTLE CARY

13/1221 Margaret Morrison, PONTELAND

13/1246 Daisy Barns Watercolours, WOMBLETON

14/1335 Mary Ann Rogers, WEST WOODBURN

14/1348 Windmill Hole Studio, BERWICK-UPON-TWEED

14/1359 Rookwood Studio Gallery, ROCK SOUTH

■ **BAKED GOODS**

1/39 Di's Dairy & Pantry, WADEBRIDGE

1/47 Proper Cornish, BODMIN

2/101 Moorland Larder, SOUTH MOLTON

2/154 Mrs Gill's Country Cakes, TIVERTON

2/216 S Moores, MORCOMBELAKE

3/283 Marshfield Bakery, MARSHFIELD

3/319 Cookie Craft, COMMON PLATT

4/521 Herschell House Foods, LEIGH-ON-SEA

5/559 Cottage Caterers, JORDANSTON BRIDGE

6/600 St Fagans Bakery (Dderwen), ST FAGAN

6/668 Hobbs House Bakery, CHIPPING SODBURY

7/736 The Flour Bag, LECHLADE

7/752 Meg Rivers Cakes, MIDDLE TYSOE

7/756 Take Two Cooks, HARBURY

7/798 Ye Olde Pork Pie Shoppe, MELTON MOWBRAY

8/908 Silver Nutmeg, EYE

9/946 Gwynle Bakery, AMLWCH

9/951 Becws Eryri, LLANBERIS

9/957 Cacennau Briwsion Cakes, PENTREFOELAS

9/963 Alwyn Thomas Bakery, DENBIGH

9/969 Megan's Kitchen, LLANGOLLEN

10/1013 High Lane Oatcakes, BURSLEM

10/1020 R & J Lodge Foods, MELTHAM

10/1033 Original Bakewell Pudding Shop, BAKEWELL

11/1070 Mrs Elizabeth King Ltd, CROPWELL BUTLER

12/1153 Lakeland Gateaux, TOWNHEAD

12/1154 The Village Bakery, MELMERBY

14/1290 Alexander Taylor at the Waterside Bakery, STRATHAVEN

14/1311 Goodfellow & Steven, BROUGHTY FERRY

14/1314 Shirra Bakery, SELKIRK

14/1315 Houstons Bakers, HAWICK

14/1317 Alex Dalgetty & Sons, GALASHIELS

14/1327 R T Hossack, KELSO

15/1386 Walkers Shortbread Ltd, ABERLOUR ON SPEY

15/1392 Mr McKenzie Biscuits, TURRIFF

● **BAROMETERS**

7/751 Peter Wiggins Restoration, SOUTHCOMBE

● **BASKETS**

2/109 Honeyford Baskets, DREWSTEIGNTON

2/203 The Somerset Willow Company, BRIDGWATER

2/204 And Beautiful Baskets, LYME REGIS

2/205 Willow Wetlands Visitor Centre, STOKE ST GREGORY

2/210 The Cane Workshop, WESTPORT

3/351 John Hayward, BEAULIEU

4/495 The Truggery, HERSTMONCEUX

4/498 Sussex Trugs Limited, HERSTMONCEUX

7/716 The Basket Maker, SOUTH LITTLETON

8/878 Rob King – English Willow Basketworks, DEREHAM

● **BATIK**

4/472 Mary Potter, LAUGHTON

■ **BEER**

1/14 Blue Anchor Inn, HELSTON

2/76 The Royal Inn, HORSEBRIDGE

2/263 Oakhill Brewery, OAKHILL

3/419 The Gribble Brewery, OVING

7/769 Bodicote Brewery, BODICOTE

7/803 The Chiltern Brewery, TERRICK

8/828 Fox and Hounds, BARLEY

13/1200 Hexhamshire Brewery, ORDLEY

3/354 High Street Pottery, KINTBURY
3/359 Ardington Pottery, ARDINGTON
3/373 Tichborne Pottery, TICHBORNE
3/375 Sidney Hardwick, UPTON
3/381 Elizabeth Gale Ceramics, SOBERTON
3/384 Blenheim Pots & Plaques, Nr WALLINGFORD
3/389 Clanfield Pottery, CLANFIELD
3/397 Farmhouse Ceramics, HARTLEY WESPALL
3/398 Coldpiece Pottery, MATTINGLEY
3/400 Selborne Pottery, SELBORNE
3/410 Rupert Spira Ceramics, LOWER FROYLE
3/416 Grayshott Pottery, GRAYSHOTT
3/428 Mary Wondrausch – The Pottery, COMPTON
3/432 Josse Davis (Arundel Pottery), ARUNDEL
4/453 Jill Pryke Pottery, DITCHLING
4/499 Peter Phillips Pottery, TROTTISCLIFFE
4/502 Hook Green Pottery, HOOK GREEN
4/527 David Sharp Ceramics, RYE
4/528 Rye Pottery Ltd, RYE
4/537 Robus Pottery & Tiles, HASTINGLEIGH
4/539 Sellindge Pottery & Crafts, SELLINDGE
4/547 Nonington Pottery, NONINGTON
4/550 Summerfield Pottery & Potters' Supplies, SUMMERFIELD
5/554 Studio Pottery, CAERFARCHELL
5/565 Begelly Pottery, BEGELLY
5/571 Michael and Carol Francis Ceramics, LLANFYRNACH
6/592 Alexander Ceramics Limited, YSTRADGYNLAIS
6/597 Marston Pottery, RHAYADER
6/615 Pembridge Terracotta, PEMBRIDGE
6/617 Old School Pottery, EDGTON
6/638 McCubbins, ST BRIAVELS
6/646 Bridget Drakeford Porcelain, FOWNHOPE
6/652 Jack and Joan Doherty Ceramics, LEA BAILEY
6/660 Homend Pottery, LEDBURY
6/662 English Country Pottery, WICKWAR
6/689 The Pottery, STROUD
6/693 Hookshouse Pottery, WESTONBIRT
6/705 Conderton Pottery, CONDERTON
6/706 Daub & Wattle (Ceramics) Ltd, BROMSGROVE
6/707 Craft Pottery, KEMBLE
7/719 Hilary LaForce Ceramics, BROOM
7/722 Louise Darby, REDHILL
7/728 Torquil Pottery, HENLEY-IN-ARDEN
7/735 Old Bell Pottery, LECHLADE
7/748 Whichford Pottery, WHICHFORD
7/749 Jan Bunyan Ceramics, BUTLERS MARSTON
7/750 Furnace Lane Pottery, MOIRA
7/764 Piggott Sculpture, BLADON
7/767 Brinklow Pottery, BRINKLOW
7/790 Design Ceramics, UPPER HARLESTONE
7/796 Frank Haynes Gallery, GREAT BOWDEN
7/801 Speen Pottery, HIGHWOOD BOTTOM
7/820 Louise Shotter Pottery, ST IPPOLLITTS
8/824 Lannock Pottery, WESTON
8/827 Clover Pottery, PIDLEY
8/837 Anna McArthur Ceramic Artist, LANDBEACH
8/838 Twentypence Pottery, WILBURTON
8/859 John and Kate Turner, NARBOROUGH
8/862 Castle Hedingham Pottery, CASTLE HEDINGHAM
8/875 Burnham Pottery, WELLS-NEXT-THE-SEA
8/883 Ryburgh Pottery, LITTLE RYBURGH
8/889 Kersey Pottery, KERSEY
8/891 The Particular Pottery, KENNINGHALL
8/897 Made in Cley, CLEY NEXT THE SEA
8/911 Carters Ceramic Designs, DEBENHAM
8/914 Paul David Jackson, CALTHORPE
8/915 A & J Young Pottery, LOWER GRESHAM
8/923 Church Cottage Pottery, WILBY
8/924 Millhouse Pottery, HARLESTON
8/925 Deborah Baynes Pottery Studio, SHOTLEY
8/929 Cat Pottery, NORTH WALSHAM
8/937 Butley Pottery, BUTLEY
8/939 Sutton Windmill Pottery, SUTTON
8/941 Jonathan Keep Pottery, KNODISHALL
8/943 Dorothy Midson Ceramics, BLYTHBURGH

■ CHEESE

2/243 Times Past Cheese Dairy, DRAYCOTT

2/247 Ashley Chase Estate, LITTON CHENEY

2/261 Chewton Cheese Dairy, CHEWTON MENDIP

2/265 J A and E Montgomery Ltd, NORTH CADBURY

3/422 Gospel Green, GOSPEL GREEN

3/435 Old Scotland Farmhouse Cheese, SHERE

4/466 Willowdown Dairy Goats, NUTLEY

4/470 Sussex High Weald Dairy Sheep Products, DUDDLESWELL

4/474 Neals Yard Creamery Ltd, IDE HILL

4/485 K W and A M Blunt, WHITESMITH

5/558 Llangloffan Farmhouse Cheese Centre, CASTLE MORRIS

5/573 Caws Cenarth, PONTSELI

5/574 Penbryn Cheese, SARNAU

5/577 Welsh Farmhouse Cheese, MAESLLYN

5/578 Teifi Cheese, FFOSTRASOL

5/580 Pen-y-Bont Goat Cheese, PEN-Y-BONT

6/669 Smarts' Traditional Gloucester Cheeses, BIRDWOOD

6/691 Ansteys of Worcester, KEMPSEY

10/1008 Staffordshire Organic Cheese, ACTON

10/1022 Ye Old Cheese Shop, HARTINGTON

11/1069 Cropwell Bishop Creamery, CROPWELL BISHOP

11/1072 Colston Bassett & District Dairy Ltd, COLSTON BASSETT

13/1233 Shepherd's Purse Speciality Cheeses, NEWSHAM

14/1274 Isle of Mull Cheese TOBERMORY

14/1280 Island Cheese Co Ltd, BRODICK

14/1297 H J Errington & Co, CARNWATH

14/1309 Thornby Moor Dairy, CROFTON

14/1322 Easter Weens Enterprises, BONCHESTER BRIDGE

14/1337 Redesdale Farmhouse Pantry, OTTERBURN

15/1380 Highland Fine Cheeses Ltd, KNOCKBRECK

■ CIDER

1/23 Callestock Cider Farm, PENHALLOW

1/71 Inch's Cider Ltd, WINKLEIGH

1/73 Saul's Farm, WEMBWORTHY

2/77 Countryman Cider, MILTON ABBOT

2/115 Stancombe Traditional Farmhouse Cyder, SHERFORD

2/127 Gray's Farm Cider, TEDBURN ST MARY

2/128 E & P Bromell, TEDBURN ST MARY

2/141 Churchward Cider, PAIGNTON

2/149 Reddaway's Farm Cider, LUTON

2/153 Clark's Farm Cider, SEVEN CROSSES

2/169 Torre Cider Farm, WASHFORD

2/177 E W Pearse, SIDBURY

2/188 R J Sheppey & Son, BRADFORD-ON-TONE

2/197 Henry's Farmhouse Scrumpy, BATHPOOL

2/202 Ashill Cider, ASHILL

2/208 Rich's Somerset Farmhouse Cider, WATCHFIELD

2/223 Somerset Cider Brandy Company and Burrow Hill Cider, KINGSBURY EPISCOPI

2/235 Wilkins and Son Farmhouse Cider, MUDGLEY

2/236 Ashwood Cider, SHIPHAM HILL

2/245 Derrick's Cider, CHEDDAR

2/248 Whitehead Cider, BARTON ST DAVID

2/275 Mill House Cider, OWERMOIGNE

3/329 New Forest Cider, BURLEY

3/366 Godshill Farmhouse Cider, GODSHILL

3/438 John Friar, ASHINGTON

4/503 Owlet Apple Juice and Cider, LAMBERHURST

4/531 Pawley Farm Cider, PAINTERS FORSTAL

6/613 Ben Crossman's Prime Farmhouse Cider, HEWISH

6/619 Richard's Cider, SMALLWAY

6/654 H Westons and Sons Ltd, MUCH MARCLE

6/656 Tony Cullimore's Services, BERKELEY

6/704 Tilley's Farmhouse Cider, GOTHERINGTON

■ CIDER AND PERRY

2/184 Bollhayes Cider, CLAYHIDON

2/213 Coombes Cider, MARK

6/614 Dunkertons Cider Co & the Cider House Restaurant, PEMBRIDGE

6/639 Franklins Cider Farm, LITTLE HEREFORD

● DOLLS' HOUSES

1/60 Treasure Houses, WIDEGATES
3/302 Honeychurch Toys Ltd, DEVIZES
12/1115 The Dolls' House Man, ULVERSTON
12/1147 Carol Black Miniatures, GREAT STRICKLAND
13/1197 Longbarn Enterprises, BAINBRIDGE

● DOVECOTES

12/1135 Connoisseur Dovecotes & Weather-vanes, KENDAL

● DRIED FLOWERS

4/484 The Hop Shop, SHOREHAM
4/490 Norpar Dried Flowers, ROMFORD
10/996 Carolyn's Flowers, MARKET DRAYTON
11/1104 Candlesby Herbs, CANDLESBY
12/1108 Pamela Bush Floral Decor, WORKINGTON

■ EGGS

3/328 Martin Pitt, CLENCH COMMON
8/926 Akenfield Eggs, CHARSFIELD

● ENGRAVING

1/4 Jack Trowbridge, NEWMILL
13/1216 The Bewick Studios, Printmaking Workshop and Museum, STOCKSFIELD

■ FARM PRODUCE

1/20 Cheese Farm Shop, TREVERVA
1/33 Trudgian Farm Shop, PROBUS
2/124 Riverford Farm Foods, STAVERTON
2/171 Combe Sudenham Country Park, MONKSILVER
3/295 Keyneston Mill, TARRANT KEYNESTON
3/348 Kimbridge Farm Shop, KIMBRIDGE
3/430 Loseley Park Farms, GUILDFORD
6/620 Brecon Court Deer Farm Shop, LLANSOY
6/630 Green Acres Organic Growers, DINMORE
6/645 The Kitchen Garden, TOCKINGTON
6/663 Taynton Farm Shop, TAYNTON
7/773 Peach Croft Farm Country Produce, ABINGDON
7/792 Seldom Seen Farm, BILLESDON
8/910 Hemingstone Fruitique, HEMINGSTONE
8/916 The Priory Farm Shop, WRABNESS

8/922 Cranes Watering Farm Shop, STARSTON
10/1027 Old Stables Farm Shop & Bakery, PACKINGTON
11/1048 Chatsworth Farm Shop, PILSLEY
14/1323 Knowes Farm Shop, EAST LINTON
14/1350 Roseden Farm Shop, WOOPERTON

■ FISH/SHELLFISH

1/12 Quayside Fish, PORTHLEVEN
1/34 Mellingey Smoked Fish & Trout Farm, ST ISSEY
1/74 Avon Oysters, BIGBURY
2/94 Head Mill Trout Farm, UMBERLEIGH
2/107 Salcombe Smokers, KINGSBRIDGE
2/152 River Exe Shellfish Farms, LYSON
2/264 Abbotsbury Oysters Ltd, FERRYBRIDGE
2/280 Whistley Crayfish, WHISTLEY WATERS
3/284 Mere Fish Farm, WARMINSTER
4/538 Seasalter Shellfish (Whitstable) Ltd, WHITSTABLE
5/562 Carew Oyster Farm, WEST WILLIAMSTON
5/584 Fish on the Quay, ABERAERON
5/588 Teifi Valley Fish, LLANYBYDDER
6/608 Crucorney Trout Farm, LLANVIHANGEL CRUCORNEY
6/671 Severn & Wye Smokery, WALMORE HILL
7/711 Preston Mill Trout Farm, CIRENCESTER
8/863 The Fish Shed, BRANCASTER
8/898 Cley Smoke House, CLEY NEXT THE SEA
8/917 The Company Shed, WEST MERSEA
8/921 Richard & Julie Davies, CROMER
8/944 Harvey's Wet Fish Shop, ALDEBURGH
9/948 Anglesey Sea Zoo, ANGLESEY
9/955 Conwy Valley Fisheries, CONWY
9/966 Forest Hill Trout Farm & Fishery, WHITFORD
10/1025 Mayfield Trout, MAYFIELD
12/1139 Ullswater Trout, TIRRIL
13/1202 Kilnsey Park & Trout Farm, KILNSEY
14/1273 Isle of Colonsay Oysters, POLL GORM
14/1275 R & M George, SALEN
14/1277 Scallop Kings plc, CRINAN

7/821 Henry Isaac, ST IPPOLLITTS
8/845 Glendale Forge, THAXTED
8/864 The Forge, GESTLINGTHORPE
8/932 Brian Reynolds Blacksmith,
PASTON
10/1045 Wentworth Forge,
WENTWORTH
12/1173 Barley Forge, BARLEY
13/1259 James Godbold – Blacksmith,
EGTON
13/1267 David Athey Blacksmith,
GARTON-ON-THE-WOLDS
14/1336 S Farrell & Co Ltd,
OTTERBURN

■ FRUIT/VEGETABLES
2/130 Dittisham Fruit Farm, CAPTON
2/199 Charlton Orchards, CREECH ST
MICHAEL
2/212 Stawell Fruit Farm, STAWELL
2/249 West Bradley Orchards,
GLASTONBURY
3/287 Gold Hill Organic Farm, CHILD
OKEFORD
3/374 West Lea Farm Shop, WEST LEA
3/403 Blackmoor Apple Shop,
BLACKMOOR
3/424 C R & B M Upton, SLINDON
3/425 Secretts Farm and Flower Shop,
MILFORD
4/481 Sepham Farm, SHOREHAM
4/534 Perry Court Farm Shop, BILTING
5/564 Greenmeadow Mushroom Farm,
KILGETTY
6/593 Baron Jackson Welsh
Mushrooms, COYCHURCH
6/605 Berryhill Farm, COEDKERNEW
8/852 Eros Asparagus, BURY ST
EDMUNDS
8/876 Crapes Fruit Farm, ALDHAM
8/890 Clay Barn Orchard,
FINGRINGHOE
8/909 Old Hall Farm, ATTLEBRIDGE
8/936 Ranworth Farms Ltd,
RANWORTH
10/982 Ellesmere Road Organic
Nursery, COCKSHUTT
12/1195 Harewood Bridge Fruit Farm,
HAREWOOD

● FURNITURE
1/58 Millthorne Chairs, HARTLAND
1/68 David Savage Furniture Makers,
BIDEFORD
2/146 Nicholas Chandler Furniture
Maker, RACKENFORD
2/155 Sugan Chairs, EXEBRIDGE

2/174 Justin Williams and Jane Cleal
Furniture, WATCHET
2/217 Moobles Design, WAYFORD
2/239 Parnham House, BEAMINSTER
2/258 Robinsons, QUEEN CAMEL
3/289 R E Hogg Upholsterer, BERE
REGIS
3/291 Southern Crafts Ltd,
DURWESTON
3/297 Belinda Ballantine School of
Painted Furniture, MALMESBURY
3/318 Trannon Furniture Ltd, WILTON
3/324 The Walnut Tree Workshop,
BREAMORE
3/378 John Nixon Fine Furniture,
ALDERMASTON
3/379 Jim Crockatt Furniture,
BRADFIELD
3/402 Screens Gallery, EMSWORTH
4/501 Barry Michael Murphy,
HERSTMONCEUX
4/522 Barry M Jones, BECKLEY
5/583 M & J Billington Pine Furniture &
Gifts, LLANDYSUL
6/604 Chris Armstrong Country
Furniture, CLIFFORD
7/712 Paul Spriggs, Woodcraftsman
and Rushworker, SOUTH CERNEY
7/723 Oxleys Furniture, CHIPPING
CAMPDEN
7/745 David E Bennett, CARTERTON
7/754 Martin Dodds Country Furniture,
CHARLBURY
7/766 Neville and Lawrence Neal,
STOCKTON
7/782 Ash Design, HOUGHTON ON
THE HILL
7/784 Bates & Lambourne, MILTON
COMMON
7/799 Hollies Farm Handcrafts, LITTLE
DALBY
8/826 ASP Cabinet Maker, ELSWORTH
8/840 David Prue, Cabinet Maker,
SAFFRON WALDEN
8/907 David Gregson Furniture,
BURSTON
10/981 Silver Lining Workshops,
ALDFORD
10/986 Michael Niblett Cabinet Maker,
BAYSTON HILL
10/995 Ray Read, COALBROOKDALE
10/1030 Steven James Furniture,
BROUGH
10/1032 Neil Clarke, KNIVETON
10/1036 Melvyn Tolley – Maker of
English Country Chairs, BRADLEY
10/1037 Nova Interiors, EYAM

14/1362 Iona Art Glass, WARKWORTH

14/1366 Corrib Crafts, CHOPPINGTON

16/1420 Shetland Glass, SCALLOWAY

● **GYPSY CRAFT**

3/401 Romany Folklore Museum &
   Workshop, SELBOURNE

● **HATS**

16/1397 Tangle Designs, STENNESS

■ **HEALTH FOODS**

7/761 Ryton Organic Gardens Shop,
   RYTON-ON-DUNSMORE

● **HERALDRY**

8/851 Dudley Bateman, Heraldic Artist,
   SOUTH WOOTTON

● **HERBS**

2/270 R T Herbs, KILMERSDON

2/273 Coach House Herbs, WEST
   KNIGHTON

6/636 Arne Herbs, CHEW MAGNA

6/688 Selsley Herb Shop,
   NAILSWORTH

8/830 N & R J Dyer, WILLINGHAM

8/868 Rafi's Spice Box, SUDBURY

8/930 Daphne ffiske Herbs,
   BRAMERTON

13/1199 Hexham Herbs,
   CHOLLERFORD

15/1379 Poyntzfield Herb Nursery,
   BLACK ISLE

■ **HONEY**

1/70 Vivian's Honey Farm,
   HATHERLEIGH

2/100 Quince Honey Farm, SOUTH
   MOLTON

4/526 Homestall Honey Farm, HIGH
   HALDEN

5/585 Welsh Honey, ABERAERON

6/594 Mr Lee's Honey Company,
   LLANAFAN FAWR

6/607 Gwent Vales Apiaries, UPPER
   LLANOVER

6/648 Teme Valley Honey Farm,
   SUTTON

9/950 Ffermfelyr Wyddfa – Snowdon
   Honey Farm, LLANBERIS

13/1269 Sneatondale Honey Farm,
   EAST AYTON

14/1341 Chain Bridge Honey Farm,
   HORNCLIFFE

15/1377 Struan Apiaries, CONON
   BRIDGE

● **HUNTING ACCESSORIES**

11/1050 Harry Boden, BONSALL

12/1169 Ivy Cottage Gun Cabinets &
   Walking Sticks, COWGILL

■ **ICE-CREAM**

1/24 Callestick Farm Dairy Ice Cream,
   CALLESTICK

1/25 Roskilly Cream and Ice Cream, ST
   KEVERNE

1/63 Thorne Farm Natural Dairy Ice
   Cream Ltd, HOLSWORTHY

2/97 Devonshire Farmhouse Ice Cream,
   CHAGFORD

2/106 Salcombe Dairy, SALCOMBE

2/136 Pure Jersey Ice Cream,
   CHERITON FITZPAINE

2/139 Langworthys Ice Cream Dairy,
   DARTMOUTH

2/201 Barnard & Gooding, PAWLETT

3/415 Blackburne & Haynes, HEADLEY

4/491 Knightsbridge Farm Dairy Ice
   Cream, GROVEBRIDGE

4/553 Solleys Farms Limited, DEAL

6/599 The Fruit Garden, PETERSTON-
   SUPER-ELY

6/609 September Dairy Products,
   ALMELEY

6/612 Shepherds Ice Cream,
   PETERCHURCH

8/874 The Manor Farm Creamery,
   THURSTON

9/949 Cadwalader Ice Cream,
   CRICCIETH

9/962 Denbigh Farmhouse Ices,
   DENBIGH

12/1107 Hartley's Ice Cream,
   EGREMONT

12/1178 Sweet Clough Dairy Ice Cream,
   SOUTHFIELD

● **JARDINIERES**

3/363 Carolyn Sheffield Designs,
   LAVERSTOKE

● **JEWELLERY**

2/126 Rebecca Edmunds, BOVEY
   TRACEY

2/241 Michael Burton Gold &
   Silversmith, HURST

3/288 Paws Jewellery (David Watts)
   Workshop, BERE REGIS

3/369 Vivian Pare, HAMPSTEAD
   NORREYS

3/383 Elisabeth Napier-Munn,
   WHITCHURCH

4/475 The Gowan Gallery,
   SAWBRIDGEWORTH

6/631 Wood Yard Gallery, LUDLOW

6/664 Newent Silver & Gold, NEWENT

■ MEAT PRODUCTS

1/29 Merrivale Charcuterie, TRURO

3/299 Sandridge Farmhouse Bacon, BROMHAM

3/307 The Sausage Shop, HORTON

12/1194 Allisons of Ferryhill, FERRYHILL

13/1225 T Appleton & Sons, RIPON

■ MEAT/POULTRY/GAME

1/72 Higher Hacknell Farm Partnership, BURRINGTON

2/84 Mid Devon Fallow, HATHERLEIGH

2/95 Heal Farm Meats Ltd, KING'S NYMPTON

2/96 Wild Beef, CHAGFORD

2/103 Tordean Farm, DEAN PRIOR

2/104 Deer Force 10, HOLNE

2/156 Burrow Products, TIMBERSCOMBE

2/167 Pipers Farm, CULLOMPTON

2/200 Somerset Ducks, NORTH NEWTON

2/259 Barrow Boar, SOUTH BARROW

2/278 Norwood, NORTON ST PHILIP

3/333 S W Pickles & Sons, NEW MILTON

3/334 Eastbrook Farm Organic Meats, SHRIVENHAM

3/349 Sutherland's of Eldon, KING'S SOMBORNE

3/405 Gabriel Machin, HENLEY-ON-THAMES

3/407 Hampshire Game Ltd, GREATHAM

3/409 Goldesborough Quail, WHEATLEY

3/412 Brunning Hams Farm Shop, FINCHHAMPSTEAD

3/440 Collins Butchers, WARNHAM

4/444 The Game Larder, CHESSINGTON

4/454 Burstye Soays, LINDFIELD

4/462 Old Spot Farm Shop, PILTDOWN

4/477 Thrushes Bush Poultry Farm, HARLOW

4/525 Wadhurst Park Speciality Foods, TENTERDEN

4/529 Marney Meats, LAYER MARNEY

4/536 Richardson's Butchers, BRIGHTLINGSEA

4/540 Peartree Farm Foods, WEELEY HEATH

5/556 Haven Ostriches, LITTLE HAVEN

5/581 Quail World, LLANDYSUL

5/582 Albert Rees, CARMARTHEN

5/590 D I J Davies Butchers, TREGARON

6/601 Graig Farm, DOLAU

6/606 C E Wells and Son, CLUN

6/611 Upper Pant Farm, LLANDEWI

6/622 Hereford Duck Company, WORMBRIDGE

6/629 Newhall Ostrich Farm Ltd, CHEPSTOW

6/650 Hicks Gate Farm Shop, KEYNSHAM

6/674 Goodman's Geese, GREAT WITLEY

6/690 Checketts of Ombersley, OMBERSLEY

6/696 Tetbury Traditional Meats, TETBURY

7/717 Kite's Nest Farm, BROADWAY

7/810 R Waller, CHESHAM

7/822 Ashwell Delicatessen, HINXWORTH

8/846 C E Brown – Licensed Game Dealer, SHUDY CAMPS

8/835 Naturally Yours, WITCHAM TOLL

8/855 R F & J Scoles, DERSINGHAM

8/858 Longwood Farm, TUDDENHAM ST MARY

8/860 Lay and Robson, SIBLE HEDINGHAM

10/985 C G Sadd, DORRINGTON

10/990 Meadow View Quail, WHIXALL

10/991 Maynards Farm Bacon, WESTON UNDER REDCASTLE

10/998 Dukeshill Ham Co, DEUXHILL

10/1003 Holly Tree Farm Shop, TABLEY

10/1009 Mooreland Foods, MORLEY GREEN

10/1016 Alan Bennett Ltd, WEDNESFIELD

11/1058 George Stafford Ltd, STANLEY COMMON

11/1077 Mrs Potter's Perfect Pork, LANGFORD

11/1079 W E Botterill & Son, CROXTON KERRIAL

11/1089 Three Kings Deer, THREEKINGHAM

11/1096 F C Phipps, MAREHAM LE FEN

11/1098 John Pettit & Sons Ltd, GRIMSBY

12/1149 C R & J Towers, HORNBY

12/1152 M F & D J Slack, ORTON

12/1193 J B Cockburn & Sons, BEDALE

12/1194 Allisons of Ferryhill, FERRYHILL

13/1230 Smithy Farmshop, BALDERSBY

13/1231 Twizell's, BISHOPTON

7/746 Paul Fischer Luthier, CHIPPING NORTON

7/772 Michael Fleming, OXFORD

7/776 Robert Goble and Son Ltd, HEADINGTON

10/1040 Northworthy Musical Instruments, HULLAND WARD

12/1134 Robert Deegan Harpsichords, LANCASTER

12/1166 Dennis Woolley Harpsichords, DENT

14/1354 D G Burleigh – Northumbrian Smallpipes, LONGFRAMLINGTON

● NEEDLECRAFTS

2/112 Presence, ASHBURTON

5/568 Glenys Sida, MYNACHLOGDDU

7/760 Traditional Cottage Crafts, AVON DASSETT

10/988 Eccles Farm Needlecraft Centre, BISPHAM GREEN

13/1210 Jennifer Davies, REETH

13/1253 The World Embroidery Shop, MALTON

13/1255 Catherine Fields, PICKERING

13/1261 All Sewn Up, SNAINTON

13/1263 Artefacts of Whitby, WHITBY

● PAINTED TILES

12/1137 Maggie Angus Berkowitz Tiles, MILNTHORPE

● PAINTS

3/305 Farrow & Ball Ltd, WIMBORNE

7/771 Biofa Natural Paints, KIDLINGTON

10/1012 Colourman Paints, COTON CLANFORD

● PAPER PRODUCTS

2/168 Two Rivers Paper Company, ROADWATER

3/298 Compton Marbling, TISBURY

4/445 Bridge House Design, LEMSFORD

6/610 Christopher Marbling, PRESTEIGNE

7/733 Comfort Farm Crafts, CLIFFORD CHAMBERS

7/779 Tic Tok Design, SILEBY

● PASTILLE BURNERS

1/21 The Dragons Lair, CARNKIE

● PETS ACCESSORIES

2/165 Comfy Pet Products, BRADNINCH

● PHOTOGRAPHY

12/1150 Ian Johnson Photography, GRAYRIGG

● PLANTS

1/22 Burncoose Nurseries, GWENNAP

1/43 Wall Cottage Nursery, BUGLE

1/51 Duchy of Cornwall Nursery, LOSTWITHIEL

1/59 Bregover Plants, MIDDLEWOOD

1/69 The Fortescue Garden Trust, Garden House Enterprises Ltd, BUCKLAND MONACHORUM

2/78 Rowden Gardens, BRENTOR

2/85 The High Garden, NEWTON FERRERS

2/89 Hostas Ann and Roger Bowden, STICKLEPATH

2/91 Glebe Cottage Plants, WARKLEIGH

2/105 Stone Lane Gardens, CHAGFORD

2/133 Peveril Clematis Nursery, CHRISTOW

2/144 Churchills Garden Nursery, CHUDLEIGH

2/173 J M Spiller Elworthy Cottage Garden Plants, ELWORTHY

2/187 Perrie Hale Forest Nursery, HONITON

2/192 Broadleigh Gardens, BISHOPS HULL

2/207 Mallet Court Nursery, CURRY MALLET

2/209 YSJ Seeds, Kingsfield Conservation Nurseries, WINSHAM

2/226 Kelways Limited, LANGPORT

2/233 Scotts Nurseries Merriott Ltd, MERRIOTT

2/250 Otters' Court Heathers, WEST CAMEL

3/301 Naked Cross Nurseries, CORFE MULLEN

3/310 Knoll Gardens, HAMPRESTON

3/311 Trehane Nursery, HAMPRESTON

3/327 Macpenny Nurseries and Woodland Garden, BRANSGORE

3/337 Apple Court Nursery, HORDLE

3/338 Steven Bailey Ltd, SWAY

3/345 Spinners, BOLDRE

3/350 Longstock Park Garden Nursery, LONGSTOCK

3/356 Hollington Nurseries, WOOLTON HILL

3/357 Exbury Gardens Ltd, EXBURY

3/377 Blackthorn Nursery, KILMESTON

3/387 Hayward's Carnations, PURBROOK

3/408 Blackmoor Nurseries, BLACKMOOR

8/942 Fisk's Clematis Nursery,
WESTLETON
9/959 Aberconwy Nursery, COLWYN
BAY
9/965 Celyn Vale Eucalyptus Nurseries,
CARROG
9/971 Oak Cottage Herb Garden,
NESSCLIFFE
10/994 Caddicks Clematis Nurseries,
THELWALL
10/997 Stapeley Water Gardens Ltd,
STAPELEY
10/1002 Bridgemere Nurseries,
BRIDGEMERE
10/1004 Hillview Hardy Plants,
WORFIELD
10/1006 Ward Fuchsias, SALE
10/1007 David Austin Roses,
ALBRIGHTON
10/1014 Collinwood Nurseries,
MOTTRAM ST ANDREW
10/1017 Barncroft Nurseries,
LONGSDON
10/1044 Rileys' Chrysanthemums,
WOOLLEY MOOR
11/1053 Highgates Alpine Plant
Nursery, BELPER
11/1060 Markham Grange Nurseries,
BRODSWORTH
11/1067 Stillingfleet Lodge Nurseries,
STILLINGFLEET
11/1068 Norden Alpines, CARLTON
11/1083 Orchard Nurseries, FOSTON
11/1090 Potterton & Martin,
NETTLETON
11/1094 Countryside Companions,
BAUMBER
11/1095 The Valley Clematis Nursery,
HAINTON
12/1162 Weasdale Nurseries,
NEWBIGGIN ON LUNE
12/1163 Hartside Nursery Garden, Nr
ALSTON
12/1164 Pinks & Carnations, BROMLEY
CROSS
12/1168 Holden Clough Nursery,
HOLDEN
13/1270 J & D Marston Fern Specialists,
NAFFERTON
14/1289 Blairhoyle Nursery,
BLAIRHOYLE
14/1306 Glendoick Gardens Ltd,
GLENDOICK
14/1319 Angus Heathers, LETHAM
14/1343 Northumbria Nurseries, FORD
15/1374 Highland Liliums, KILTARLITY
BY BEAULY

■ **POULTRY**
7/718 Domestic Fowl Trust,
HONEYBOURNE

■ **PRESERVES**
1/13 Phillimore Fine Foods,
PORTHLEVEN
1/45 Trevervan Jams, TREWARMETT
2/134 Heaven Scent Herbs, CREDITON
3/317 Olives Et Al, SALISBURY
5/572 Wendy Brandon Preserves,
BONCATH
5/575 Welsh Rarebit Products,
GLYNARTHEN
6/684 Farthing Fayre, HORSLEY
7/753 Shaken Oak Products, HAILEY
7/816 Les Fines Herbes, STAMFORD
8/848 English Country Chandlers Ltd,
GREAT DUNMOW
8/938 Garden of Suffolk Preserves,
YOXFORD
10/983 The Hollies Apiary and Farm
Shop, WELSHAMPTON
10/987 Taylors Original English Mustard
Co, GREAT BARROW
10/1034 Connoisseurs of Bakewell,
BAKEWELL
11/1061 Womersley Crafts,
WOMERSLEY
12/1171 Island Cottage Crafts,
NENTSBERRY
13/1219 Rosebud Preserves, HEALEY
14/1299 Scone Palace, SCONE
14/1346 Oxford Farm Shop, ANCROFT

● **ROCKING-HORSES**
2/222 Margaret Spencer & Co,
CREWKERNE
3/325 Robert Mullis Rocking Horse
Maker, WROUGHTON
3/436 Clive Green Rocking Horses,
RUSTINGTON
8/831 Michael Pearson Fine Rocking
Horses, HARSTON
9/961 A P E S Rocking Horses,
LLANNEFYDD
9/973 Greenwoods Rocking Horses,
TARPORLEY
11/1074 The Rocking Horse Shop,
FANGFOSS
12/1159 Heirlooms, DUFTON

● **ROPE**
12/1175 W R Outhwaite & Son, HAWES

● **RUGS**
11/1051 Tessa Badcock, handweaver,
BONSALL

14/1276 Macdonalds Smoked Produce, GLENUIG
14/1278 Colfin Smokehouse, PORTPATRICK
14/1281 Inverawe Smokehouses, TAYNUILT
14/1282 Ritchies of Rothesay, ISLE OF BUTE
14/1283 Crannog Scottish Seafoods, BLAR MHOR
14/1288 Galloway Smokehouse, CARSLUITH
14/1291 Swanswater Smokehouse, SAUCHIEBURN
14/1326 The Teviot Game Fare Smokery Ltd, KELSO
14/1365 Gourmet Goodies Ltd, LONGHOUGHTON
15/1372 Summer Isles Foods Ltd, ACHILTIBUIE
15/1378 Sargasso Ltd, ALNESS
16/1417 The Shetland Smokehouse, SKELD

● SMOKING PIPES
3/309 Tilshead Pipe Co Ltd, TILSHEAD

● SPINNING WHEELS
7/791 Timbertops Spinning Wheels, ASFORDBY

● STENCILS
13/1213 The Stencil Library, STOCKSFIELD

● STONE
3/300 Tony Viney, CORFE CASTLE
3/336 Lloyd of Bedwyn, GREAT BEDWYN
7/777 Nigel Owen, YELVERTOFT
12/1123 Kirkstone Galleries, SKELWITH BRIDGE
15/1381 Orcadian Stone Company Ltd, GOLSPIE
16/1399 Frances Pelly Stone, EVIE

● STRAWCRAFT
8/881 Corn-Craft, MONKS ELEIGH
16/1407 Scapa Crafts, KIRKWALL

● TAXIDERMY
7/732 Natural Craft Taxidermy, EBRINGTON

● TEXTILES
1/3 Noah's Ark Studio, PENZANCE
1/64 South Worden Farm Enterprises, BRADWORTHY
2/269 Dianne Davies Designs, HIGHER BRATTON SEYMOUR

3/380 Daffodil, STREATLEY
3/406 Geraldine St Aubyn Hubbard, NUTBOURNE
5/555 The Woollen Mill, SOLVA
5/557 Melin Tregwynt, CASTLE MORRIS
5/567 Studio in the Church, WHITLAND
6/634 Woodstock House Craft Centre, BRIMFIELD
6/670 Roger Oates Country Warehouse, EASTNOR
6/676 Colin Squire and Janice Williams, EPNEY
6/682 Margaretha Bruce-Morgan, GUARLFORD
7/768 Sharon J Webb, WHITWICK
7/813 Pheasant House, BERKHAMSTED
8/869 Vanners Mill Shop, SUDBURY
8/879 Sheila Rowse Designs, GREAT WALSINGHAM
8/880 Peter and Jason Collingwood, NAYLAND
9/947 Cefyn Burgess, LLANDWROG
9/970 Isaf Design Ltd, MOLD
10/1010 The Mill Shop, STYAL
11/1092 Timberland Art & Design, TIMBERLAND
12/1119 Coniston Woollen Mill Ltd, CONISTON
12/1120 Countryman John & Co Ltd, CONISTON
12/1124 Fibrecrafts, ELTERWATER
12/1186 Helyg Pottery and Textiles Workshops and Gallery, ADDINGHAM
13/1228 Northumbria Weavers, BLYTH
13/1268 Ankaret Cresswell, WYKEHAM
14/1312 Eden Valley Woollen Mill, ARMATHWAITE
14/1352 Shepherd's Cottage, LEMMINGTON HILL HEAD
15/1382 Hunters of Brora, BRORA
15/1384 Johnston's of Elgin, ELGIN
16/1393 Tait & Style, STROMNESS

● TOYS
1/28 It's Childsplay, TREWORTHAL
2/79 Hilary Bix Puzzles, BIDEFORD
2/121 David Plagerson, TOTNES
2/163 Eric Horne Collectors Toys, TOPSHAM
2/230 Jean George Designs, SALWAYASH
3/330 Hill Top Toys, FARLEY
4/442 Sue Godber Crafts, RUDGWICK
4/544 Canterbury Bears Ltd, LITTLEBOURNE

4/524 The Harbourne Vineyard, WITTERSHAM
4/542 Elham Valley Vineyard, BREACH
4/548 Staple Vineyard, STAPLE
4/551 Ash Coombe Vineyard, ASH
4/552 St Nicholas Vineyard, ASH
5/563 Cwm Deri Vineyard, NARBERTH
5/586 Gwinllan Ffynnon Las Vineyard, ABERAERON
6/596 Glyndwr Vineyards, LLANBLETHIAN
6/598 Cariad Wines, HENSOL
6/621 Offa's Vineyard, LLANVIHANGEL-YSTERN-LLEWERN
6/633 Tintern Parva Vineyards, TINTERN
6/635 Bodenham English Wines, BODENHAM
6/658 English and Country Fruit Wines, OXENHALL
6/666 Three Choirs Vineyards, NEWENT
6/667 Coddington Vineyard, CODDINGTON
6/681 Tiltridge Vineyard, UPTON-ON-SEVERN
6/683 Astley Vineyard, ASTLEY
6/701 Crickley Windward Vineyard, LITTLE WITCOMBE
7/744 Edby Wines, BAMPTON
7/793 Waddesdon Manor Gift and Wineshop, WADDESDON
7/814 Frithsden Vineyard, FRITHSDEN
8/829 Coton Orchards, COTON
8/843 Chilford Hundred Wine Company, LINTON
8/853 Felsted Vineyards, CRIX GREEN
8/857 Boyton Vineyard, STOKE BY CLARE
8/867 Gifford's Hall Vineyard, HARTEST
8/882 The Leaping Hare Café and Country Store, STANTON
8/885 Elmham Wines Ltd, NORTH ELMHAM
8/887 Harling Vineyards, EAST HARLING
8/888 Carters Vineyards, BOXTED
8/918 Pulham Vineyards Ltd, PULHAM MARKET
8/920 Stradbroke Vineyard, BATTLESEA GREEN
8/931 Staverton Vineyard, EYKE
8/933 Bruisyard Vineyard and Herb Centre, BRUISYARD
8/935 Wissett Wines, WISSETT
9/968 Ty Brethyn Meadery, FRON BACHE
10/984 Carden Park Vineyard, CARDEN

11/1056 Leventhorpe Vineyard, WOODLESFORD
11/1063 Eglantine Vineyard, COSTOCK
15/1376 Highland Wineries, MONIACK CASTLE

● WOOD
1/11 Roy Hewson Woodcarver, ST ERTH
1/56 Lynn Muir, MARHAMCHURCH
2/92 Woodturners Craft Centre, MODBURY
2/98 Wood & Rush, CHAGFORD
2/117 Bill Hooper Wooden Bathroom Furniture and Small Gifts, PARFORD
2/123 Rendle Crang Woodcraft, TOTNES
2/143 One Good Turn, CHUDLEIGH
2/179 Paul McHardy Woodworker, MILVERTON
2/185 Sunshine Designs, FITZHEAD
2/229 Somerset Creative Products, CRICKHAM
2/242 Yandle & Sons Ltd, MARTOCK
2/253 Dansel Gallery, ABBOTSBURY
3/339 Mike Bradley, Craftsman Woodturner, FARINGDON
3/343 Nether Wallop Trading Company, NETHER WALLOP
3/368 Chrisken, KINGSCLERE
3/388 Pendennis Crafts, LOVEDEAN
4/543 Jali Ltd, BARHAM
5/561 Robintree, FISHGUARD
5/570 Old Forge Crafts, LLANGLYDWEN
6/603 From the Wood, HAY-ON-WYE
6/675 Lark Designs, BATHEASTON
6/694 Painswick Woodcraft, PAINSWICK
7/731 Julian Stanley Woodcarving and Furniture, LONGBOROUGH
7/739 Burford Woodcraft, BURFORD
7/742 Carol & Peter Moss Woodcarvers, ARMSCOTE
7/755 Swanalong, TASTON
8/913 John Anderson, BLICKLING
10/977 A B Woodworking, GOBOWEN
11/1086 Tamcraft Woodworks, CAENBY
12/1121 Lathe and Chisel, BOUTH
12/1122 Maurice Mullins, CALDBECK
12/1138 Peter Hall & Son, STAVELEY
12/1141 The Wood Revolution, OVER KELLET
12/1160 John J Rudd & Sons, DUFTON
12/1179 David Tippey, KIRKBY MALHAM